THE LAND-COMING

Common murres are sea-birds which spend most of their lives far off shore. Early in the spring, with the urge to breed far stronger than their fear for safety, they approach land to seek the traditional nesting sites which have been occupied by their kind for untold ages

THE NEST-SITE

The traditional nest-sites for common murres are certain cliffs and small remote islands where they are safe from land predators and where turbulent currents provide abundant food. Each pair scarcely requires one square foot to raise its single chick

THE COLONY

Common murres nest on broad flat ledges or the rubble strewn tops of small islands where they can crowd together. Each colony is composed of a core of experienced birds surrounded on the fringes by young birds breeding for the first time. They lay their eggs on the bare rock

THE GUARDIANS
The chicks sometimes attempt to go to sea before they are able to survive the shock of the cold waters. When this happens, adults form a protective barrier at the edge of the land to prevent such a disaster

THE PROSPECTORS

Late in the breeding season, each colony is visited by prospecting birds not yet fully mature. They are making their first contact with the land which they left as chicks. On the following year, they will return to breed on the fringes of the colony

THE SEA-GOING

Scarcely half grown and unable to fly, common murre chicks follow the adults down to the edge of the land and plunge or leap into the sea where, if they survive, they will remain for at least two years before returning to land once more

THE THICK-BILLED MURRE
*The thick-billed murre, the only other species of
murre, prefers to nest on narrow ledges and
vertical cliffs where its chick must leap from
great heights into the sea*

THE MURRES

CANADA

Department of
Northern Affairs and National Resources
National Parks Branch
Canadian Wildlife Service

Issued under the authority of the
Honourable Walter Dinsdale, P.C., M.P., Minister of
Northern Affairs and National Resources

THE MURRES · *their distribution, populations and biology*

a study of the genus Uria

by Leslie M. Tuck

Ottawa, 1960

Roger Duhamel, F.R.S.C., Queen's Printer and Controller of Stationery, Ottawa, 1961

Price $3.00   *Cat. No. R66-2161.1*

Contents

List of Tables

List of Figures

Introduction

Murres are relatively large sea-birds, weighing on the average two pounds, with sharply defined bi-coloured plumage. They are highly specialized for catching small fish under water. Specialized development for this purpose includes reduction of the length and area of the wing and so great modification of the bones and muscles of the legs that these birds walk very little and very awkwardly. They nest in large, compact colonies on steep cliffs facing the sea.

Murres are essentially marine species and approach land only during the breeding season. They obtain most of their food by flying *under* water. They are the only sea-birds in the Northern Hemisphere which habitually lay their eggs in exposed situations on bare ledges and rocks. They brood but a single egg and yet they are probably the most abundant sea-birds in the Northern Hemisphere.

There are two species; the common murre (*Uria aalge*), with some tolerance for warmish water, and the thick-billed murre (*Uria lomvia*), largely restricted to arctic waters. They occupy in the Northern Hemisphere an ecological niche similar to that occupied in the Southern Hemisphere by penguins, which they resemble superficially in coloration and postures.

The habit of nesting in large colonies (some colonies contain more than one million individuals) has made the species of substantial economic importance in some parts of the Northern Hemisphere. Their eggs, and to a lesser extent the birds themselves, have been traditionally used in the Old World for food, and were so used for a brief and over-enthusiastic period in the New World. Recent investigations indicate that there is more nourishment in a murre's egg than in the equivalent volume of a domestic fowl's. The utilization of murres, with some minor exceptions, has been outlawed in the New World for more than half a century. Elsewhere utilization has decreased in some places (e.g., Great Britain), remained the same (e.g., the Faeroes), or increased (e.g., Russia). There is no evidence that murre populations are appreciably less numerous today than they were in historical times.

Nesting murres require scarcely one square foot of territory per individual. Such compact colonies are possible because the food of murres is almost unlimited in summer. Murres provide a vital link in the ecology of the species which are their food. Their excrement, rich in potash, is important to the growth, and so to the abundance, of small marine organisms. Their colonies are in many respects the fertilizing factories of the northern seas.

A murre colony (loomery or bazaar) is an orderly aggregation of birds. It is basically composed of a core of experienced adults, surrounded on the submarginal fringe sites by less experienced birds or those breeding for the first time. Early in the breeding season, mature murres take part in communal displays in the sea at the base of the cliffs. It is believed that those communal displays not only stimulate the birds to breed but enable them to "synchronize" their breeding cycles so that the maximum number of young are raised in a comparatively short period.

The eggs and chicks are subjected to many dangers, not the least of which is the likelihood of being knocked off the narrow ledges. The surviving chicks are led to sea, and to comparative safety, by single adults, not necessarily their parents. In other ways also, murres show communal interest in the welfare of the eggs and chicks of the colony.

The foregoing sketchy account suggests that murres are peculiar and extremely interesting sea-birds. The purpose of this monograph is to document what is presently known about their biology, distribution and populations, and also to examine the probable reasons for their remarkable success.

My interest in sea-birds, especially murres, began about 1940 and has progressively increased since then. One of my very first projects with the Canadian Wildlife Service was to commence, in 1950, an investigation of their biology. This study was initiated because murres were of substantial economic importance to the new Province of Newfoundland. The Canadian Wildlife Service (almost as new) had little information about the species on which to base a management program. Since 1950, I have spent annually part or all of each summer at a murre colony and many days during each winter within sight of murres on their feeding grounds. I have examined every known colony in Newfoundland and along the Labrador Coast, and representative colonies in Ungava Bay, Hudson Bay and Lancaster Sound. The story of the murres is far from complete: a great deal more will be known about them twenty years hence.

Many people have given me invaluable assistance at one time or another during the course of these studies. Special thanks are due members of the Royal Canadian Mounted Police both in Newfoundland and the Canadian Arctic, including Corporals Jack Carroll, Ray Johnson and D. S. Moodie, Constables A. C. Fryer, Blake Macintosh, Jake Coyne, the late Clayton Gilbert and many of the men on the patrol vessels *Irvine* and *MacBrien*.

John Miller remained with me on Akpatok Island during the summer of 1954, and Jim Lowther spent the wet and stormy summer of 1955 with me in Hudson Bay. I think with great affection of my Eskimo friends, especially Toonga and Mucktar, who were often my sole companions for many weeks. Douglas Pimlott, Biologist with the Newfoundland Department of Mines and Resources, assisted me in various ways, and Ron Harper, while stationed at Torbay with the Royal Canadian Air Force, gave freely of his leave in three consecutive years to band murres on Green Island. Alan Loughrey banded murres on Coats Island in two consecutive summers.

I thank Captain Baxter Blackwood of the trawler *Blue Spray* and Captain Arch Thornhill of the trawler *Blue Foam* for pleasant and valuable trips to the Grand Banks. I wish to thank Father H. Mascaret, Oblate Missionary, Ivugivik, and Jimmie Ford and Dave Stevenson, of the Hudson's Bay Company at Payne Bay and Pond Inlet. Dr. Cater Andrews, Professor of Biology, Memorial University, gave advice and encouragement. Dr. Wilfred Templeman, Director, and Hubert H. Squires, Biologist, of the Fisheries Research Station, Newfoundland, provided laboratory facilities and assistance in identification of murre food.

Information on murre colonies was generously given by Dr. William H. Drury, Jr., Professor V. C. Wynne-Edwards, Derry Ellis, Laidlaw Williams, Alex Walker, Stanley G. Jewett, Tom J. Cade, Dr. Finnur Gudmundsson and Arne Nørrevang, among others.

The background material in this account, especially a great deal of the information on the location of colonies and comparative populations, has been abstracted from the literature. I have borrowed freely from many writers, whose names are included in the list of references.

I am especially grateful to James Fisher for critical reading of the manuscript and for placing his well-equipped personal library at my disposal, and to Dr. Finn Salomonsen who reviewed parts of the manuscript and assisted me in many other ways. Dr. David Lack was most helpful with my work at Oxford. For Russian translations, I am indebted to Professor Hans Johansen and Dr. J. M. MacLennan, and for translations of Swedish and Norwegian papers to Dr. David Sergeant.

This account of murres would not have been possible without the guidance and encouragement of W. Winston Mair and David A. Munro of the Canadian Wildlife Service. Harrison F. Lewis edited the manuscript. His criticisms and corrections were most helpful. Miss D. Darwin prepared the figures.

PART I: EVOLUTION AND ADAPTATION

CHAPTER I

The Evolution of Murres

Twenty species of the family Alcidae, to which murres belong, now survive (Table 1). One species, the flightless great auk (*Pinguinus impennis*), became extinct within historical times. It was last recorded in 1844 or possibly 1845 (Grieve, 1885).

Fossil evidence shows that murres existed in the Pacific in the Pleistocene and in the Atlantic as long ago as the Pliocene and possibly the Miocene epoch (Miller and Peabody, 1941). The Alcidae as a group may have originated in or not far from the Bering Sea (Fisher and Lockley, 1954). From that point, they evolved into the various species presently known. Storer (1952) suggests that the murres originated in the Atlantic.

Concerning the two species of murres presently known, Sergeant (1951) wrote: "We may assume that the two were once a common stock that became separated into northern and southern forms, reproductively isolated, by some climatic barrier associated with the Pleistocene glaciation." Storer (1952) reasoned that the thick-billed murre (*Uria lomvia*) developed into its present specific form somewhere north of Siberia. Eventually it spread southwards and met the common murre (*Uria aalge*) as the more northerly populations of that species became adapted to colder conditions. Those species overlap now in much of their breeding range. They are not known to interbreed.

Both species of murre are relatively large sea-birds, weighing on the average two pounds. The species are superficially similar. Generally speaking, the thick-billed murre can be distinguished from the common murre in the breeding season by its thicker bill and white gape marks on the upper mandible. A slightly greater extent of white on the head of the common murre and a black mark running back from the eye distinguish it in winter from the thick-billed murre. The various subspecies differ to a minor extent in size and length of bill and in dorsal coloration, which ranges from light brown to nearly black. All murres are characterized by dark upperparts, white underparts and short wings. They are essentially a marine species, breeding only in close proximity to the sea and spending the non-breeding season in the shallow parts of the ocean extending to the edge of the continental shelf. The sexes are alike at all times of the year. Like all Alcidae, they are restricted to the Northern Hemisphere.

The basic coloration of murres, dark upperparts and white underparts, is an adaptation to their cold environment. The cells of white feathers are filled with air, which is a poor conductor, while the cells of dark feathers are filled with small melanin granules, which, in proportion to their density, are able to conduct heat (Freuchen and Salomonsen, 1958). The advantage of white feathers on the underparts of murres is their insulation

Table 1: *Distribution of the Alcidae*

	North Pacific	North Atlantic
Great auk (now extinct)		x
Razorbill		x
Common murre	x	x
Thick-billed murre	x	x
Dovekie		x
Black guillemot		x
Pigeon guillemot	x	
Marbled murrelet	x	
Kittlitz's murrelet	x	
Xantus's murrelet	x	
Craveri's murrelet	x	
Ancient murrelet	x	
Cassin's auklet	x	
Parakeet auklet	x	
Crested auklet	x	
Least auklet	x	
Whiskered auklet	x	
Rhinoceros auklet	x	
Common puffin		x
Horned puffin	x	
Tufted puffin	x	

of the vulnerable body organs against the chilling waters. The advantage of dark feathers on the upperparts is their conduction of heat from the sunshine.

The tendency to reduce projecting body parts is so general among arctic animals that it is called Allen's rule, after its formulator. A well known example is the rounded face and short ears of the lemmings, as compared with corresponding parts in the mice of more southerly regions. A striking example in the bird world is the hoary redpoll (*Acanthis hornemanni*), which is restricted to the Arctic in winter as well as summer. Its bill is shorter and more robust than those of any of the redpolls which breed or winter in more southerly regions. The thick-billed murre, which is completely arctic in its distribution, even in winter, has a shorter and heavier bill than the common murre. Furthermore, one subspecies of the common murre breeds and winters in the low-arctic parts of Europe. This subspecies has a shorter and more robust bill than any of the other forms of the common murre and in this way approaches the measurements of the thick-billed murre.

The structure of the short, narrow wings of the murre is admirably adapted for underwater locomotion. This manner of locomotion may well be called sub-aqueous flight, because as a process it is very similar to flying in the air. During sub-aqueous flight the wings are half opened, with the primaries more or less closed. In this position they form powerful paddles, which aid the feet in causing the bird to move rapidly through the water.

The legs of murres are also admirable instruments for propelling these birds at high speed when submerged. Specialization of these limbs for this purpose includes great muscular development, necessarily accompanied by enlargement of bony areas of attachment for large muscular bundles.

Young murres that have not yet entered the water can walk and run in a normal manner because the joints of their legs move freely. But development of the leg as a highly specialized swimming organ involves such exceptional enlargement of muscles and of bony areas of muscle attachment that movement of the joints of the leg is greatly restricted. The legs of the adult murre move readily and powerfully in limited arcs, as required for most effective propulsion through the water, but they can no longer be straightened out sufficiently to enable the bird to walk well. The sub-aqueous speed necessary for the bird's success in the environment in which it lives has been attained at the cost of bearable limitation of ability to walk and to fly.

Murres are the most social of the alcids and form, during the breeding season, closely packed loomeries or bazaars, scarcely requiring one square foot per individual. In this respect also they resemble penguins. Murres concentrate in large numbers on the wintering areas and may thus be considered gregarious at all seasons.

Murres brood only one egg, though some alcids have two. Both sexes share in the duties of incubation and care of the young. They do not build nests, but lay and incubate the single egg on bare rock in an exposed situation generally on a steep cliff.

Many of the behaviour patterns of murres, especially during the breeding season, have important survival values. The breeding season is necessarily compressed to take advantage of the maximum production of plankton and small fishes within operational range of the colony. Mass displays in the vicinity of the loomeries undoubtedly stimulate ovulation. Consequently, most of the eggs are laid within a comparatively short period. Such a mechanism also protects the eggs and young from extended predation.

Specialization and adaptation

Murres fly in a straight line, with a somewhat bee-like whirring of wings. The rapid beating of the wings gives the impression of great speed and power, but that is an illusion, for they make little progress against a strong wind and are easily outdistanced by gulls, whose wings beat in a leisurely fashion. They are unable to manoeuvre efficiently in the air.

Murres have very short rectrices. Consequently, they have little directional stability in flight. The feet, stretched out behind, function as rudders (in place of a tail) when they are flying or diving. Because their wings are short and narrow, taking flight and alighting are both difficult and clumsy feats. On level ground the birds hastily waddle

21

away, using their wings to help them along, until sufficient momentum is gained to enable them to become airborne. They are reluctant to leave the sea or their nesting colonies during strong winds. When caught on the windward side of the land, with no "sea room" to manoeuvre, they are occasionally blown inland to their doom. Such occurrences are commonly called "wrecks".

Since murres are unable to walk or run on land or even to take flight from land with rapidity, they have developed few adaptations which are of advantage on the land. Perhaps that explains why they nest on cliffs near the sea or on small islands free from land predators.

The murre literally dives into the air from its nesting ledge. In a few seconds, it thus gains sufficient momentum to make level flight possible. The flight is direct, with practically no manoeuvring, and changes of direction are in long curving routes. Fig. 1 shows the flight direction of murres going out to sea and returning to land on August 10, 1955, when a rather strong northwest wind blew directly on the cliffs at Digges Island. A half hour's count at a windward ledge on that date indicated that fewer than three birds out of five were able to alight the first time round. Those unsuccessful slanted downwards towards the sea, joined the out-going birds which were low over the water, and shortly afterwards swung over and joined the land-coming procession in another attempt at landing. Murres going out to sea to feed or to bring in food invariably hurtle

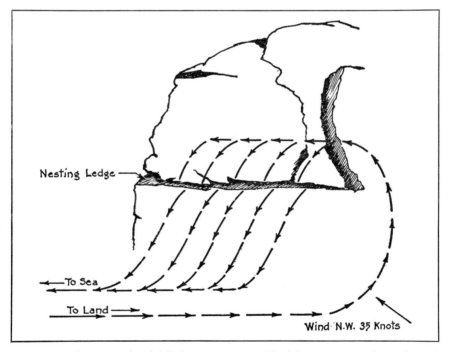

FIGURE 1. *Flight pattern of thick-billed murres at Digges Island during strong northeasterly winds*

downwards from the cliffs and proceed seawards at low altitudes. Murres returning to land invariably fly at higher altitudes. This seems especially necessary since the birds must be positioned slightly above the ledge before they can alight. Furthermore, a procession of murres going seawards at low altitude and one returning at high altitude lessens the chance of collision. I have sometimes observed mid-air collisions, which would appear to be inevitable in crowded colonies.

The murre can rise from the water rather easily when waves are present, using the crest of a wave as a trampolin. On calm days, it becomes airborne only after a long run, the wings striking the water to increase acceleration. To alight on the nesting ledge, the murre directs its flight not at the nest but at a point directly below it, and reduces speed by rising vertically just before reaching the ledge. On a large flat nesting area, the murre literally "plunks" onto its nesting site with little finesse or grace.

A precise note on the speed of a murre is recorded by Baxter and Rintoul (1953). Mr. D. C. Anderson wrote: "On 30th July I saw an interesting example of the speed of a [murre]. The destroyer was proceeding at 31 knots (35 mph) and was slowly overhauled by a Common [Murre] whirring low above the sea about 50 yards from the ship. The 'race' continued for some miles, the bird slowly gaining, and the contest arousing no little amusement among the crew as the ship was on speed trials and was being beaten. Finally, the bird turned on a spurt and gained sufficiently to cross our bows, thus doing a steady 36 mph with a burst of about 45 mph." Another race between a ship and murre is recorded by Portaz (1928). In that instance, the murre was keeping pace for a while with H.M.S. *Hood*, which was cruising at 30.5 knots (34.4 m.p.h.) into a head wind of about 15 m.p.h., and then drew ahead. The actual air speed of that particular individual was in excess of 50 m.p.h. Frohawk (1928) estimated the speed of a common murre under rather similar conditions to be more than 60 m.p.h., which is probably about its limit.

The murre moves under water with great speed and agility. It may stay submerged frequently for as long as one minute and sometimes much longer. The greatest depth to which it can dive is unknown. Murres have, however, occasionally been caught off Newfoundland on longline trawls set at 40 fathoms or more (Tuck and Squires, 1955). Depending on their choice of food, they probably rarely go below 30 fathoms.

Only a few mammals have become adapted to an aquatic existence and it is noteworthy that those which are most successful have developed a method of posterior propulsion similar to but not identical with that of a fish. Although the pectoral fins of a fish and the fore-flippers of an aquatic mammal are analogous to the wings of a murre, the former are used mainly for balancing and not, as in the case of the murre, for propulsion. The long-extinct, foot-propelled *Hesperornis*, which evidently also pursued its prey under water, became so specialized towards this end that only the vestiges of the wings eventually remained. The great auk and the penguins of the Southern Hemisphere lost the power of aerial flight as they perfected sub-aqueous flight.

Murres, then, may be considered eminently successful biologically in that they have compromised by retaining sufficient wing surface to permit both methods of flight. They are exceeded in this respect possibly only by the cormorants, which are found in both hemispheres and which have developed a method of posterior propulsion while retaining the large wing surfaces so necessary for aerial flight[1].

Water is a heavier medium for locomotion than air. Therefore, a large wing surface would be a hindrance to sub-aqueous flight. The murre in adapting itself to this method of movement has done so at the expense of its wing surface. The murre's wings are very short in comparison with its body length, but are not yet reduced to the extent of those of the penguin. Murres are not normally required to make long sustained flights. They depend to a large extent on ocean currents for both food supplies and dispersal.

It has been suggested that compressing of breeding territory, or colonial nesting, can be developed only in species whose food resources in the nesting season are normally superabundant. This seems to be the case with murres, which feed on various kinds of crustaceans and fishes. Such a situation involves a great tolerance of others during the critical period of nesting. This tolerance is highly developed in murres, breeding birds generally living in reasonable harmony with their neighbours. The older birds appear also to tolerate disturbance arising from other causes. When disturbance is continuous, only the individuals on the periphery of the colony (the least experienced and most expendable birds) desert their eggs or young.

It would appear that a species with such a compressed breeding territory, and a restricted nesting period, is especially vulnerable to meteorological or geological disasters. The extinction of the great auk may have been precipitated by the volcanic submergence of the Geirfuglasker off Iceland in 1830. Otherwise, as Grieve (1885) pointed out: "It seems likely that this skerry on which these birds principally bred might have been their home to the present time." However, most authorities insist that the extermination of the great auk was due to over-exploitation.

Murres are not as specialized as the great auks were. They are widely distributed over the coastal regions of the Northern Hemisphere. Their nesting requirements are less rigid than were those of the great auks. In fact, they show a certain amount of flexibility in their choice of nesting sites within a particular colony. Although only fragments are known of the life history of the great auks, their known distribution suggests that they were less tolerant of low temperatures and less catholic in their selection of food than are murres. It seems very unlikely that any meteorological or geological catastrophe would have other than a minor and local effect on a particular murre population.

The murres have evolved special characteristics to adapt them to their present way of life. At the critical time in incubation the brood patch is single. Earlier, however, there are two oval patches separated from each other and symmetrically located, one on each side of the sternum. This characteristic was the basis of Kaftanovski's (1951) opinion that during the process of evolution the murre was transformed from a layer of several (two) eggs to a single-egg species.

Storer (1952) suggested that the murre's habit of nesting on open ledges was developed through nesting in large caves and was evolved along with, and made possible by, their

[1]A flightless auk, *Mancalla*, existed in the Pliocene era (Miller and Howard, 1948). It had progressed much farther towards the development of a truly penguin-like swimming wing than had the great auk.

extremely colonial habits. He said: "As the density of the populations on the nesting ledges increased and the nest territories became crowded together, many of the ancestral behaviourisms likewise became compressed or lost, and the upright posture may have developed through this type of pressure. The large colonies of birds, located on isolated cliff ledges and islands, suffered less predation and hence had high nesting success. This made it possible for the species to maintain itself through each pair's producing but a single egg per season. The single egg can be rested across the tarsi, incubated in this position, and even carried short distances by a shuffling adult. Finally, the push given the egg as the parent departs hurriedly from the ledge, lunges at a potential predator, or fights with a neighbour, was probably the selective factor responsible for the evolution of the extreme pearlike form of the egg. This in turn has made possible the successful nesting of murres on narrow ledges".

Both species of murre sometimes place small pebbles in close proximity to their feet before or after the egg is laid. It is not clear whether this might be vestigial nest-building —all that remains from a period when murres actually built nests—or a tendency to develop the nest-building habit. Many eggs are prevented from rolling off the sites by a few pebbles gathered together and cemented by excrement and sediment. As such, they offer protection to the egg—which, after all, is the practical purpose of any nest.

Increase in stability of the egg on the ledge towards the end of incubation is very important to the survival of the species, as the possibility of a second laying by the bird rapidly decreases during incubation. This stability is provided both by changes taking place within the egg and by the adhesive quality of the accumulating excrement.

Fewer eggs fall toward the end of the incubation period than at its beginning. This may partly be explained by increasingly assiduous incubation, but also important are changes taking place within the egg which aid its stability. As incubation proceeds, the radius of the curve described by the egg when disturbed is diminished. Consequently, the chance of rolling off the ledge is similarly reduced.

A murre chick, raised in a small niche or crevice at a distance from a concentration of others, voids its excrement clear of the nest site. Murres raised in captivity and provided with ample room void in one particular corner of their compartment. Adults make no particular effort to keep their nest sites clean, nor is that normally possible with such compressed territories. It seems likely that the habit of voiding clear of the nest is inherent but impossible to follow later in life. It suggests that murres either occupied individual nests at one time in their evolution or that their breeding territory was formerly less compressed.

A murre's egg is enclosed in a porous shell of varying thickness. The large end of the egg is covered by a thin shell layer (0.4 to 0.6 mm.). The thickness of the shell gradually increases towards the narrow end, reaching a maximum at the centre of the narrow half and at the small end (0.6 to 0.8 mm.), i.e., at the parts in contact with the rock surface. The thickening of the shell at the most vulnerable parts of the egg may be considered an adaptive feature, developed in murres because of the absence of nest-construction. In black guillemots and puffins—birds nesting under cover—the thickness of the shell is uniform.

The eggs of no other species show such great variation in markings and ground colour. The ground colour of individual eggs varies from almost pure white to various shades of blue, green and brown. The markings vary from mere small spots to fantastic scrawls and blotches of brown, lilac or black. Our studies have indicated that a murre which replaces a lost egg lays a replacement of identical background colour and markings. Thus the particular colouring of an egg is inherent.

Several writers have suggested that a murre can recognize its egg by its special colour and markings. I have carried out experiments to determine to what extent a murre can recognize its egg. I have been unable to determine that either colour or shape is important in egg recognition by murres. It seems possible, however, that the great variations in background colours and marking have some biological significance.

In 1953, I experimented with egg selection by great black-backed gulls at Green Island, Newfoundland, by exposing a murre's egg and a white puffin's egg side by side to a marauding great black-backed gull on nine different occasions. Since puffins nest in tunnels in the turf, it was probable that the gull had never encountered a puffin's egg before. The gull chose the white puffin's egg in preference to the coloured murre's egg on seven occasions. This short experiment is not conclusive, but it suggests that the variations in background colour and the markings on a murre's egg make it less conspicuous. The natural camouflage would therefore have some survival value.

I have never seen a pure white murre's egg, but a few closely approach this colour, although they show faint markings. If it is a characteristic of gulls to take the more conspicuous eggs, then murres with the inherent ability to lay only white or nearly white ones would not be especially successful.

Regardless of whatever camouflaging effect the colouring of the eggs may have, murres do not normally leave their eggs or chicks unattended. One of the pair almost continuously incubates the egg until it is hatched or looks after the chick until it leaves the nest site.

When the young are ready to leave the nesting colony, they merely plunge into the sea or hurtle off the high ledges. The lack of primaries and rectrices at the fledging stage is no disadvantage to the young. Those parts of plumage are not truly essential to the murre until it must return to land to breed.

CHAPTER II

Variations and the Vernacular

Both species of murre occur in the arctic marine zone, while only the common murre occurs in the boreal marine zone. Although there may be considerable overlapping of both species in the arctic marine zone, the thick-billed murre has the more northerly distribution and is the only species occurring in the high-arctic marine zone (Fig. 2). Storer (1952) states: "*Uria lomvia* arose in the arctic, probably north of Siberia. Perhaps a small or fluctuating population of murres was able, through preadaptation or a rapid evolution, to remain in the north after most of the ancestral species moved south. Continued rapid evolution in the north, where feeding conditions were extremely favourable but other conditions less favourable, led to the development of *Uria lomvia*. This species spread southward and met *Uria aalge*, which was spreading northward as its more northern populations became adapted to colder conditions. Finally by the time the two species came together they had developed reproductive isolation".

Thick-billed murres have a distinctive white gape mark in the breeding season, and at that time of the year the white on the throat terminates in a sharp peak. Neither of these is apparent in the common murre. In full winter plumage, the common murre has a narrow black line running back from the eye into the white of the cheek, a line which the thick-billed murre lacks. Those are the best distinguishing marks.

Geographic races of murres have small differences in wing length, tarsal length, length of culmen, bill depth and colouring. The dorsal colouring is subjected to the most geographic variation, but even so the dorsal colouring of northern populations of common murres may be similar to that of thick-billed murres. The under-coverts of both species may vary from predominately white in certain populations to predominately dark in others.

The smallest murres seem to be the Iberian population of common murres, the maximum wing-length of which is 195 mm. The largest seem to be the Kamchatka population of thick-billed murres, the maximum wing-length of which is 240 mm. The length and thickness of the bill, while an important taxonomic feature of geographic populations, does not appear to be a reliable characteristic where both species of various ages and several races are mixed on the wintering grounds (Table 2). The common murres have the longest bills, in that the length of the culmen of the smallest race parallels the length of the culmen of the largest race of thick-billed murres. The depth of the culmen of the nominate race of common murre may actually exceed that of the depth of the culmen of the nominate race of thick-billed murre. The depth of the culmen of *Uria aalge hyperborea* is greatest of all murres. For this reason, thick-billed murre is not an apt vernacular name for *Uria lomvia*.

Four somewhat isolated populations have been assigned to the subspecies *Uria aalge aalge* by Salomonsen and others. Those are, from west to east, the common murres of

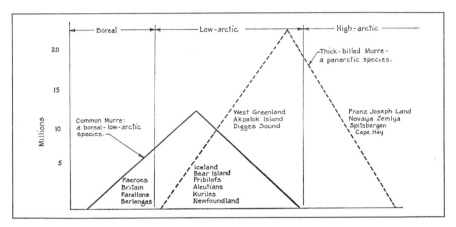

FIGURE 2. *Optimum murre populations in relation to the boreal, low-arctic and high-arctic marine zones*

Table 2: *Variations in culmen length and depth of murres (from Salomonsen, 1944; Storer, 1952; Portenko, 1944; and Bernis, 1949).*

	Culmen length		Culmen depth	
	Males	Females	Males	Females
COMMON MURRE				
albionis	42.5 – 51.0	43.0 – 50.0	11.8 – 14.2	12.1 – 13.7
ibericus	38.0 – 47.0	38.0 – 47.0	11.0 – 13.5	11.0 – 13.5
intermedia	45.0 – 51.0	43.0 – 48.0	12.9 – 14.7	13.8 – 14.8
aalge	41.5 – 49.5	39.0 – 51.5	12.6 – 16.0	12.5 – 14.5
spiloptera	44.0 – 53.5	47.0 – 50.0	12.4 – 13.3	12.6 – 13.1
hyperborea	46.0 – 48.0	42.0 – 47.0	17.5 – 18.0	15.0 – 16.0
californica	43.0 – 53.5	41.5 – 52.0	12.5 – 15.6	12.5 – 15.2
inornata	43.5 – 53.0	42.0 – 52.0	12.6 – 16.2	12.4 – 15.9
THICK-BILLED MURRE				
lomvia	30.5 – 41.0	33.0 – 41.5	12.7 – 15.6	12.0 – 15.8
arra	35.0 – 47.0	35.0 – 48.0	13.6 – 16.1	12.9 – 15.6
heckeri	34.8 – 40.0	33.9 – 41.5	— —	— —

FIGURE 3. *Breeding distribution of common murres in relation to geographical races*

FIGURE 4. *Breeding distribution of thick-billed murres in relation to geographical races*

eastern North America, those from Iceland, those from Scotland and the Hebrides, and those from southern Norway. Those populations, although not differing from each other sufficiently to warrant taxonomic separation, are not identical. The common murres from southwestern Scandinavia are intermediate between *Uria aalge hyperborea* of northern Norway and *Uria aalge albionis* of the southern British Isles and Heligoland. Similarly, the murres of northern Scotland are intermediate between *albionis* and *Uria aalge spiloptera* of the Faeroes (Storer, 1952). *Uria aalge aalge* intergrades with *Uria aalge spiloptera* in the Shetlands and with *Uria aalge hyperborea* along the coast of Norway.

The foregoing comments and Figs. 3 and 4 indicate the geographic variation in murres. Taxonomic treatment is given in Salomonsen (1932 and 1944), Storer (1952), Portenko (1944), and Bernis (1949). I am accepting all subspecies without reservation. It seems likely, however, that more material should be available before the most recently described races, namely *ibericus*, *arroides*, *eleonorae* and *heckeri*, are accepted as valid races under the present taxonomic rules.

THE COMMON MURRE

Uria aalge aalge (Pontoppidan)
Type locality: Iceland
Breeding range: Along the coast of Labrador from the Gannet Islands to Nunarsuk Island; in the Gulf of St. Lawrence from Bradore Bay and Bonaventure Island to the Magdalen Islands; at Funk Island, Baccalieu Island, Green Island and Cape St. Mary's, Newfoundland—the latter being its most southerly limit in eastern North America; in southwestern Greenland (at Sermilinguaq Fjord only); Iceland; Norway to the Vesteraalen, where it intergrades with *Uria aalge hyperborea*, and Scotland to Ailsa Craig, where it intergrades with *Uria aalge albionis*.

Uria aalge albionis Witherby
Type locality: Flamborough, Yorkshire, England
Breeding range: Along the coasts of the British Isles from the Farne Islands and Ailsa Craig south, Heligoland and Brittany.

Uria aalge ibericus Bernis
Type locality: Sisargas Islands, Spain
Breeding range: The Iberian Peninsula, intergrading with *Uria aalge albionis* in south Brittany.

Uria aalge intermedia Nilsson
Type locality: The Baltic Sea
Breeding range: Restricted to the Baltic Sea.

Uria aalge hyperborea Salomonsen
Type locality: Bear Island
Breeding range: Bear Island, Norway north of Vesteraalen, the Murman coast and Novaya Zemlya.

Uria aalge spiloptera Salomonsen
Type locality: The Faeroes
Breeding range: The Faeroe Islands, intergrading with *Uria aalge aalge* in Shetland.

Uria aalge californica (Bryant)
Type locality: The Farallon Islands, California
Breeding range: California south to Hurricane Point—the latter being the southern limit of the common murre in western North America. It intergrades in Washington and Oregon with *Uria aalge inornata*.

Uria aalge inornata Salomonsen
Type locality: St. Matthew's Island, Bering Sea
Breeding range: Point Hope, Alaska, south to Triangle Island, British Columbia; the islands of the Bering Sea, the Aleutians and Komandorskie Islands and as far south in Japan as Tsugaru Strait.

THE THICK-BILLED MURRE

Uria lomvia lomvia (Linnaeus)
Type locality: Greenland
Breeding range: Bird Rocks in the Gulf of St. Lawrence; from Cape St. Mary's Newfoundland (its southernmost limit in the Northern Hemisphere) along the Labrador coast and in the eastern Canadian Arctic as far north as Coburg Island and as far west as Prince Leopold Island; Greenland, Bear Island, Spitsbergen, the Murman coast and Novaya Zemlya.

Uria lomvia arra (Pallas)
Type locality: Kamchatka
Breeding range: Alaska, the coasts and islands of the Bering Sea, the Kuriles and the Sea of Okhotsk, and as far south as Tyulena Island, South Sakhalin.

Uria lomvia arroides Portenko
Type locality: Hooker Island, Franz Josef Land
Breeding range: Franz Josef Archipelago.

Uria lomvia eleonorae Portenko
Type locality: Preobraschenje Island, Khatanga Bay
Breeding range: Siberia and New Siberian Islands, Khatanga Bay.

Uria lomvia heckeri Portenko
Type locality: Cape Waring, Wrangel Island
Breeding range: Wrangel Island and the northern coast of Chuckchee Peninsula.

Genetic variations

Genetic variations occur quite commonly in the alcids. Probably the best known in murres is the "ringed" or "bridled" phase, a form of the common murre in which a narrow white line extends around the eye and for a short distance backward and downward.

This form was once considered a separate species, *Uria ringvia*. Bridled murres are known only from among the Atlantic populations of the common murre. There is no indication that they prefer to mate among themselves. Mating in a mixed colony of bridled and "normal" common murres appears to be at random.

Southern (1939 and 1951) organized counts of the percentages of bridled murres throughout Britain and in other parts of their range in 1939 and again in 1949. Two main conclusions were apparent from his study: first, in Britain the percentages of bridled murres increased from south-southeast to north-northwest but the reverse was the situation in Iceland; and secondly, the percentage was not always the same in one area. Possibly the possession of a bridle gives a murre an advantage over other murres in some areas, and a disadvantage in others, though it is not known why.

Bridled murres occur in the common murre populations in eastern North America. Dr. H. F. Lewis found 17.7 per cent in the colonies along the North Shore of the Gulf of St. Lawrence (Lewis, 1930). James Fisher and I found 17.3 per cent bridled murres at Cape St. Mary's colony in 1953, and 20.8 per cent bridled at Green Island, Witless Bay, in 1959. At Funk Island, on the east coast of Newfoundland, a count of common murres in 1956 showed 21 per cent to be bridled individuals: similar counts in 1958 and 1959 showed 17.3 and 19.9 per cent respectively. Several Labrador colonies at the Gannet Islands were 32 per cent bridled in 1953. In the same year at Nunarsuk Island, the northerly limit of the species in eastern North America, where the population was small, bridled murres comprised 71 per cent of the common murre population.

Abnormal plumages caused by a lack of pigment (albinism) or an excess (melanism) occur in murres, but not very commonly. There are several published records of full or partial albino common murres in the literature. In 1956, a full albino chick and a partial albino chick were found on Funk Island. The latter's plumage pattern was retained, but the normally black feathers were replaced by feathers of buff. In 1958, three albinistic chicks, pale buff in colour, were observed on Funk Island. Albinistic conditions also occur in both species when feathers, such as those on the head, grow back after an injury.

Albinism probably occurs more frequently in the thick-billed murre. Winge (1898) records several from West Greenland. Storer (1952) mentions five specimens in various American museums. I have examined six shot during winter in the coastal waters of Newfoundland. Three of those were full albinos and the other three were partial albinos. In the latter instances, the plumage pattern was retained, but the normally black feathers were grey.

Melanistic conditions occur even more rarely. Storer (1952) mentions three museum specimens of common murre from the Pacific coast, one of which was completely melanistic and two others in which many of the flank feathers were entirely dark. Winge (1898) records several melanistic thick-billed murres from West Greenland. A completely melanistic thick-billed murre was shot in Trinity Bay, Newfoundland, during the winter of 1952. Its normally white feathers were brownish-black, not quite as dark as the back feathers. This specimen is now in the National Museum of Canada.

The vernacular names of murres

The scientific classification of birds is a comparatively recent invention. Each genetic type is given a generic, a specific, and if necessary, a subspecific name, all in latinized or graecized form, by which it is recognized by scientists the world over. In by-gone days, before the exchange of ideas was as swift as it is today, scientists, unknown to each other, sometimes gave different names to the same species. Thus it is that over the years the generic names of *Colymbus*, *Alca*, and *Uria* have been applied to murres. Today, nomenclature boards (in North America, a committee of the American Ornithologists' Union) have been set up in several areas to stabilize the scientific naming of birds and to prevent duplication.

While such boards or committees can decide upon an internationally acceptable scientific name for a species, the vernacular names are part of the common language of each country and sometimes reflect regional variation in speech. Thus the species are known in the vernacular in North America as murres, in Great Britain as guillemots, in Denmark as lomvi and so on. The most commonly used vernacular names of murres in some of the countries in which they occur are listed in Table 3.

Because a subspecific form, which is merely a distinct or local population, may also have a vernacular name, the labelling of birds is especially confusing to the layman. The race of the common murre occurring in the eastern North American regions was formerly known as the Atlantic murre; the more southerly race in the Pacific as the California murre. Some forms may not have vernacular names, although the Faeroe population is sometimes referred to as the Faeroe murre and the Baltic population as the Baltic murre. The subspecies of thick-billed murre occurring in eastern North America was formerly known as Brünnich's murre; that occurring in part of the Pacific as Pallas's murre.

A common vernacular name for the murre in Newfoundland is "turr". It is used for either species and especially for a bird in winter plumage. More than a century ago, the Reverend Philip Tocque (1846), perhaps the first Newfoundland author, referred to "turs" or "merrs", and ever since both names have been used somewhat indiscriminately. Unfortunately, the confusion in usage of the names has occasionally led to the mistaken belief that turrs are a different species from murres. Bonnycastle (1842) called them "the guillemot or merr of Newfoundland". "Baccalieu" (or Baccalo) birds is a traditional name in Newfoundland for the murres nesting on Baccalieu Island, and is usually used only when the birds are in summer plumage.

According to Hatton and Harvey (1883), the name given to the murres by the aborigines of Newfoundland (the Beothucks) was "geonet". The Eskimos call them "akpa".

Table 3: *Some Vernacular Names for Murres*

Country	Common Murre	Thick-billed Murre
Denmark	Lomvi	Kortnaebbet lomvi
Germany	Trottlellumme	Dickschnabellumme
England	Guillemot	Brünnich's guillemot
North America	Common murre	Brünnich's murre
Spain	Aràu	Guillemote
France	Guillemot de troil	Guillemot de Brünnich
Iceland	Langvia	Stuttnefja
Italy	Uria	Uria grosse
Holland	Zeekoet	Groote zeekoet
Norway	Lomvi	Spitsberglomvi
Poland	Nurzyk podielaly	Nurzyk Brunnicha
Portugal	Aìro	
Finland	Etalänkiisla	Pohjankiisla
Sweden	Sillgrissla	Sptiesbergsgrissla
Japan	Umigarasu	Hashibuto umigarasu

CHAPTER III

The Environment

Murres are tied to the land by breeding requirements but they spend most of their lives at sea. Their entire existence is controlled by the marine environment. Common murres breed in the boreal and low-arctic marine zones. Thick-billed murres breed in the low-arctic and high-arctic marine zones.

Many geographers and explorers have attempted to define the arctic regions by various criteria, all of which are terrestrial in application. Washburn (1951) suggested that the arctic lands be those north of the 50°F. isotherm for the warmest month of the year, provided that the mean temperature for the coldest month is not more than 32°F. Such criteria would not aptly apply to the oceans of the Northern Hemisphere because the sea is a more homogeneous environment than the land. Except for such outstanding surface areas as the Gulf Stream, the seasonal temperature variation of the ocean's surface is less than five per cent. The surface temperature of the northern oceans seldom falls below 29°F.

Throughout the oceans, proportions of the various inorganic salts are quite uniform. Thus, whatever the concentration, chloride ions constitute about 55 per cent of the dissolved salts (Sverdrup *et al.*, 1942). Except near continental shores, where land drainage affects the constitution of the sea or where other special conditions may prevail, differences in the composition of sea water from place to place and from time to time are differences of concentration. Consequently, the composition of any particular mass of water is determined by the amount of chloride which it contains. The salinity is then calculated by multiplying the chlorinity, stated in grams per kilogram, by 1.805 and adding 0.03. It is expressed in parts per thousand, using the symbol 0 /00.[1]

High-arctic waters are those with a low salinity (below 34 parts per thousand) and low temperatures. The temperature of the Arctic Ocean is always close to the freezing point of water of that salinity (i.e. between $-1.5°$ and $-1.8°C$.). Low-arctic waters, because they contain some Atlantic or Pacific waters from the more temperate regions, are higher in temperature and also in salinity.

The criteria for the arctic marine zones should not follow, then, the limits of the terres-

---

[1]Actually, the determinations are not nearly so simple as this brief account may seem to imply. For one thing, they involve the use of "normal water" which was formerly prepared and distributed from the hydrographical laboratories of the International Commission for the Exploration of the Sea in Copenhagen, and is now available from the Woods Hole Oceanographic Institution, Massachusetts.

trial zones in the same regions set out by Washburn (1951) and others. Rather, the low-arctic[2] marine zone may be defined as the area between the northern limit of surface flow of non-arctic water and the southern limit of surface flow of arctic water (Dunbar, 1955a).

The zones of the marine environment in the Northern Hemisphere may be, then, as follows:

High-arctic zone: Regions where pure polar waters (setting aside land drainage) are found at the surface.

Low-arctic zone: Regions where both polar and southern (boreal) waters are found at the surface.

Boreal zone: Regions of pure Atlantic or Pacific waters.

The approximate position of the low-arctic marine zone, as defined here, and its boundaries with the high-arctic zone on the north and the boreal zone on the south are shown in Fig. 5. Those boundaries correspond fairly well with the 5°C. and 15°C. surface isotherm for the warmest month (August) of the year.

A large part of the Polar Basin is permanently covered by ice. For a great part of the year large expanses of both the high-arctic and the low-arctic marine regions are unsuitable for sea-birds because of pack ice.

Perhaps no natural power on earth is more destructive than the constant battering of ocean waves or the tremendous thrust of pack ice with millions of tons of pressure behind it. The coastline of Newfoundland and Labrador shows clearly the results of those tremendous forces. Thomas Stevenson developed the instrument known as a wave dynamometer and with it studied the waves that battered the coast of his native Scotland. He found that in winter gales the force of a wave might be as great as 6,000 pounds to the square foot. More precise instruments have measured greater forces.

The environment of murres is subjected to violent storms. A great part of their environment is crossed by an unending procession of intense cyclones. This is owing largely to the existence of the so-called "permanent" low-pressure areas commonly known as the "Aleutian low" and the "Iceland low". Meteorologists refer to those two regions as the Pacific and Atlantic storm belts. The Atlantic storm belt has its axis from Labrador to the Shetlands and Scandinavia. Consequently, the sector from Newfoundland across Iceland to Novaya Zemlya is almost continuously stormy.

While waves may have their destructive effects, they are also creative. Headlands and islets are modified so that they provide nesting sites for murres. Concurrently, the same force may slowly render many traditional sites unsuitable.

In the high-arctic regions and in some parts of the low-arctic, ice or early winter storms may affect the breeding success of murres. In the eastern Canadian Arctic regions which I have studied, the murre colonies are situated in proximity to areas of coastal turbulence and become ice-free early in the season. Uspenski (1956) states that the common murre's preference for warmish water and for regions which are early in becoming

---

[2]Dunbar used "subarctic" to define this zone. The word "subarctic" appears to have several meanings in North American literature. On that account, I prefer to follow the terminology used in Europe. See, especially, the introductory chapter in Freuchen and Salomonsen (1958).

ice-free prevents it from extending its range in Novaya Zemlya. Presumably the continued warming of the waters of the Barents and Kara Seas and the west coast of Greenland will create more favourable conditions for a wider distribution of this species.

A late season in the Arctic or a bad "ice year" may have an adverse effect on the breeding biology of murres. This is dealt with in more detail in Chapter XV. Early winter storms may have two effects, both detrimental. The young may perish from exposure or pack ice may temporarily cut off the food supplies. Normally, this should affect only a small percentage of a colony, the young birds which have laid late in the season and for the first time.

The major currents of the Northern Hemisphere are shown in Fig. 6. A brief discussion of oceanic circulations in the western North Atlantic is necessary for the understanding of the importance of the ocean currents to murres.

The arctic waters flow out of the Polar Basin along the west coast of Greenland and through the islands of the eastern Canadian Arctic and then spread over Baffin Bay, Foxe Basin and Hudson Bay (Dunbar, 1955a). The waters pouring out from Hudson Strait and Davis Strait converge off Cape Chidley to form the Labrador Current. The Labrador Current flows along the coast of Labrador and the east coast of Newfoundland. It eventually dissipates in the warm waters of the Gulf Stream at the edge of the Grand Banks. It is the Labrador Current which brings southwards vast quantities of plankton in the summer months. Each spring it also brings southward the pack ice, which a few months earlier existed as an unbroken cover in Baffin Bay and the eastern Canadian Arctic. At times, pack ice has extended in late March from Newfoundland to the west coast of Greenland. A similar current, with pack ice in spring, flows southwards along the Kamchatka coast in the Bering Sea.

Murre chicks are unable to fly when they first leave the nest sites. At about the same time, the breeding adults undergo a post-nuptial moult. Both the chick and the flightless adult accompanying it then swim northwards against the current. Murres from Newfoundland breeding colonies, for example, move north along the Labrador coast, remaining in the more productive cold waters until they are able to fly. Thick-billed murres from the Canadian and Greenland colonies reach the Newfoundland area in late October but by that time they are able to fly and most of the northern seas and the coast waters of Labrador have begun to freeze over.

In parts of their breeding range where they are not affected by ice, murres are largely sedentary. Juvenile birds, however, are more inclined to wander southwards in winter. At that time of year they are strong flyers.

In the Aleutians and in parts of Europe where murres are not affected by late ice in the spring, they nest at least a month earlier than in Labrador and the eastern Canadian Arctic. The nesting phenology of murres in Southwest Greenland, which is not affected by ice in late spring, is earlier than that of the thick-billed murres in Canada.

Except for a few small isolated basins, all land drainage is towards the oceans. The seas taken together constitute a great catch-basin for everything that leaches from the land or is washed from its surface. Obviously the ocean water must be a great chemical *pot-pourri*, carrying in solution the salts of all the elements. The nutrient salts utilized

FIGURE 5. *Breeding distribution of murres in relation to the surface August isotherms. The approximate limits of the low-arctic marine zones are the 15°C and 5°C surface isotherms for that month. The approximate southern limit of the high-arctic marine zone is the 5°C surface isotherm for that month*

FIGURE 6. *Breeding distribution of murres in relation to principal marine currents*

by the marine organisms are returned to the sea on death of those organisms or to the surface by the excrement of sea-birds which live on marine organisms.

Most chemicals in solution in the marine regions become directly or indirectly nutrient to organisms that live there. Nowhere in all the sea does life exist in such bewildering abundance as in the surface waters. A cupful of water may contain millions upon millions of diatoms, tiny plants, each of them far too small to be seen by the human eye; or it may swarm with an infinite number of animal creatures, none larger than a dust mote, which live on plant cells still smaller than themselves (Carson, 1950).

The plankton—of which diatoms are the most important forms in arctic and temperate seas—makes the mineral wealth of the seas available to the larger animals. Feeding directly on the diatoms and other groups of unicellular plankton are the crustaceans and the young of many fishes—the zooplankton.

The cold climate and waters of the Arctic are extremely favourable for the growth of phytoplankton. Because of this, they are the most highly productive regions of the oceans. As a direct result, the world's great fisheries are carried on in the low-arctic marine regions.

The maximum growth of phytoplankton in those marine regions occurs mainly in the spring and to a lesser extent in the autumn. The surface waters of the Northern Hemisphere absorb the cold during the winter, become more dense and slowly sink, displacing warmer layers below. This internal circulation is largely checked in the spring and summer when warm surface layers, such as the Gulf Stream generally prevent vertical mixing. But currents such as the Gulf Stream exert a strong influence, carrying warmth into marine regions to the north and providing energy for vertical mixing. At the strongest surge of those warm currents, where the salinity and temperatures most strongly differ, upwellings of the buried layers of cold waters take place. Since those upwellings from arctic waters are rich in nutrients, they provide the basic food for the phytoplankton. The maximum amount of light, which occurs at that season, also stimulates the growth.

The sudden awakening of the simple plant life, which was largely dormant during the winter, and its explosive reproduction, is one of nature's great phenomena. But the phytoplankton holds sway in the sea for only a short period. Almost at once its reproduction is matched by an increase in the small animals of the zooplankton, which feed on the abundant plant growth and in turn become the food of larger creatures. It is at that time of the year that murres forsake the open sea and converge on islands and cliffs which are their traditional breeding places and where they are assured of a supply of zooplankton and fishes for their young.

For some reason, perhaps connected with the comparatively recent freeing of the arctic waters from the Pleistocene glaciation, the fishes, as a group, have not yet managed to invade the coldest waters with any success (Dunbar, 1955a). Moreover, such fishes as are found in the arctic waters are benthonic forms, living close to the bottom. The most abundant fish in the arctic waters is probably the polar cod (*Boreogadus saida*). This little cod is an important food species for murres. The lack of pelagic[3] fish is sur-

---

[3]Fish or organisms living free in the water, particularly in the upper layers of the oceans, are called "pelagic", as opposed to "benthonic" or bottom-living forms.

41

prising, since the plankton of the high-arctic waters, though less abundant than that in the low-arctic, is nevertheless substantial.

In the low-arctic zone there are many more species of fish of both pelagic and benthonic forms. The low-arctic capelin (*Mallotus villosus*) may well be the single most important winter food item of murres. Murres feed to some extent on the young of such commercially important fishes as Atlantic cod (*Gadus callarias*), Greenland cod (*Gadus ognac*), and Greenland halibut (*Reinhardtius hippoglossoides*).

This environment, the high-arctic part rich in plankton but poor in fishes and the low-arctic part rich in both plankton and fishes, is shared by a number of large marine mammals. The principal ones are the Phocidae or hair seals, the walrus, the Otariidae or eared seals of the Pacific, and the beluga (*Delphinapterus leucas*) and the narwhal (*Monodon monoceros*) of the high-arctic. In the summer months, various species of fish-eating whales inhabit the low-arctic marine regions and plankton-eating whales inhabit the high-arctic marine regions.

Life is not evenly distributed over the seas. There are deserts in the sea, with little organic content, and there are areas where in season marine life is prolific. As a rule, the farther one moves from the equatorial belt towards the poles, the more the species-composition of life is restricted. Simultaneously, the biological productivity of the ocean and the number of creatures inhabiting it increases (Uspenski, 1956).

Regions of vigorous vertical circulation are especially prevalent in the Antarctic and there penguins and petrels live in immense numbers. Such regions also occur off the west coast of Africa, famous for its large gannet and pelican colonies, and off Peru, famous for its large cormorant and pelican colonies.

In the Northern Hemisphere such regions are found in the Bering Sea, along the west coast of Greenland, in the Barents Sea and along the west coast of Novaya Zemlya. In all those regions, great murre loomeries are located. Elsewhere in the low-arctic and high-arctic regions of the Northern Hemisphere, the optimum hydrographical conditions for a prolific marine life are induced more perhaps by coastal and bank turbulence than by actual vertical circulation. Such regions are situated along the east coast of Newfoundland, along the coast of Labrador and in many localities in the eastern Canadian Arctic. Regions of vigorous turbulence occur especially where there are sudden changes in the depth of the sea. They are invariably good commercial fishing regions. It is not a mere coincidence that the murre colonies situated along the east coast of Newfoundland and along the Labrador coast are close to excellent commercial fishing areas.

The existence of adequate food supplies is in itself not sufficient to determine the location of a murre colony. A feature of great importance in this respect is the nature of the coastline. There are lengthy gaps in the breeding distribution of murres in the European Arctic and in the western Canadian Arctic because the coastline is low in those regions and does not provide steep seaward-facing cliffs.

Murre colonies are located only on rocky coasts, usually where there are steep seaward faces from which the colony rarely expands to flat cliff-tops and low islands. Low-lying islands, such as Funk Island, off the east coast of Newfoundland, are exceptions.

They are presumably attractive because of their remoteness and their freedom from predators.

The type of rock in murre colonies may vary greatly. Large colonies are located on basalt, limestone, chalk, granite and many other geological formations. Stratification, which provides ledges, or the presence of weathered pinnacles and other projections, appears to be an important requirement.

PART II: DISTRIBUTION AND POPULATIONS

CHAPTER IV

Murre Colonies of the Polar Basin

It is surprising but pleasant that modern sailing instructions, which contain the latest information on obtaining positions by loran, should at the same time advise the navigator to be guided, like the Norseman of old, by the flight of birds. The Norway Pilot has this to say about the colonies on Jan Mayen: "The presence of sea fowl in large numbers will give an indication of the approach of land and the noise of their rookeries may be useful in locating the shore".

The murre colonies at Jan Mayen have been visited by a number of ornithologists, a recent one being Cullen (1954), who spent the summer of 1950 there. No precise estimate of the populations of the murres on Jan Mayen has been published, but Fisher and Lockley (1954) state: "Jan Mayen has at least a million sea-birds". The most abundant sea-bird, by far, nesting on Jan Mayen is the thick-billed murre.

Northeast of Jan Mayen is Bear Island. The Norway Pilot has this to say about the murres of Bear Island: "The sea around the island teems with guillemots. These flocks and the direction of their flight on approaching, together with the use of the lead, are of great value in making the island when it is foggy".

Bear Island is so situated that branches of the North Atlantic Drift flow along its coast. Consequently, although the locality is within the range of the thick-billed murre (*Uria lomvia*), the more southern species breeds there also. As a matter of fact, Bear Island is the type locality of the arctic form of the common murre (*Uria aalge hyperborea*), which also has a northern outpost on Novaya Zemlya and breeds from Vesteraalen eastward along the coast of the Polar Basin.

Concerning the relationship of the two species of murres on Bear Island, Duffey and Sergeant (1950) showed that in 1948 the very large colonies on the southern cliffs were composed of common murres and thick-billed murres in a ratio of roughly two to one. In the smaller colonies on the west, north and east coasts, there was a majority of thick-billed murres. They wrote: "This seemed in part to be due to a preference of the latter species (i.e., common murres) for nesting in smaller groups on the more open, irregular ledges, such as are typical breeding sites of the razorbill on British coasts, and which are plentiful on these lower more broken cliffs, though restricted to the very top of the high southern dolomite cliffs. At the latter, Brünnich's were mixed freely with Common Guillemots on the typical long ledges, but predominated at the cliff-top. However, at the two localities where the guillemots extended to the flat top of the cliff, it was only the Common Guillemot that did so."

A similar distribution of the two species was found on Bear Island by the Oxford Expedition of 1921 (Jourdain, 1922), and by the Cambridge Expedition of 1932 (Bertram and Lack, 1933). James Fisher (*in litt.*) observed the same kind of thing in the mixed colonies on the Westmann Islands, off southern Iceland. In the mixed colonies in Newfoundland and Labrador, the narrow ledges are occupied solely by thick-billed murres, while both thick-billed and common murres breed on the wider ledges.

Some of the buttresses of Bear Island rise 400 feet from the sea and, as Bertram and Lack (1933) state: ". . . have been described with justice as the finest bird-cliffs in the Northern Hemisphere."

Regarding the population of murres on Bear Island, Fisher and Lockley (1954) write: "The miles of cliffs round Bear Island (especially at its south end) harbour millions— (an unknown number of millions) of Brünnich's and Common Guillemots."

North from Bear Island is Spitsbergen, famous for its teeming multitudes of sea-birds. There are large thick-billed murre colonies on many of the Spitsbergen headlands, such as the Vogel Hoek of Prince Charles Foreland; Clover Cliff, the headland of the northwest; the Alkrange in Hinlopen Strait; Mount Congress, Cape Diabas, Phantom Point and Hyperit Hat in Ice Fjord; and Cape Sofia in Horn Sound. Elton (in Longstaff, 1924) wrote of the Alkrange: "It is impossible to describe the multitudes of the [murres] on the bird cliffs. The place was teeming with them; literally hundreds of thousands. The cliffs are made of columnar dolerite which weathers into pinnacles and which rise several hundred feet sheer out of the sea. On the numerous and narrow ledges the birds were so crowded that there was room for no more."

Fisher and Lockley (1954) state: ". . . there may well be millions at more than several places in Spitsbergen."

The breeding murre of Spitsbergen is the thick-billed murre (*Uria lomvia lomvia*). There is no positive evidence that the common murre breeds there at all. Thus, Jourdain (1922) wrote: "The only positive record of *Uria troile* from Spitsbergen is that of one obtained in August, 1898, on Barents Island by the Prince of Monaco, though possibly one was shot by Herr Dreyer in 1881".

There are many colonies of thick-billed murres breeding on the basalt cliffs and capes of Franz Josef Land. Somewhere in that area are the most northerly murre colonies in the Polar Basin. The northeasterly section of the area borders the permanent ice pack.

Little is known about the murre colonies in Franz Josef Land except that they are vast. Clarke (1898) mentions large loomeries at Cape Crowther, Cape Grant and Cape Stephen. Other breeding localities in Franz Josef Land which are mentioned in the literature are Auk Point (on Rudolf Island), Bell Island, and the vast loomery at Cape Fisher, Salisbury Island, which Nansen paused to watch on his famous journey from the *Fram.*

The Novaya Zemlya murre bazaars are so large and important that the Soviet Government has carried out special studies to determine the feasibility of their economic exploitation (Gorbunov, 1925; Krasovski, 1937; Kaftanovski, 1938; Uspenski, 1956).

In Bezymyannaya Bay, near Gribovaya Bay, there existed not long ago the greatest of all Novaya Zemlya bird bazaars. The colonies are situated on the coast to the north of Bezymyannaya (the North Bezymyannaya bazaars), and on Kutoff Island. A detailed description of them is given by Krasovski (1937).

The total length of the North Bezymyannaya bazaars is nearly 12 kilometres, and of the South Bezymyannaya bazaar eleven kilometres. The predominant nesting species is the thick-billed murre, although small numbers of puffins, kittiwakes and glaucous gulls nest on the cliffs also. The Kutoff Island bazaar, rather less than one kilometre in length, is occupied entirely by thick-billed murres.

In 1933-34, the murre population in Bezymyannaya Bay, according to a census made by Krasovski (1937) in all three areas, totalled 1,644,503 individuals. This total comprised 116,557 in the northern bazaars, 1,510,946 in the southern bazaars, and 17,000 on Kutoff Island. Another census of those colonies was made in 1942 by L. O. Belopolski (Uspenski, 1956), who found that because of heavy utilization the total population had dwindled to 600,000 (100,000 in the northern bazaars and 500,000 in the southern bazaars and on Kutoff Island). In 1948, the colonies continued to decrease and the total number was officially recorded as 290,000 (200,000 in the southern bazaars, 80,000 in the northern bazaars and 10,000 on Kutoff Island). Protective measures were taken in 1947 and the coasts of Gribovaya and Bezymyannaya Bays were made a preserve. Beneficial results of that measure were not slow in appearing (Table 4). Since that date, the northern bazaars, which had suffered least from excessive exploitation, have been completely restored. The population of the southern bazaars has increased substantially, the average annual increase in breeding populations during the period of protection being approximately ten per cent (Uspenski, 1956).

Table 4: *Composition of Bezymyannaya Bay bird bazaars in 1950.*
(In individuals, after Uspenski, 1956).

Bazaar	Kittiwakes	Murres	Puffins	Glaucous Gulls
S. Bezymyannaya	5,620	240,000	—	120
N. Bezymyannaya	2,040	120,000	46	84
Kutoff Island	—	11,000	—	8
Total:	7,660	371,000	46	212

The largest bird bazaars in Novaya Zemlya at present are in Archangel Gulf. Their length is about 1.5 kilometres, but because of the tremendous height of the cliffs an innumerable multitude of birds finds shelter there. A brief but colourful description of the bazaar is given by Rusanoff (1910): "The southern shore of Archangel Gulf is amazingly picturesque. The sea murmurs lazily. Around it are piled up, one above another, wild and terrible cliffs. They are eroded by the waves beneath, shattered by frost above. In every crevice, on every projection of the cliffs, birds roost; gay, swift-winged dovekies, great far-extending flocks of murres . . . On the mountain peaks snowy owls sit motionless ... Gulls wheel in the air with piercing screams ..." Later descriptions of that bazaar were given by Schaaning (1923) and Gorbunov (1929). In 1942, L. O. Belopolski, leader of an economic expedition to Novaya Zemlya, estimated the numbers of thick-billed murres in the gulf at 400,000. Subsequent exploitation of the bazaars in that area was so irregular and on such a small scale, that the numbers of murres nesting there at present may be approximately the same (Uspenski, 1956).

Not far from Archangel Gulf there is, in Vilkitski Bay, another large bird bazaar. An excellent description of that bazaar is also given by Rusanoff (1910): "The whole north shore of the bay is occupied by a great glacier, which usually reaches the sea. On the east side one's attention is caught from a distance by a tall cliff, looking like a high stone wall. That cliff is occupied from top to bottom by birds, thanks to which an enormous quantity of guano is piled up at its foot; and on the soil so enriched there grows vegetation which for Novaya Zemlya is luxuriant. It includes the mosses, king-cups, and a few herbaceous plants generally found in Novaya Zemlya. But such an amazing difference! In other places that sparse yellowish herbage scarcely rises above the surface of the earth, but here the stout stems of king-cups reach a height of 20 to 30 cm. and are covered with dense green, succulent leaves. The seed-laden grasses sway heavily, and a thick mossy cover spreads over the low places." Belopolski in 1942 estimated that the number of murres in the Vilkitski Bay bazaar was 300,000.

There are a number of murre colonies in Novaya Zemlya south of Admiralty Bay. The most important one is situated on Cape Tchernetski. This bazaar is low and easily accessible and consists of 13 separate sections, with a total length of about six kilometres. The wide, long and horizontal ledges are very suitable for nesting sites for murres, as well as for human exploitation. In 1942, Belopolski determined that the number of murres nesting at Cape Tchernetski exceeded 200,000. Exploitation of the bazaar began in 1930 and by 1950 only some 55,000 murres were nesting there (Uspenski, 1956).

The most northern bird bazaars in the south island of Novaya Zemlya are those in Gribovaya Bay. They are situated on the south shore of the bay and on Golets, Topori-koff (Shestakova) and Pestovy (Veselovo) Islands. A bazaar on the south shore, about two kilometres in length, is occupied by murres (including common murres), kittiwakes, puffins, black guillemots and glaucous gulls. The bazaar on Golets Island is occupied by murres (including a few common murres) and puffins. The Toporikoff Island bazaar has a similar bird population. Pestovy Island bazaar is occupied only by thick-billed murres and kittiwakes. In 1950, 104,000 murres nested in Gribovaya Bay (Uspenski, 1956).

There are fairly large bird bazaars in Pukhovy Bay, mostly on the west coast and on two capes north and south of Pukhovy Island. Those bazaars were first studied and de-scribed by Gorbunov (1925). Thick-billed murres, small numbers of common murres and a few puffins nest on Pukhovy Island. Thick-billed murres nest at the capes. In all three localities and also outside them along the shore of the bay, black guillemots and small numbers of glaucous gulls nest. In 1950, there were 121,000 murres nesting in Pukhovy Bay (Uspenski, 1956).

On the section of coast between Pukhovy Bay and Gusinaya Zemlya (Goose Land) Peninsula, bird bazaars are situated in the northwest part of Srednyaya Bay, on Kuvshin

Island in Little Karmakulskaya Bay, on the north shore of Little Karmakulskaya Bay (the "dog" bazaar), at the north end (the Vily) of Karmakulski Island, at the south end of Karmakulski Island and Mhramtsoff Peninsula (the "Home" bazaar), and in the northwest part of Obsedya Bay. Descriptions of several of those bazaars are given by Portenko (1931).

The main element in the population of those bird bazaars, as elsewhere in Novaya Zemlya, is the thick-billed murre. In the "Home" bazaar and on Kuvshin there are also kittiwakes, on Kuvshin, common murres, and in the "Home" bazaar possibly puffins. Black guillemots and glaucous gulls nest in all of the localities. There are, according to Uspenski (1956), approximately 20,000 murres nesting on Kuvshin; 40,000 in the Vily, and 25,000 in the "Home" bazaar. Presumably those colonies were larger formerly, as Uspenski mentions that they have been unduly depleted because of exploitation.

The coast of Goose Land Peninsula is mostly low and the scattered nesting areas there are located on the few coastal cliffs and rocky islands, mostly found at river mouths. There are bird bazaars at the mouth of the River Talbey-Yaga, on several promontories and rocky islands at the mouth of the River Sautchikha, on Cape Ne Bazaar Sale (the "Woman's bazaar"), on Cape Lilye and the rocky islet of Kuvshin in front of it, at the mouth of Belusha Bay. A description of the Cape Lilye bazaar is given by Gorbunov (1929) and of Cape Lilye and the bazaars at the mouth of the Sautchikha by Portenko (1931). The population of those bazaars consists only of thick-billed murres, black guillemots and glaucous gulls. The largest of the bazaars listed is located at the mouth of the Sautchikha and numbers presently from 15,000 to 18,000 birds. The bazaar on Kuvshin Islet is one of the few places in Novaya Zemlya where thick-billed murres nest on the horizontal surface of an island.

The nesting places at the mouth of the Sautchikha and Cape Lilye are accessible and regularly exploited. In 1925, Gorbunov estimated the number of murres there at 200,000; in 1930, Portenko reported 30,000; in 1938, no more than 20,000 were estimated; and finally, in 1950, only 1,000 (Uspenski, 1956).

There are also murre colonies on the south coast of Novaya Zemlya. The largest are at Yartseff Island (15,000), on Cape Shadrovski (16,000), on Cape Lebediny (30,000), at the "Obmanny" bazaar on Mezhdusharski Island (20,000), in Black Gulf (25,000) and in Sakhanikha (15,000 to 20,000). Descriptions of several of those bazaars are given by Gorbunov (1929) and Portenko (1931). The Black Gulf bazaar, especially, has been regularly exploited since 1930. According to a trapper named Voronin (Uspenski, 1956) there were, comparatively recently, other large murre bazaars on the east coast of the peninsula bordering the Black Gulf. They ceased to exist in the 1920's because of coastal erosion and destruction of the nesting ledges.

There are at present nearly fifty bird bazaars in Novaya Zemlya occupied predominantly by thick-billed murres. The total number of both species of murres nesting in all the bazaars is about 2,000,000 (Uspenski, 1956).

Large common murre colonies have been reported from the coasts of Norway near Tromso, on islands off Vardo and other parts of east Finnmark, from Reeno, Tamos in Porsanger Fjord, Mageroy, Karlsoy, and Helgoy and doubtless on many bird cliffs in between. Thick-billed murres do not breed in this coastal region of the Polar Basin, but at Vesteraalen the nominate race of the common murre intergrades with the arctic form (*Uria aalge hyperborea*), which is the form of the common murre breeding at Bear Island, Novaya Zemlya and along the Murman coast.

Both species of murre breed on the Murman coast of Russia. The colonies are reputedly of great size, but I have been unable to determine their relative abundance. The common murre reaches its easterly limit in the Polar Basin in that region.

The low tundra of northeastern Russia and western Siberia does not have the rocky coasts essential for murre breeding colonies. Consequently, on the mainland coast there are no large colonies between Novaya Zemlya and Prebraschenie Island in Khatanga Bay.

Thick-billed murres are reportedly abundant in the Siberian Sea, but little information is available concerning their breeding populations in that region. Two colonies in Severnaya Zemlya (Northland) are mentioned by Dementev *et al.*, (1951). Those are in the north of the island at Mys Molotova and in the east at Fjord Matuseevecha.

Colonies of thick-billed murres are reported for the New Siberian Islands on Bennet, Henrietta, Wilkitsky, Bielkowsk and probably Stolbovoi Islands.

There are reportedly large colonies on Anadyr, Koliutschin, Herald and Wrangel Islands. E. W. Nelson (1887) must have been mistaken when he identified the murres (among which he actually climbed and walked) of Wrangel and Herald Islands as common murres. They are undoubtedly thick-billed murres.

I once talked with a merchant marine captain who was ship-wrecked on Wrangel Island during World War II. He told me that the colonies on that island are immense and were the important factor in the crew's survival.

Thick-billed murres (*Uria lomvia arra*) breed east of Bering Strait, in Kotzebue Sound. Grinnell (in Bailey, 1948) reported that on July 9, 1899, they were breeding in immense numbers on the Chamisso Islands, at which time all eggs were fresh. Hersey (in Bailey, 1948) reported the breeding colony at Cape Lisburne, where fresh eggs were secured on August 8.

Large numbers of thick-billed murres migrate northward along the coast to Barrow, but where they go is unknown. Hendes (in Bailey, 1948) reported them extremely abundant at Wainwright in the spring, flying over the ice in flocks of hundreds on May 9 and 10, 1922. There was no open water at the time, but the flight continued for several days, whenever it was calm or the wind was from the south.

Brower (in Bailey, 1948) stated that those thick-billed murres must nest to the eastward of Barrow, for they migrated over the open leads in the spring and returned each autumn. They passed along in strings, one after the other, not in compact flocks.

It has long been assumed that murre colonies were absent from the western Canadian Arctic because of the low coastline. Clarke (1944) recorded that he was informed by an Eskimo of Banks Island, that murres were one of the component species of a large seabird colony at Nelson Head. Manning *et al.* (1956) visited Nelson Head on September 4, 1951, and again in late July, 1952, but did not find murres there or anywhere along the south coast of Banks Island. Clarke (1944) saw several thick-billed murres at Cape Parry in Amundsen Gulf on August 18, 1942, but could not determine that they bred there. Höhn (1955) found about 100 pairs of thick-billed murres breeding at Cape Parry on August 13, 1953, and thus established that an outpost of this species did exist in the western Canadian Arctic.

There is some confusion about the status of common murres in this region of the Polar Basin. Nelson (1883) stated definitely that "they were not observed by us during the cruise of the *Corwin* in the Arctic" but later (1887) goes into detail on the great numbers seen. Since Nelson obviously confused the breeding species of Herald and Wrangel Islands, little faith can be placed in his murre observations. Bailey (1948) failed to secure specimens of the common murre on the Diomedes or in the Bering Strait during migration and was convinced that the northern limit of the common murre in that region was the Bering Sea. However, Jacques (1930) obtained a specimen of the common murre on the Diomedes and two others at Point Hope, near Cape Lisburne, on August 5, 1931. Those specimens have been referred by Bailey (1948) to the North Pacific form of the common murre (*Uria aalge inornata*).

There is, then, an amazing total population of murres, especially thick-billed murres, breeding in the Polar Basin. Novaya Zemlya, with its census of two million, is the only locality for which there is a reasonably accurate idea of the breeding population. It seems likely that the total numbers of murres breeding on both Bear Island and Spitsbergen exceed the Novaya Zemlya population. Jan Mayen has "at least a million" and Franz Josef Land, Wrangel and Herald Islands undoubtedly have large breeding populations. In addition, there are the many other presumably large colonies in the Siberian Sea and on the New Siberian Islands. The minimum total I can attribute to those localities is 15 million thick-billed murres.

Common murres are components of the "unknown numbers of millions" of murres occurring on Bear Island. All the colonies along the coasts of Norway are of common murres, but elsewhere in the Polar Basin this species has only small outposts. Perhaps a total of one million common murres in the Polar Basin is a conservative estimate.

CHAPTER V

Murre Colonies of the Eastern North Atlantic

The only region of East Greenland in which murres are found is in Scoresby Sound, in the same latitude as Jan Mayen. This locality could just as reasonably have been considered part of the Polar Basin. According to Salomonsen (1951), there is a colony of 5,000 thick-billed murres at Rafle Island off the Liverpool coast on the north side of the entrance to Scoresby Sound; a colony of 10,000 pairs at Cape Brewster, the southern entrance to Scoresby Sound; and "great numbers" along the coast between Cape Brewster and Stewart Island. The common murre is not known to breed in that locality.

Murre colonies are found on all four coasts of Iceland. Dr. Finnur Gudmundsson, Director of the Museum of Natural History, Reykjavik, has informed me that the Iceland colonies are huge but no attempt has ever been made to determine their populations. In fact, some of the colonies have never been visited by an ornithologist. Both species of murre breed in Iceland. In the north and northeast, as at Grimsey and Rauinpur, thick-billed murres outnumber common murres, on Grimsey by more than three to one (Foster *et al.*, 1951). In the northwest, thick-billed murres greatly outnumber common murres on the great loomeries of Hronjarg and Haelavikurbjarg. A little westward, at Latrabjarg, the two species breed in approximately equal numbers, and the common murre outnumbers the thick-billed murre at Ritur (Loppenthin, 1932). In the southwest (Hafnaberg) and south (Westmann Islands) common murres outnumber thick-billed murres. The Westmann Islands are the most southerly locality in western Europe where thick-billed murres are found.

Common murres formerly bred along the south coast of Norway near Stavanger and in Oslo Fjord. Their breeding distribution in Norway is now from just north of Bergen to the Lofotens and Vesteraalen. The largest colonies in Norway are just north of the Arctic Circle.

A subspecies of the common murre (*Uria aalge intermedia*) is restricted to the Baltic Sea in summer and largely confined to that region in winter. In the first half of the nineteenth century, Baltic murres nested on the Danish Island of Bornholm in the southern Baltic, on some skerries off Kalmar, and on the beautiful Karlsoarna, west of Gotland. By 1880, the Baltic murre population had been reduced to at most 20 birds. They have since increased notably and by 1942 were estimated to be 15,000 (Wahlin, 1944). They have re-occupied Bornholm (Salomonsen, 1943).

From Heligoland south along the coast of Europe and on the west coast of Britain the race of common murre is known as *Uria aalge albionis*. It is an extremely pale race.

The murre is now extinct along the Normandy coast, although it nested in the last century far up the English Channel and even beyond the chalk cliffs of Picardy. The most northern outpost of the southern common murre (*Uria aalge albionis*) in Europe is on the sandstone cliffs of Heligoland. In spite of the "saturation" bombing of the island during World War II, about 2,000 eggs are still laid on the ledges every year (Schultz, 1947).

Common murres breed along the coast of Brittany. There are colonies in the Bay of Douarnenez and at Toulinguet in Finistère and on Rouzic in the Sept Isles. It appears that murres formerly bred more extensively along the Brittany coast, but there are still colonies, although admittedly small ones, on the Autelets, l'Etac de Serk, Ortac and other islets of the Casquet group and Alderney.

Common murres are very abundant in the Faeroes and Shetland. It will be recalled that thick-billed murres do not breed south of Iceland in that part of Europe. Salomonsen (1932) separated the Faeroe birds as *Uria aalge spiloptera*. His data show that there is a cline in coloration from south Britain to the Faeroes from the typical *albionis* through dark *aalge* to the darkest *spiloptera;* the birds of Iceland and Norway (*aalge*) being lighter again. More recent unpublished data (Salomonsen, *in litt.*) strengthen the validity of *spiloptera* as a distinct race.

Ferdinand (1947) published an excellent map of the murre colonies in the Faeroes which shows that all are "as near as possible to the open sea and on the steepest places of the coast exposed to north and south." Some of the islands with colonies are Dimunar, Stremoy, Eysturoy and Fugloy. The most enormous colonies are on northwest Stremoy, and on Skuvoy, Hestur, Stora Dimun, Dumumak and Mykines. No attempt has been made to determine the murre populations of the Faeroes, but Arne Nørrevang, who has spent much time in studying the sea-birds of that region, has informed me that several millions breed there.

Hundreds of thousands of common murres, possibly more than a million, breed in Shetland. The murre cliffs of Foula are especially famous. It is impossible to list all the loomeries in Shetland, but there are large colonies on the northern cliffs, stacks and skerries of Unst and on the eastern cliffs and stacks of Noss. There are colonies on Sumburg Head and Fitful Head in the south; on Papa Stour and its attendant drongs, holms and skerries; on the Ramna Stacks, Hascosay, Fetlat and the Out Skerries. Perry (1948) counted 4,224 bridled murres on Noss and tells us that the well-known Shetland ornithologist, G. T. Kay, estimated that murres "from Noss passed out to the Atlantic fishing grounds at the rate of 3,830 an hour . . ."

The pioneer Shetland ornithologist, H. L. Saxby (1874), wrote that "Noss Head and Unst are the chief breeding stations of the guillemots, but from all accounts the numbers now will bear no comparison with those of fifty years ago, so great has been the havoc committed by shooting parties". In some years of the present century, the Royal Society for the Protection of Birds at Unst has reported increases—never decreases. This is slender evidence on which to base a case that the Shetland murre population has changed importantly within historical times.

It is also impossible to list all the many colonies in Orkney. The greatest is on the vast

1,100-foot sandstone cliffs of West Hoy. To the east of this loomery there is another large colony on Copinsay and one on the southeast of Shapinsay. There are many colonies in the North Isles of the Orkney group, of which those on the Calf of Eday and the Noup of Westray are probably the largest.

The resident breeding murre of England, Wales and Ireland is the southern common murre, *Uria aalge albionis*. This race also breeds in Scotland off the coast of Galloway and includes at least part of the population of Ailsa Craig (Gibson, 1951). On Britain's eastern coast the boundary between the two subspecies coincides with the Scottish Border, for north of it *Uria aalge aalge* breeds on St. Abb's Head and south of it *Uria aalge albionis* breeds on the Farnes.

At Ailsa Craig in Scotland, the only colony in the Firth of Clyde, both the southern race (*Uria aalge albionis*) and the dark northern race (*Uria aalge aalge*) occur (Gibson, 1951). There are numerous colonies on the west coast of Scotland, but most of them are small. A colony at Barra Head in the Hebrides, however, is large and has been described as one of the finest bird-stations in Britain.

The present murre population of Britain's famous sea-bird station, St. Kilda, is surprisingly low. In 1939, only about 20,000 pairs were nesting on the entire St. Kilda group (Fisher, *in litt.*) and more recent estimates confirm that the size of the present population is of that order.

North Rona is St. Kilda's rival for the honour of being the most remote British island ever to have been inhabited. As a result, it has been visited by a succession of ornithologists. Nobody has been able to count or estimate the murre population there. Indeed, the best anybody has done has been to suggest "thousands" or "thousands and thousands". Some thousands also nest on Sula Sgeir, eleven miles west of Rona.

There are large murre colonies on both west and north coasts of Sutherland. The most southerly, and perhaps the largest, is on Handa. This famous bird colony has been visited by most of the great Scottish naturalists and all agree that it is enormous.

There is a common murre colony, although apparently only a small one, on the Bass Rock in East Lothian. A colony on the Isle of May, off the coast of Fife, has been known since 1684. Its population in 1888 was reported to be 300 pairs, but in 1936 Southern (1939) counted 2,080 pairs. The Isle of May is now a bird sanctuary and carefully watched by ornithologists.

In Northumberland, the only colony is on the Farne Islands, where some thousands occupy every part of the flat top of the Pinnacles. Murres also breed or have bred on the Megstone, North Wamese, Harcars, Brownsman, Staple, Skeney Car, and even the Inner Farne.

The only colony in Yorkshire appears to be at Flamborough Head, where the scaling of the cliffs for eggs, known as "climming" is a traditional sport.

On the west coast of northern England, the common murre breeds only at St. Bee's Head in Cumberland, which substantial colony has been known since 1675. These murres breed also on the steep and inaccessible cliffs and rocks of the Isle of Man.

In North Wales, colonies are confined to Caernarvonshire and Anglesey. In South Wales there is a colony in Glamorgan and many colonies of varying sizes from St.

Margaret's Isle in Pembrokeshire round the coast of that rugged country at least as far as New Quay Head in Cardiganshire.

Murres breed on both the north and the south coasts of Devon. A colony on Lundy, in Bristol Channel, commenced to increase in 1922 and in 1939 contained some 38,000 breeding birds. It has since shown a marked decrease. The Lundy Field Society considered that there were likely not more than 10,000 birds breeding in that colony in 1949.

The common murre breeds in a number of places in Cornwall. It formerly bred on the Scilly Isles, but all the present colonies in Cornwall appear to be on the north coast.

There are colonies of hundreds of murres on the ledges of Durlston in Dorset, and previously there used to be others. "We went to the Bill of Portland to shoot murre", wrote George Cartwright in his diary for May 18, 1773, and there are still a few murres breeding at Portland Bill.

The principal colony on the Isle of Wight is at Freshwater, at the west end of the chalk cliffs. Until recently there was also a small colony at Culver Cliffs at the east end of the Isle.

It is now many years since murres nested on Beachy Head in Sussex. They were driven away, it is said, by rock falls about 1879, though twice since then a few have started to lay.

A colony in Kent, on the chalk cliffs between Dover and St. Margaret's Bay, is now extinct, although a century ago it was large. By 1895 it contained about 60 pairs, by 1908 about 36, and by about 1910 it was deserted, also probably as the result of rock falls.

Common murres nest at many places along the coast of Ireland. There are colonies, for instance, along the coast of Kerry and Cork. What may possibly be the largest colony in Ireland is at Loop Head, on the limestone cliffs of Moher.

There are colonies along the west coast of Ireland, at Galway, for example. There are several colonies in Mayo. Murres breed in at least two localities in Sligo and there are several colonies in Donegal. The southernmost colony in northern Ireland is at the Gobbins on Island Magee, just north of Belfast Lough.

In all there are more than two hundred common murre colonies in Britain. No special effort has yet been made to estimate the total breeding populations of those colonies. Most of them are probably small. It is also likely that the ornithologists who have described some of the larger ones as "enormous" had not seen the truly enormous colonies of murres in the Polar Basin or even the Canadian Arctic. I do not think that the total murre population of Britain exceeds one million individuals. Except in one or two regions, it is generally agreed that the murre is a decreasing species in Britain and the general belief is that the decline is caused by oil pollution. There is scarcely an annual ornithological report from any British bird-watching organization covering an important part of the coast that does not comment on the messy destruction of murres by oiling.

There seems to be only one murre colony in Portugal. It is in the same latitude as that of the California murres in the Pacific, and is the southernmost colony of the common murre in the Atlantic. The Portuguese colony is on the Berlenga Islands, some miles off Cape Carvoeiro, where Tait (1924) found them abundant, and where Lockley (1942) estimated the population to be 6,000 pairs in June, 1939. Tait was informed by the Portuguese ornithologist Reis, that murres also "nested exceptionally on the Aquilheira rock, near Villa de Conde", in northern Portugal, but Tait saw none when he landed there in June, 1918.

Murres breed on some of the islands along the northwest coast of Spain. Tait saw murres at the Cies Islands in 1882, and he received eggs from Santillo, a little farther north. He also saw murres on the Sisargas Islands, west of Corunna, in June, 1914, and was informed by the lightkeeper that they bred there. This seems to be so, for in June, 1948, Bernis (1949) found a colony of 310 on Sisarga Major and one of 350 on Sisarga Mediana. Bernis also confirmed the Cies Islands as a breeding-station. He proposed a separation of the Iberian murres as *Uria aalge ibericus*.

I have assigned one million common murres to the British coasts, although some British ornithologists think the population is higher than that. The Shetland population possibly exceeds one million individuals. The largest murre colonies in the eastern North Atlantic are found in Iceland and the Faeroes. The Faeroe Island population, from the personal accounts of ornithologists who have studied that region, is at least several million—say three million. The population of Iceland is more difficult to estimate. I suspect that it is four or five times as large as that of the Faeroes. A total estimate of the murres breeding in the eastern North Atlantic may thus reach at least ten million. Approximately half of those are thick-billed murres in Iceland and the east coast of Greenland; the remaining five million are common murres, more widely distributed southwards, but generally existing in smaller colonies.

CHAPTER VI

Murre Colonies of the Western North Atlantic

The first reference to murres in the New World was probably made by Jacques Cartier when he described the "Isle of Aves", off the northeast coast of Newfoundland, which was later known as Penguin Island and finally as Funk Island. When Cartier arrived at Funk Island on May 21, 1534 (old calendar), he was understandably impressed with the fresh meat provided by the "Aporath" or great auks, which then inhabited the island which he had discovered. He wrote in his log: "In less than halfe an houre we filled two boats full of them, as if they had bene stones, so that besides them which we did eat fresh, every ship did powder and salt five or sixe barrells full of them" (Hakluyt, 1660).

Cartier also described the "Margaulx" of Funk Island, which obviously were gannets and another species, "Godets", but with less precise language: "There is another kinde of bird which hover in the aire, and over the seas, lesser than the others, and those doe gather themselves together in the island, and put themselves under the wings of other birds that are greater; those we called Godets" (Hakluyt, 1660). When I first read this account, I thought that the birds which "hover in the air" might have been terns. Steenstrup (1885) states: "The name Godet[1] appears to have been applied in a general way to the black-feathered birds of the genus *Alca*". However, Cartier's descriptions: ". . . doe gather together . . ." almost certainly referred to murres. The razorbill prefers crevices for nesting and therefore probably was never abundant on Funk Island within historical times. Much less was it likely that they would ". . . gather together . . ." or nest in colonies. The only other alcid to which the description might apply would be the puffin, but puffins almost certainly did not nest on Funk Island until soil built up on the decomposed remnants of the exterminated great auk. Underneath the soil in which puffins now burrow, the bones of both great auks and murres are intermingled. So murres did indeed breed on Funk Island when Cartier discovered it, but it is impossible to say how abundantly.

In 1535, Cartier took birds at Funk Island once more and in 1536, the Hoare expedition obtained "penguins" there. Sir Humphrey Gilbert's expedition visited Funk Island in 1583 and took on loads of great auks and other sea-birds for food. Subsequently every ship which came into that vicinity during the summer visited the island. The tragic story of the extinction of the great auk in Newfoundland, largely due to a commercial venture when its oil and feathers were utilized, is fairly well known.

[1]The word seems to be of Breton origin. It is remarkably similar to the Beothuck "geonet", p. 34. The modern French equivalent in Quebec is "gode" but is restricted to the razorbill.

John Milne (1875) visited Funk Island on July 20, 1874, and recorded a great abundance of birds still nesting there, especially terns and murres. Lucas (1888) visited Funk Island on July 22, 1887, and wrote: "The number of murres and razorbills was comparatively insignificant and the few eggs of these species were placed in the most secluded spots attainable".

Wynne-Edwards (Johnson, 1940) recorded an estimate of 10,000 pairs of common murres breeding on Funk Island on June 29, 1934. In another part of the same paper, Johnson tabled 10,000 individuals (rather than pairs) as the population of Funk Island.

Gilliard (1937), who landed on Funk Island on July 20, 1936, estimated that there were 10,000 pairs of breeding murres on the sloping southwestern side of the island.

The next scientific visit to the island was by Peters and Burleigh (1951), who estimated 15,000 pairs of common murres on July 5, 1945. More recent observations made by me indicate a substantially increased population. Population estimates are presented in Table 5.

Table 5: *Estimates of Funk Island common murre populations*

Date	Estimate	Authority
July 20, 1874	"Great abundance"	John Milne
July 22, 1887	"Insignificant numbers"	F. A. Lucas
June 29,1934	10,000 pairs	V. C. Wynne-Edwards
July 20, 1936	10,000 pairs	E. T. Gilliard
July 5, 1945	15,000 pairs	Peters and Burleigh
July 10, 1951	40,000 pairs	L. M. Tuck
July 9, 1952	50,000 pairs	L. M. Tuck
July 11, 1953	50–60,000 pairs	L. M. Tuck
July 6–17, 1956	150,000 pairs	L. M. Tuck
July 10–15, 1958	400,000 pairs	L. M. Tuck
July 14, 1959	500,000 pairs	L. M. Tuck and James Fisher

Although these recorded visits to Funk Island were by ornithologists, the literature contains several discrepancies concerning the status of the murres on Funk Island.

Aldrich and Nutt (1939) reported sight records of thick-billed murres (*Uria lomvia lomvia*) off Funk Island on July 13, 1938. In their account they made no mention of the common murre and attributed the species breeding on Funk Island to the thick-billed murre on the authority of Lucas (1888) and Gilliard (1937). Actually neither Lucas nor Gilliard mentioned what species of murre was found on Funk Island.

Wynne-Edwards (Johnson, 1940) mentions only common murres (*Uria aalge aalge*) breeding on Funk Island. Peters and Burleigh (1951) stated that the thick-billed murre is "not known to nest in Newfoundland".

The murres on Funk Island are largely common murres, which now occupy three separate areas, one on either end of the narrow island and one in the central valley. Those colonies have increased twenty five-fold during the past eight years. The probable reason for their increase will be dealt with elsewhere.

A small outpost of thick-billed murres is entrenched on some narrow ledges in Indian Gulch on Funk Island. A careful investigation of that site has shown that approximately 250 pairs nest there and that their number did not change appreciably from 1951 to 1959.

Like those of Funk Island, the sea-birds of Baccalieu Island played an important part in the early history of Newfoundland. In fact, most of the early voyagers attempted to strike land at Baccalao (Basque for "cod"), as it was then called.

The first estimate of the numbers of murres breeding on Baccalieu Island was made in 1934 by Wynne-Edwards (Johnson, 1940): "At Baccalieu Island, there may have been 1,000 pairs, possibly less—(say 500–1,500)". Peters (1942) visited the nesting site on June 24, 1941, and estimated 5,000 pairs at that time.

I have made two visits to Baccalieu Island, but since neither was at the height of the breeding season, it was not possible to estimate the population. Both thick-billed murres and common murres breed on the narrow ledges of Baccalieu Island.

Roger Tory Peterson estimated only 2,500 pairs on Baccalieu Island on July 11, 1959. The present available nesting sites suitable for murres on Baccalieu Island are limited. It seems likely that this is one of several known colonies in Newfoundland which has no room to expand.

There is a comparatively new murre colony on Green Island in Witless Bay. Puffins have been known to breed there within the memory of the oldest settlers in the area, but all agree that the murre is a newcomer, first breeding there about 1936. Green Island is a small lump of an island about half a mile square and with nearly vertical faces. The murres breed wherever there are available ledges, but mainly on the flat shelves at the top of the cliffs. Like most murre islands, Green Island is rather difficult of access, but, as it is so near St. John's, it has been visited during each breeding season since 1950.

Peters and Burleigh (1951) record 3,000 pairs of common murres as the breeding population for Green Island on July 1, 1941. Their estimate, however, was made from a boat from which the upper ledges could not be seen and is thus probably too low. There were roughly 10,000 pairs breeding there in 1951 and nearly 20,000 in 1953. In 1959, James Fisher and I estimated the astonishing total of 50,000 breeding pairs.

Though the most abundant species on Green Island is the common murre, two separate colonies of thick-billed murres, totalling about 1,500 pairs, are entrenched on the narrow ledges.

There is a small outpost of common murres on South Cabot Island in Bonavista Bay. Other sea-birds breed on South Cabot Island and the nesting sites are not suitable for any further expansion of the murre population. The total breeding population does not exceed 150 pairs.

Peters and Burleigh (1951) recorded a small colony of murres on Gull Island in Witless Bay. I have noted murres loitering there, but have seen no evidence of breeding.

There is one other important colony in Newfoundland, at Cape St. Mary's (46° 49'), the most southerly colony in eastern North America. Residents of the Cape Shore in

Newfoundland associate Cape St. Mary's with the intrepid collector, J. C. Cahoon, who in 1890 was the only person foolhardy enough to climb Bird Rock. Once on the top he was unable to get back down but, after a lengthy stay, was eventually rescued by a "bosun's chair" rigged by the residents. Soon after he had recovered from that ordeal, Cahoon was killed by slipping from a ledge while attempting to collect raven's eggs. Had he lived, the written history of the Cape St. Mary's bird colonies might have been available earlier. As it was, outside attention was not drawn to the colony until 1918 (English, 1918).

Both species of murre nested at Cape St. Mary's during Cahoon's visit, as they do today. His specimens of both species and their chicks are in the Museum of Comparative Zoology at Cambridge, Massachusetts. The thick-billed species was, however, apparently overlooked both by Wynne-Edwards and by Peters and Burleigh, who stated that only common murres nested there.

Wynne-Edwards, writing to Johnson (1940) in connection with the murres at Cape St. Mary's said: "I do not think I should exaggerate if I said there were 5,000 pairs; there may have been two or three times that number." Peters and Burleigh (1951) visited the colony on June 28, 1942, and recorded 2,500 pairs. Our estimates during the past several years have remained at between two and three thousand pairs. In 1959, James Fisher and I estimated 2,500 pairs at Cape St. Mary's.

We also estimated that 11.4 per cent of the visible murres at Cape St. Mary's on April 15, 1953, were thick-billed murres. Later in the season W. I. Campbell, working with a smaller sample (on June 20, 1953), estimated that 20 per cent were thick-billed murres. Thus there is the interesting biological phenomenon that at Cape St. Mary's, Newfoundland, both the common murre and the thick-billed murre nest together at their extreme southern limit in eastern North America.

Records of murres breeding in eastern North America south of Cape St. Mary's are not well substantiated. Certainly, there is no major breeding station south of the cape.

Hardy (1897) wrote: " I will say that over 50 years ago my father obtained the egg and parent of the Brünnich's murre at either one of the Duck Island or Marshall Island in Penobscot Bay. I think I have the identical egg in my collection, but am unable to look it up at present." This record for Maine was considered doubtful by both Allen (1909) and Palmer (1949). Norton (1923) reported that before 1870 common murres bred on the Green Islands off western Penobscot Bay, but did not document that statement.

Boardman (1862) stated that common murres bred on the Murre Ledges in Grand Manan. An egg in the Lord collection was taken at Grand Manan on June 20, 1901 (Squires, 1952). Boardman (1862) and Baird, Brewer and Ridway (1884) recorded thick-billed murres breeding in the Bay of Fundy but, according to Squires (1952), those reports are not substantiated.

Bayley (1925) wrote: "Lying six miles offshore from Great Bras d'Or entrance, Cape Breton Island, Nova Scotia, there is a little group of islands (Ciboux and Hertford Islands) . . .

"The murres are not as numerous as the puffins and razorbills. Probably not more than a dozen pairs are nesting here now, though they are said to have been very plentiful in former years. They nest on the higher ledges some fifty feet above water." Bayley does not mention which species he was referring to but Godfrey (1958) wrote that Taverner saw two common murres there in 1929. Mr. James O. Seamen of the Massachusetts Audubon Society has informed me that he saw no murres on Ciboux and Hertford Islands in July, 1958.

The most southerly breeding outpost of murres in the Gulf of St. Lawrence is at the Bird Rocks, near the Magdalen Islands. Murres were quite abundant there at one time, but have now dwindled to a remnant population, as they have elsewhere in that area. Both species are recorded for the locality.

In 1860, Bryant (1861) estimated the comparative numbers of the Bird Rock population as two common murres to one thick-billed murre. Maynard in 1872 "unaccountably overlooked" the common murres at Bird Rocks (Brewster, 1883), but Brewster found both species of murres still breeding there in "amazing numbers . . . but they are said to be diminishing" and estimated that 75 per cent were thick-billed murres and 25 per cent were common murres. Lucas (1888) merely mentions that young murres on the Bird Rocks had hatched on July 9, 1897. Bishop (1889), who spent from June 21 to July 8, 1887, in the Magdalen Islands, found common murres on Bird Rock and Bryon Island, but thick-billed murres only on the Great Bird Rock, where "it breeds abundantly". A. C. Bent (Gurney, 1913) visited Bird Rock on June 24, 1904, and recorded 1,600 thick-billed murres and 1,500 common murres—a ratio of practically one to one.

Townsend (1920) estimated that 1,000 common murres bred on Bonaventure Island in 1919. Murres still breed there. It seems that it is almost impossible to obtain a satisfactory count, because a great many of them incubate in small caverns which open high on the face of the cliff and are difficult to examine.

There are a number of published accounts of the sea-birds of Anticosti Island and from those accounts we are able to trace the history of the murres breeding in that locality.

Verrill (1865) stated that common murres bred "in large numbers along the eastern and northern shore of Anticosti" in 1861. He said, also, that about half of them were bridled murres. Brewster (1883) " . . . saw none at the eastern end of Anticosti". Schmitt (1904) stated " . . . some nest at Bird Bay". Dionne (1920) wrote: "formerly common now very rare". Lewis (1924) quoting Frits Johansen: "Recorded Common Murres . . . at High Cliff Point, August 4, 1923, . . . on the cliffs east of Cape Sandtop, August 5, 1923 . . . at Fox Point, August 2, 1923."

Johnson (1940) wrote: "There are no reliable data regarding the number of breeding murres for the Island of Anticosti . . . Two deputy wardens visited the vicinity of the bird cliffs near Fox Bay on the northeastern coast and have given an estimate for the number of breeding birds there. From their report Dr. Lewis considers there are at least 20,000 breeding there." Johnson estimated 20,000 common murres for Anticosti Island on Dr. Lewis' authority. From correspondence with Dr. Lewis, I have learned that this figure "would not be an unreasonable estimate for the total number of sea-birds of all species breeding at Gull-cliff Bay. It may be that the deputy wardens intended it for that and that at some point in the chain of communication from them to Dr. Johnson misunderstanding crept in. I am confident that very few murres breed on Anticosti. Probably there are none along the south shore of the island, for it is a low coast. In June, 1940, I travelled along the entire north shore of the island in a small motorboat manned by two game wardens of the staff maintained by the island's proprietors. We had fine weather and passed close to all cliffs, so that I might see and count the birds there. These cliffs are not continuous. Except in Gull-cliff Bay, near the east end of the island, they are generally confined to headlands of the eastern half of the north shore . . . I recorded . . . murres only at Gull-cliff Bay, where some time, perhaps two hours, was spent on June 9, 1940. As a result of counts and estimates, I recorded at that bay . . . 220 Common Murres".

A century ago murres bred in fairly large numbers from Perroquet Island, off Mingan Channel, as far east along the North Shore of the Gulf of St. Lawrence as Bradore Bay. In the late nineteenth century that region was heavily exploited by the "Halifax eggers" (Frazar, 1887). Johnson (1940) estimated that as many as 750,000 murre eggs were harvested annually.

Audubon (1840) described the Murre Rocks thus: "Not far from Great Mecatina Harbor lie the Murre Rocks, consisting of several low islands, destitute of vegetation and not rising high from the waters. There, thousands of guillemots (i.e., murres) annually assemble in the beginning of May to deposit each its single egg and raise its young. As you approach these islands the air becomes darkened with the multitudes of birds that fly about; every square foot of the ground seems to be occupied by a guillemot planted erect, as it were, on the granite rock, but carefully warming its cherished egg. All look toward the south, and if you are fronting them, the snowy white of their bodies produce a very remarkable effect, for the birds at some distance look as if they were destitute of head, so much does that part assimilate the dark hue of the rocks on which they stand. On the other hand, if you approach them in the rear, the isle appears as if covered with a black pall." Coues (1861) and Bryant (1861) both commented on the decrease of murres in that region since Audubon's visit.

Brewster (1883) visited Perroquet Island in 1881. He wrote: "When we first saw the place the water was covered with murres, and hundreds were sitting on their eggs along the ledges of the western end of the island." Charles W. Townsend and A. C. Bent explored the southern part of this region in 1909, cruising much of the time in a small boat among the islands, but saw "only nine murres, although we were constantly on the lookout for them".

Frazar (1887) spent the summer of 1884 in the vicinity of Cape Whittle and reported the murres as "very common, but rapidly diminishing". Dr. C. W. Townsend explored Cape Whittle in 1915 (Bent, 1919) and found only two breeding colonies of about a thousand each.

Although the slump in the breeding population of murres in the Gulf of St. Lawrence, which probably occurred in the early twentieth century, has been attributed to excessive exploitation, other factors, such as changes in the marine environment, may have prevented any significant recovery.

Murres have been legally protected in Canada since 1918 and federal bird sanctuaries were set up along the North Shore of the Gulf of St. Lawrence in 1925 with the specific interest of those dwindling sea-bird populations in mind. Data in Table 6 show a slight increase during the first decade of sanctuary protection and a 25 per cent decrease from 1940 to 1945. There has been no significant trend of change for the past two decades.

Common murres were first observed at Fog Island in 1925 (Lewis, 1931) and increased considerably in that locality during the subsequent decade. The erection of a lighthouse and alarm station at Cape Whittle in 1929 undoubtedly precipitated the decline in that locality. The comparative censuses (Table 6) indicate that the Cape Whittle nesting birds moved to Fog Island. In any case, the Cape Whittle Sanctuary was cancelled on March 16, 1937, ". . . because of its small and dwindling bird population" (Lewis, 1942). A slump in 1955 in the Fog Island breeding population and a rise of similar magnitude in numbers of murres at Bradore Bay, seems to indicate an eastward shift in the murre population of the region. The colony at Wolf Bay showed an increase after sanctuary protection, but it reached a static condition very quickly.

In addition to the murre colonies in the sanctuaries along the North Shore of the Gulf of St. Lawrence, small colonies probably still exist near Kegaska, Washikuti, Frenchman's Bay, Audubon Islands, Wolf Bay, Cape Whittle, Etamamu River, Boat Islands, Great Mecatina Island and Kécarpoui. Johnson (1940) gave their total population as 3,222 individuals.

Table 6: *Comparative counts of common murres in sanctuaries along the North Shore of the Gulf of St. Lawrence.*

	1925	1930	1935	1940	1945	1950	1955
Fog Island	64	2,586	4,000	3,300	2,000	2,400	670
Wolf Bay	314	208	1,840	2,310	2,000	2,180	2,054
Cape Whittle	3,062	900	—	—	—	—	—
St. Mary Island	3,600	4,204	6,338	6,846	5,248	6,862	7,070
Bradore Bay	200	150	30	104	120	180	2,500
Totals:	7,240	8,048	12,208	12,560	9,368	11,622	12,294

Sources: Lewis (1931, 1937, 1942); Hewitt (1950); Tener (1951); Lemieux (1956).

The dominant breeding species of murre in the Gulf of St. Lawrence is the common murre. As recorded above, thick-billed murres breed with common murres at Bird Rocks in the Magdalen Islands. Johnson discovered a pair of thick-billed murres nesting at Cliff Island (St. Mary Island sanctuary) in 1938 (Lewis, 1942). It became the custom for visiting scientists to seek out that site. Allen (1948) wrote: "For ten years now, a single Brünnich's Murre has claimed foothold on a narrow shelf of Cliff Island facing the sea. Here he stands in the middle of a flock of Common Murres—the tenth bird to the right and the fifteenth from the left. Storms may rage, but nothing budges him from this particular spot. Of course he leaves it to go fishing, but he returns soon to the same few square inches." Gabrielson (1952) noted two thick-billed murres (and probably four) at the same site on June 19, 1947. It is an excellent illustration of the tenacity with which this species holds to a traditional nesting site.

Audubon failed to see thick-billed murres on his 1833 trip to southern Labrador. In fact the only specimen he saw and the one from which he drew his plate "... was sent to me in ice ... from Eastport, Maine ... on the 18th of February, 1833."

The most southerly murre locality along the eastern coast of Labrador is at the Bird Islands south of Gready. This name appears on the very oldest charts and therefore suggests a traditional nesting site. There is at present a long distance between the north-easternmost murre colonies along the North Shore of the Gulf of St. Lawrence and the southernmost along the eastern coast of Labrador. Austin (1932) did not record any murres at Bird Islands during his coastal explorations from 1926 to 1928, but on July 14, 1953, I found two small colonies of common murres there, one on Wester Bird and the other on Little Bird, the two totalling 250 pairs by actual egg count. There appeared to be competition for nesting sites between the murres and the razorbills. The latter out-numbered the murres six to one on the Bird Islands and the murres were nesting there in small pockets or crevices.

The Gannet Clusters and the Outer Gannet are the most spectacular of the sea-bird colonies along the eastern coast of Labrador. Puffins, razorbills and murres are the principal species nesting there. The early records of murres for that locality referred to the common murre. Macoun and Macoun (1909) say: "Mr. Dicks collected a large series of the eggs of this bird at the Gannet, July 2, 1895." Austin (1932) found four small scattered groups of murres totalling about 250 individuals on the Gannet Clusters. He stated that the thick-billed murre was the prevalent breeding species and found none of either species on the Outer Gannet.

Robert Grayce (1947), who accompanied Commander MacMillan on the 1946 Labrador Expedition, recorded that the centre of abundance of common murres in Labrador was at the Gannet Islands. He said: "I averaged, during a brief visit to the chief island, not more than 50 nesting pairs." Of the thick-billed murre, Grayce said: "A few birds rested on the waters of the Gannet Clusters on which islands they unquestion-ably nested." Apparently, Grayce did not visit the Outer Gannet, which lies about three miles off the Gannet Clusters. Harold Peters cruised around the Outer Gannet on August 22, 1944, and in an unpublished report to the Department of Mines and Resources stated that there were some 400 pairs of thick-billed murres and 500 pairs of common murres breeding there at the time.

In 1952 I was in that region for the period of July 14-20, on August 2 and 4, and dur-ing the period August 9-14. During that summer I made careful counts of eggs and found 28 small groups comprising 2,750 pairs of common murres and 15 pairs of thick-billed murres on the Gannet Clusters. Those groups were generally well scattered under boulders, in crevices and even in shallow sinkholes. In 1952, the common murre popula-tion of the Outer Gannet was 8,900 pairs and 300 pairs of thick-billed murres nested there. Except for a few isolated pockets, the common murres on the Outer Gannet nested in a valley strewn with large boulders, among which there were numerous flat areas. Because of the physical features of the island, murres in flight would funnel through the valley rather than fly around in erratic circles as they usually do. The thick-billed murres on the Outer Gannet were restricted to several steep cliff faces on the northwestern part.

Since Austin (1932) did not record any murres on the Outer Gannet from 1926 to 1928, it can be safely assumed that either this is a recent breeding location or that they have become re-established there. My own visits in 1952 and again in 1953, indicate that Peters' late August visit was too late in the season to obtain a reliable breeding index, so that the increase may have been spread over a larger interval of time than the recorded data suggest.

Turner (1885) recorded thick-billed murres breeding abundantly on the coast of Labrador in 1882, notably on the outlying islands of Hamilton Inlet, Davis Inlet, Cape Mugford and Cape Chidley. In 1912, A. C. Bent cruised the length of the coast, as far north as Cape Mugford, and "saw only one solitary Thick-billed Murre". However, Bent did not visit the Gannet Islands or the other islands on which murres now breed.

The Bowdoin expedition in 1891 took specimens of adult and downy common murres from the Herring Islands (Austin, 1932). Austin did not visit this group of two fairly large islands in the Hamilton Inlet. Horr (1947) writes: "North of Hamilton Inlet, seven miles below Indian Harbour, are the two Herring Islands. These proved to be the two outstanding bird islands we encountered on the Newfoundland Labrador, for there were thousands of puffins, auks and murres, the ground being literally honeycombed with them." I visited the Herring Islands on July 29, 1952, and found that the puffin popula-tion was indeed very high—something like 10,000 pairs. The murres were not especially abundant; 475 pairs of common murres and no thick-billed murres.

There is no specific reference in the literature to murres on Quaker Hat, but in 1952 I found a single small colony of 30 pairs of common murres under a large boulder on Quaker Hat and the several steep and narrow ledges were fully occupied by about 75 pairs of thick-billed murres. Quaker Hat, consequently, small as the total breeding number of murres is, is the only known location along the coast of Labrador where thick-billed murres predominate.

The most northerly island on the Labrador coast on which murres are known to breed is Nunarsuk Island (56° 03'N). It is a small island some 20 miles northeast of Cape Harrigan and is not indicated on most charts. It is about 100 feet high, steep on its south-western and northwestern sides, with three rounded domes on top. In 1928, Austin (1932) found a few common murres there and about 300 thick-billed murres. On August 10, 1953, I found 150 pairs of common murres and 175 pairs of thick-billed murres breeding there. Apparently the breeding status of the murres in that locality had not changed appreciably since Austin's visit. Nunarsuk Island, also, is the most northerly known outpost of the common murre in eastern North America[1]. The few available cliff

---

[1]Common murres apparently breed locally and in small numbers in Sermilinguaq Fjord, West Greenland (Salomonsen, 1951).

ledges were occupied by thick-billed murres, and the common murres were nesting under rocks and in fissures.

There is one other possible breeding location of murres in Labrador and that is on the Button Islands. Turner (1885) stated that thick-billed murres bred near Cape Chidley. Hantzsch (1908) recorded that species breeding on the Button Islands and in the neighbourhood of Cape Chidley, from which the Canadian Neptune Expedition is said to have taken eggs (Low, 1906). More concrete evidence is given by Gross (1937): "On July 23 (1934) fifteen Thick-billed Murres were noted while we were crossing the Gray Straits to the Button Islands and on July 29, I saw a large raft of them on the sea off Lacey Island of the Button group. Although Thick-billed Murres undoubtedly breed in northern Labrador and on the Button Islands we were unable to find their nests. They probably breed on some of the large number of inaccessible cliffs."

The most southerly murre colony in the eastern Canadian Arctic is on Akpatok Island in Ungava Bay. Akpatok is roughly 500 square miles in area and is composed of Ordovician limestone of geological formation similar to that of the eastern section of Foxe Basin. Hudson is reported to have sighted the island in 1610, but the first white man to examine it was Dr. Robert Bell of the Canadian Government Survey, who landed there for a few hours in 1885. Hantzsch (1908) drew attention to the murre colonies on Akpatok Island: "Very large numbers, the name meaning 'where there are Akpa in great numbers' ", although he personally did not visit the island. An Oxford University Expedition spent from August 19 to September 19, 1931, on the southeast coast of Akpatok Island (Davis, 1936). No precise information on murres was obtained by the expedition.

In 1954 John Miller and I, with Eskimo assistants, spent from July 10 to August 29 on the island, studying the murre colonies in particular.

There are two large colonies of thick-billed murres on Akpatok Island, one of 900,000 birds at the northern end and another of 300,000 at the southern end. The nesting sites are on horizontal limestone shelves at approximately 600 feet above sea-level on vertical 800-foot cliffs. The birds were censused by defining various sections of the cliff faces, counting the number of birds occupying those sections, and mathematically determining the percentage of the colony so examined.

The Digges Sound colonies are even more sensational than those of Akpatok Island. There are also two separate colonies in that locality, one on Digges Island and another on the adjacent mainland. There are numerous references in the literature to a murre colony at Cape Wolstenholme, but they actually refer to Digges Island and the mainland nearby. Cape Wolstenholme is a low and inconspicuous point of land and there is no murre colony at that precise location. The names Cape Wolstenholme and Digges Sound may be regarded as synonymous in reference to murre colonies.

The two murre cliffs in Digges Sound are remarkably similar in many respects. Both are of granitic schist, with numerous gulches and ledges. Both have numerous isolated stacks, which are specially favoured nesting sites and are occupied on all sides. The Digges Island colony extends unbroken for some three miles on cliffs averaging about 700 feet in height. The mainland colony, except for a hiatus caused by a steep valley and

Table 7: *Breeding populations (pairs) of common murres* (Uria aalge) *in eastern North America. Most recent estimates.*

Location	Population	Year	Authority
Newfoundland			
Funk Island	500,000	1959	Tuck and Fisher
S. Cabot Island	100	1945	Peters
Baccalieu Island	2,500	1959	Peterson
Green Island	50,000	1959	Tuck and Fisher
Gull Island	50	1942	Peters
Cape St. Mary's	2,500	1959	Tuck and Fisher
Gulf of St. Lawrence			
Bird Rocks (Magdalens)	700	1904	Bent
Bonaventure Island	500	1919	Townsend
Anticosti Island	110	1940	Lewis
North Shore Sanctuaries	6,147	1955	Lemieux
Other colonies	1,617	1926–33	Johnson *et al.*
Coast of Labrador			
Bird Island	250	1952	Tuck
Gannet Clusters	2,750	1952	Tuck
Outer Gannet	8,900	1952	Tuck
Herring Islands	475	1952	Tuck
Quaker Hat	30	1952	Tuck
Nunarsuk Island	150	1953	Tuck
Total:	576,779 pairs		

a rounded headland with no available nesting sites, extends for a total of two miles. The mainland cliffs are higher and extend upwards to 1,000 feet. They are also occupied to a greater height, in most cases up to 900 feet. With few exceptions, the Digges Island cliffs are not occupied above the 500-foot level. Both colonies face into Digges Sound and thus towards each other. They at first give the impression of formidable and sheerly vertical cliffs. Closer inspection reveals numerous gulches, inclines and outcrops. Immense sections of the cliffs have fallen or slipped away leaving the stacks mentioned above and, in some instances, sloping banks on which grasses and nitrophilous plants fertilized by murre excrement grow unusually large. Very deep water extends right up to the cliffs.

The breeding population of the Digges Sound thick-billed murre colonies will probably never be precisely determined. It is much larger than is indicated by several scientists who had had only a brief glimpse of part of the colonies from ships. In 1955 it was not less than two million birds, but most likely not more than three million. It seems likely that those colonies are the largest in the eastern Canadian Arctic and compare favourably with Cape Shackleton in West Greenland and indeed with the largest in the European Arctic.

The only other murre location in Hudson Bay is at Coats Island. Sutton (1932) drew attention to the thick-billed murres nesting in that area when he wrote: "Mr. Ford visited the nesting colony at Cape Prefontaine several times while he lived at Coats Island. He told me that hundreds of birds laid their eggs on the ledges above the sea, in such numbers that the breasts of the incubating birds, as seen from a distance, made solid bands of white[1] against the rock-face."

Alan G. Loughrey, Canadian Wildlife Service, visited Coats Island in late July, 1953. He reported two colonies, of 10,000 and 20,000 birds respectively, at 62° 57'N; 82° 01'W and 62° 57'N; 81° 59'W, in the vicinity of Cape Pembroke.

Very little is known concerning murre colonies on Baffin Island, largely because of the lack of extensive exploration in the coastal regions. Hantzsch (1908) wrote: "On the 25th of July, 1906, I observed a splendid colony of Thick-billed Murres on a green bird-mountain near Cape Bluff on the northeast of Resolution Island." Soper (1946) wrote: "It appears from Eskimo reports that breeding places may exist on the cliffs on Resolution Island and possibly on the sheer rocky promontories of the opposite coast along Gabriel Strait." Further evidence of murre colonies in that locality is provided by Wynne-Edwards (1952), who wrote: "On July 27, 1937 when off Acadia Cove, hundreds were seen proceeding to and from Hatton Headland, the southeast of Resolution Island. They would have been obliged to round the headland in order to reach a colony some-where on the east side of the island". Wynne-Edwards informed me that on July 28, 1953, when passing along the south side of Lok's Land, he again saw great numbers of murres. Those points are about 40 miles south and 25 miles north, respectively, from Cape Bluff, where Hantzsch originally reported a breeding colony. Wynne-Edwards also told me that he was sure there are a good many colonies in southeast Baffin Island and had evidence of others in the neighbourhood of Lok's Land and also on the coast between Cyrus Field Bay and Grinnell Bay.

Soper (1946) wrote: "There is further indication that breeding colonies also occur somewhere along the coast between Frobisher Bay and Cumberland Sound. The birds are not known to nest anywhere in the latter sector, but Eskimos report large nesting colonies of them in the vicinity of Merchant's Bay". Kumlien (1879) mentions large murre colonies in Exeter Sound and at Cape Walsingham and Cape Mercy. Wynne-Edwards (1952) wrote: "On August 8, 1936, we passed some 25 miles off Monumental and Lady Franklin Islands and noted a large number of murres coming and going, as Kumlien did in the same region 'about Grinnell Bay'. Evidently, no colony is situated on Lady Franklin Island, because Kumlien . . . would certainly have mentioned any breeding murres. Many murres were seen by us that day along the north side of Frobisher Bay and they were especially numerous off the southeast coast of Lok's Land." Later, Wynne-Edwards wrote me: "I am rather sorry I made the statement in my 'Auk' paper

[1]Incubating thick-billed murres lie in a semi-prone position or against the cliff and show little white. Mr. Ford's visits were apparently late in the sea- son, when loitering birds and unoccupied breed-ing birds were facing the sea.

that 'evidently no colony is situated on Lady Franklin Island', because there might well be, after all."

There is also a murre colony, probably a large one, some ten miles south of Reid Bay. The presence of that colony was determined by various persons, none of whom had actually seen it. Wynne-Edwards (1952) said: "There must be a very large colony there. I understood the place to be the large island in the mouth of Reid Bay, marked (as a peninsula) on Boas's map as "Agpan", which means murre-place." Mr. D. V. Ellis (*in litt.*) wrote: "The location of the colony, as generally stated, is incorrect." He determined, from Eskimo reports, that the colony is situated at 66° 54′N; 61° 45′W.

Kumlien (1879) also mentioned a murre colony at Padlie Island, Exeter Sound. That particular colony has not been recorded since and Wynne-Edwards (*in litt.*) wrote: "This is perhaps the same island, centered on 66° 13′N; 62° 12′W, as the one on which the Fulmar colony is situated, namely, the largest island in Exeter Sound."

Our present knowledge of murre colonies on the east coast of Baffin Island is therefore scanty. The facts that Davis Strait is especially productive of plankton and that large colonies exist along almost the entire length of West Greenland lead to the supposition that there may be large colonies on the east coast of Baffin Island. It may well be, however, that the presence of large amounts of pack ice along the coast in early summer renders it less attractive to murres (Fig. 7).

There is a small colony of thick-billed murres at Cape Graham Moore (near Button Point) on Bylot Island. The first recorded mention of it was by M'Clintock (1859), although it was undoubtedly utilized by the various whalers who visited Pond Inlet during the previous several decades. On July 29, 1858, M'Clintock wrote in his log: "During my absence our shooting parties have twice visited a loomery upon Cape Graham Moore and each time have brought on board 300 looms." Corporal D. S. Moodie estimated that 40,000 murres bred at Cape Graham Moore in 1952. I spent several days there in late May, 1957, but the birds had not yet settled in for the season. An examination of the cliffs and the potential nesting ledges, at that time, gave the impression that Corporal Moodie's estimate was a reasonable one.

The only specific record of a murre colony at Cape Hay in Lancaster Sound was also made in 1858 by M'Clintock, who was searching for the lost Franklin expedition. M'Clintock was prevented by moving pack ice, which kept him three miles from the coast, from "levying a tax" upon the colony. There is mention in the Franklin literature of a load of coal cached at or near Cape Hay at Lady Franklin's request, but no other mention of the large murre colony in that vicinity. The reasons seem clear. M'Clintock at the time intended to investigate an Eskimo report of a shipwreck near Cape Hay. The other rescue ships had no desire to loiter in Lancaster Sound and in fact, except for a brief period in August, would not, because of drifting pack ice, be able to reach the murre cliffs.

It is likely then, that Corporal Ray Johnson, Royal Canadian Mounted Police, and I were the first white men ever to see the Cape Hay murre colony from the land and the first to see it at all for a century. Early in the spring of 1957, we reached Cape Hay by travelling on the sea ice from Pond Inlet to Navy Board Inlet and going overland in the vicinity of the Wollaston Islands. Johnson, with the ice breaking up behind him, returned to Pond Inlet by way of Lancaster Sound and the glaciers of the eastern part of Bylot Island. Mucktar, an Eskimo from Pond Inlet, and I spent the summer at Cape Hay, returning to Pond Inlet by canoe in late August.

The colony is not precisely at Cape Hay, but five miles west of it, towards Navy Board Inlet. The cliffs are of Silurian limestone and generally vertical. They extend for two miles, but, because of deep indentations, cover slightly more than three lineal miles of coast. They are some 200 feet high at the eastern extremity and 100 feet high at the western, but the greater part of the central portion is from 1,000 to 1,500 feet in height. Murres nest wherever there are suitable ledges or crevices, right to the top. Large sections of the cliffs are chair-formation: a drop of several hundred feet, then several hundred feet of benched scree, below which the cliffs fall off again. The murres attain their highest breeding density in those areas. A careful appraisal of the cliffs during the summer of 1957 indicated that approximately 400,000 pairs of thick-billed murres nested in the Cape Hay colonies. Thus, including non-breeding birds, the actual population of the cliffs was close to one million individuals.

The most northerly murre colony in the Canadian Arctic of which there is a record is at Coburg Island, between Devon and Ellesmere Islands. The first mention I have of this colony is from Commander David C. Nutt (*in litt.*), who observed a large colony there while passing the island with Captain "Bob" Bartlett, "prior to the war". Corporal A. C. Fryer, Royal Canadian Mounted Police, stationed at Craig Harbour, visited the Coburg Island colony on August 16, 1953. He wrote: ". . . the number of murres nesting here exceeds the number of murres on Bylot Island, but the cliffs on Coburg Island are more inaccessible". I suspect that Corporal Fryer in referring to Bylot Island meant the Cape Graham Moore colony, which he had also seen, and not the large Cape Hay colony.

The only other known Canadian colony in the High Arctic is at Prince Leopold Island. That island is about five miles wide and eight miles long. It is of limestone, with precipitous cliffs up to 1,000 feet high. Sir Edmund Parry, who named the island in honour of His Royal Highness, Prince Leopold of Saxe-Coburg, on August 4, 1819, records the "numerous" murres, fulmars and kittiwakes near the island, but could only get within four or five miles of it because of pack ice. M'Clintock wintered at Fort Leopold on Somerset Island for eleven months in 1848-49, and reported a large colony in that vicinity. A. G. Loughrey (*in litt.*), from an aircraft in 1952, noted: ". . . large numbers of murres flying to and from the abrupt coastal escarpment at Cape Clarence, Somerset Island, and Prince Leopold Island."

In 1958, T. W. Barry of the Canadian Wildlife Service carried out a biological reconnaissance of Somerset Island and its vicinity, spending from August 13 to August 19 on Prince Leopold Island. He confirmed that there was a large colony of murres, fulmars and kittiwakes on Prince Leopold Island. He found murres nesting along the northern and eastern sides, occupying about ten miles of cliff. Barry estimated that there were 350,000 thick-billed murres nesting on Prince Leopold Island, but none actually at Cape Clarence.

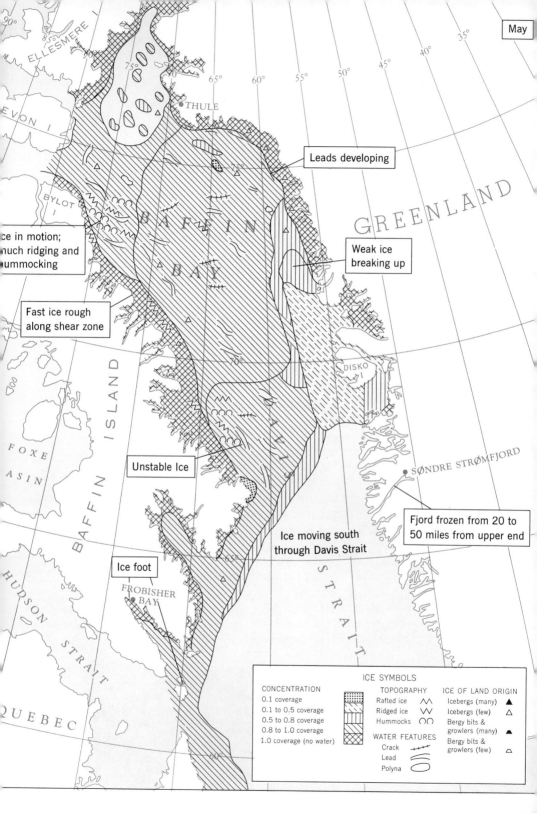

May

Leads developing

Weak ice
breaking up

Ice in motion;
much ridging and
hummocking

Fast ice rough
along shear zone

Fjord frozen from 20 to
50 miles from upper end

Unstable Ice

Ice moving south
through Davis Strait

Ice foot

ELLESMERE I.

THULE

GREENLAND

BYLOT I.

DEVON I.

BAFFIN BAY

DISKO

SØNDRE STRØMFJORD

BAFFIN ISLAND

FOXE BASIN

FROBISHER BAY

DAVIS STRAIT

HUDSON STRAIT

QUEBEC

ICE SYMBOLS

CONCENTRATION
0.1 coverage
0.1 to 0.5 coverage
0.5 to 0.8 coverage
0.8 to 1.0 coverage
1.0 coverage (no water)

TOPOGRAPHY
Rafted ice   ᴧᴧ
Ridged ice   ᴠᴠ
Hummocks   ◠◠
WATER FEATURES
Crack   ┼┼┼
Lead   ⬯
Polyna   ◯

ICE OF LAND ORIGIN
Icebergs (many)   ▲
Icebergs (few)   △
Bergy bits &
growlers (many)   ◣
Bergy bits &
growlers (few)   ◿

FIGURE 7. *Distribution of ice in Baffin Bay and Davis Strait in May (after Technical Report TR-13 of U.S. Hydrographic Office, February, 1955)*

Vague references in the Franklin literature suggested that there was another colony off the northwest coast of Somerset Island, possibly on Limestone Island. Barry, from an aircraft, saw murres in the vicinity of Limestone Island, but bad weather prevented his confirming that they actually nested there. It is most likely that they do. In fact, from what I could learn about this region of sounds, channels and straits centred about Viscount Melville Sound, where the pack ice is almost always in motion in summer, there are likely to be other unrecorded colonies there as well as on the east coast of Baffin Island (Fig. 8).

The thick-billed murre is a common breeding species along the west coast of Greenland. In that region, it breeds in extensive colonies which have occupied the same coastal cliffs for centuries. Salomonsen (1951) has studied most of the west coast colonies and estimated the size of the breeding population in each.

The northernmost colony in Greenland is situated on Hakluyt Island in Thule District at 77° 25'N latitude. It is well known and has been visited by a number of explorers, including Gibson, Macmillan, Rasmussen and Koch. It appears to be very large, but Salomonsen could view it only from ship at some distance and did not estimate the population.

There are additional breeding localities in the Thule District: Carey Island, two colonies, each of about 10,000 pairs; Saunders Island, 200,000 pairs; Igsivigsoq (76° 09'N), small colonies; and Agpat (76° 05'N), 100,000 pairs.

Upernavik District is the main stronghold of the species in West Greenland. The chief colonies are located at Agparssuit (73° 48'N), 1,000,000 pairs; Qiparqo (73° 43'N), 30,000 pairs; Torqussaq (73° 25'N), about 8,000 pairs; Middle Kingigtaurssuk (72° 42'N), 10,000 pairs; Qaersorssuaq[1] (72° 42'N), 100,000 pairs; Agparssuit at Kingigtoq (72° 40'N), 100,000 pairs; Agpatsiat (72° 42'N), 10,000 pairs; Tingmiakulugssuit (72° 39'N), 5,000 pairs; and smaller colonies at Umiasugssik, Qornoq Angissoq and Kingigtuarssuk North.

There is a large colony on Sagdleq Island (70° 56'N), in the Umanaq District. Bertelsen estimated that there were 500,000 pairs breeding at that locality in 1921. In 1949, however, Manager O. R. B. Hansen informed Salomonsen that he considered the population had decreased to half of that size, as a result of persecution. Salomonsen made a census of the Sagdleq colony on August 3, 1949, when a great number of the breeding birds had already left with their young, and estimated that there were 150,000 pairs still present. There are seven other colonies in the Umanaq District, but they are small, not exceeding 3,000 pairs in any locality.

There is only one large colony in Disko Bay and that is located at Ivnaq on Arveprinsen's Island, just north of Ritenbenk. The colony formerly contained several hundred thousand pairs, but in consequence of persecution had decreased. Salomonsen estimated 50,000 pairs breeding in that locality in 1949.

---

[1] John Davis on June 30, 1587, named this island "Sanderson His Hope" in gratitude to the most generous of his supporters, and in the "hope" that the passage beyond was the sought-for Northwest Passage. Here they saw hundreds of thousands of murres. Davis seems to have been the first person to describe a thick-billed murre colony in the New World.

There is a colony in Sermilinguaq Fjord in the Sukkertoppen District. During a visit in 1925, Salomonsen found murres breeding on both the north and the south of the Fjord, "probably more than 100,000". In 1946, however, he estimated that there were only about 5,000 pairs in that locality. Other small colonies in that region have also disappeared as a result of persecution.

The southernmost breeding locality in West Greenland is on Qiope (60° 42′N), where Salomonsen found a colony of 1,000 pairs in 1949.

The foregoing accounts of murre colonies in West Greenland refer primarily to thick-billed murres, but apparently common murres breed locally and in small numbers in Sermilinguaq Fjord. They have not actually been observed nesting, but specimens in breeding condition have been collected at that locality.

Johnson (1940) tabled 60,626 individuals as the known breeding population of common murres in North America up to 1936. As pointed out, both Funk Island and Anticosti were erroneously tabled (an error of some 10,000 birds). Thus Johnson's table should have read 50,000 individuals or 25,000 pairs. Since that time, the common murre population in Labrador and Newfoundland has increased by more than 500,000 pairs (Table 7). This increase occurred entirely along the Labrador coast and the eastern coast of Newfoundland—i.e., in those regions most strongly affected by the Labrador Current.

Although there are along the east coast of Baffin Island some murre colonies of which there is scanty knowledge, it is possible to account for some 4,700,000 thick-billed murres at three large loomeries in the eastern Canadian Arctic. The estimated breeding populations at Coats Island, Prince Leopold Island, Cape Graham Moore and Coburg Island account for another 500,000. It is likely then, that a total of five million thick-billed murres breeding in the eastern Canadian Arctic is a conservative estimate.

Salomonsen (1951) states that the total breeding population of thick-billed murres in West Greenland amounts to about two million pairs, half of which inhabit the gigantic loomery at Agparssuit or Cape Shackleton. This estimate does not include the non-breeding birds, such as those prospecting the colony but not breeding. I suspect that it is a very conservative estimate and cannot concede that fewer than five million thick-billed murres inhabit the west coast of Greenland during the summer months.

There are then, at least five million thick-billed murres in the eastern Canadian Arctic and five million along the west coast of Greenland. The total population of common murres, including non-breeders is probably in excess of one and one quarter million individuals. Ten million thick-billed murres and one and one quarter million common murres as the total population for the eastern North American section of the North Atlantic, is, I am sure, a very conservative estimate.

FIGURE 8. *Breeding distribution of thick-billed murres in the eastern Canadian Arctic, including suspected colonies*

LEGEND/FIGURE 8
● ACTUAL MURRE COLONIES
▲ SUSPECTED MURRE COLONIES

CHAPTER VII

Murre Colonies of the North Pacific

The common murre is widely dispersed along the coasts of Washington, Oregon and California. "Large and small nesting colonies are found from the Strait of Juan de Fuca south to Gray's Harbour off-shore rocks" (Stanley G. Jewett, *in litt.*).

There are colonies of common murres off the coast of Marin County at Point Reyes, off Bear Valley and off Double Point (Jewett and Storer, *in litt.*); off the coast of San Mateo County on a rock near Devil's Slide (Storer, *in litt.*); and off Monterey County at Hurricane Point (Jewett, *in litt.*). Those are all small colonies, however, the largest (Point Reyes) having a population of about 3,000 birds.

One of the largest and certainly the most famous of the breeding localities of the common murre is on the Farallon Islands. Those islands have an interesting historical background as the following descriptive note by Emerson (1904) will show: "From the old Spanish chronicles we learn of the discovery of the Farallon Islands in 1543 by Ferrelo. It was Sir Francis Drake, however, who gave us the first particular description of the 'Islands of St. James' as they were then known. Drake, it seems, landed to replenish his larder with seal meat. Doubtless he laid in a stock of eggs, for a man is never too old a boy to collect eggs where they may be had for the taking. In 1775 Bodega and Maurells, on their way up the northwest coast, named the islands 'Los Farallones de los Frayles' in honour of the monks who had discovered San Francisco Bay in 1769, the same year that the Franciscans founded their first mission in Alta California, at San Diego. The first settlers on the islands, we know, were Russians from the north, who came with Aleuts to fish and seal hunt. There remain today, on the southwestern part of the island, the well-preserved stone walls of their low huts, but the date of their occupancy is unknown.

"The islands are formed of crystalline granite, a ridge rising many hundred feet above the ocean floor. Sugar Loaf Rock in Fisherman's Bay is an exception, being a conglomerate of coarse gravel, standing isolated 185 feet above sea level. South Farallon Island is the largest of the group. At water line the rocks are of a blackish brown where the surf beats, and then above high water mark change to a yellow or a light grayish tone over all the island, where not occupied by the roosting or nesting areas of the sea fowl or changed by the presence of introduced plants. The granite readily yields to a pick and offers a firm footing but is rather hard on shoe leather. Shore lines are all cut up into great channel-like troughs, with arched grottos running far into the rock and filled with gorgeously tinted marine life. There are natural bridges, pot holes, and shelving ledges of all descriptions."

Ray (1904) gives an account of the main breeding colonies on the Farallons as follows: "The largest rookeries on the main island are in Great Murre Cave and at Tower Point, on East End, on the rocky shelves and terraces below Main Top Peak, and on the dizzy sides, from sea to summit, on the Great Arch, the natural bridge par excellence, on West End. The birds also breed abundantly all along the ridge and in the numberless grottos along the seashore, while the surrounding islets are covered with them in countless thousands. Great Murre Cave, which runs in from the ocean on Shulbrick Point, with its vast bird population is a wonder to behold. All ledges and projections, as well as the cave floor, were murre covered, and on our approach the great colony became a scene of animation, with a vast nodding of dusky heads and a ringing concert of gurgling cries."

Another important colony on the Pacific coast, Three Arch Rocks in Oregon, now a National Wildlife Refuge, appears recently to have increased in size. Stanley G. Jewett informed me: "A few years ago an estimated 750,000 birds were nesting there, a considerable increase over the population found there during the summer of 1914, my first visit to the Rocks". Mr. Jewett added: "Large colonies nest on the rocks off Bandon, Coos County, and off Port Orford and off the mouth of Pistol River in Curry County. Other smaller colonies are found in between those listed but so far as I know no qualified person has visited them."

Mr. Alex Walker provided me with additional information on the present distribution of California murres. He wrote: "In regard to the number of murres on Cape Lookout, I do not believe there are more than 2,500 or 3,000 . . . There are several colonies along the Tillamook County coast in Oregon besides the Cape Lookout colonies and the large, best known colonies on the Three Arch Rocks. The other colonies would include those on the Two Arches off Cascade Head, where two of the three rocks are occupied by murres; Cape Mears, where some nest on ledges on the cape and others on an offshore rock; and another smaller colony on a rock off Falcon Cove."

The only known colony of murres along the British Columbia coast is one of common murres (*Uria aalge inornata*) on Triangle Island. Guiguet (1950) "conservatively estimated" the breeding population in 1949 on Triangle Island at 3,000 birds.

The major colonies of common murres in southeastern Alaska are near Sitka, on St. Lazaria Island, on the Hazy Islands in Chatham Strait and on Forrester Island (Gabrielson and Lincoln, 1959).

Both the thick-billed murre (*Uria lomvia arra*) and the common murre (*Uria aalge inornata*) breed in mixed colonies at Kodiak Island, as their subspecific counterparts do in the low-arctic North Atlantic. There are other mixed colonies westward of Kodiak Island, throughout the Aleutian Islands, and Komandorskie Islands (Bent, 1919), the Kurile Islands as far west as the coast of Japan (Yamashina, 1931), in the Sea of Okhotsk, on Kamchatka Peninsula, and possibly on Sakhalin (Salomonsen, 1944), on the Pribilof Islands and St. Matthew Island in the Bering Sea (Bent, 1919) and northwards to Sledge Island (Cade, 1952).

The common murre breeds from Olyutorski (60° N) south along the east coast of the Kamchatka Peninsula. It breeds all along the chain of the Kuriles from Paramushir to

Kunashir. Some of the colonies in the Kuriles are immense.

In the Sea of Okhotsk, common murres breed off the north coast of Hokkaido (Yezao), and at Tyulena Island (Kaihyo-to) in South Sakhalin, where at least 300,000 birds breed (Austin and Kuroda, 1953), on the Shantarski Islands, and probably at Ayan (where they have been observed during the summer); and on Taigonos Peninsula (in the northeast section of the Okhotsk Sea). They have not been recorded from the western coast of the Kamchatka Peninsula.

Breeding colonies of common murres in the Sea of Japan are few and the populations probably small. There is a colony at Dikastri, on the mainland of Tartar Strait. Austin and Kuroda (1953) report small colonies on Teurejimo, off western Hokkaido, and on Koshimo, a small island off the western entrance of Tsugaru Strait. Several Russian and Japanese authors write that *perhaps* common murres breed in Korea, but I have been unable to find any positive recorded evidence that it is so. Therefore, Tsugaru Strait (41° 31′N) may be the southernmost locality of the common murre in the western Pacific.

Thick-billed murres breed along the Koryaski coast and mix with common murres at Olyutorski Gulf (60° 30′N). Both thick-billed and common murres breed together along the eastern Kamchatka coast and in the Kuriles as far as Matua (48° 45′N).

Thick-billed murres also breed in mixed colonies in the Sea of Okhotsk, along the coast of Sakhalin, in the Shantarski Islands, at Matkyil Island, at Moneron, where five per cent are thick-billed murres (Gizenko, 1955), at Allen Island (near Matkyil), where no common murres are recorded, and on the Taigonos Peninsula, the most northerly colony in the Sea of Okhotsk. Moneron Island (46° 20′N) is the southernmost known breeding site of the thick-billed murre in the western Pacific.

Probably the best known murre colony in the Aleutians is on Bogoslof Island, which Bent (1919) visited on July 4, 1911. He wrote: "The largest breeding colony of Pallas's Murres, probably the largest breeding colony of any kind, that I have ever seen was on the famous volcanic island of the Bering Sea, Bogoslof Island, about 70 miles northwest of Unalaska. Considering the wonderful volcanic performance of this interesting island, it is surprising that the murres still resort to it as a breeding ground, for at each of its frequent eruptions many thousands of these poor birds have been killed; but still the 'foolish guillemots', as they have been well called, return to it again next season. The violent eruptions of the summer of 1910 threw up enough material to join together the three little islands forming the Bogoslof group. In 1911 the volcano had subsided and the towering peaks of Castle Rock, from 200 to 300 feet high, were literally covered with nesting murres. I could hardly hazard a guess as to how many hundred thousand murres were breeding on this and other portions of the island. On the steep sides of the rocky peaks, every available ledge, shelf or cavity was occupied by murres, sitting as close as they could, in long rows on the narrow ledges and in dense masses on the flat rocks below the cliffs". Common murres (*Uria aalge inornata*) also bred on Bogoslof Island during Bent's visit but they were in the minority, actually only "several small compact colonies . . . in close bunches of 15 or 20 pairs".

The Bogoslof Island colony compares in size with any in the Polar Basin or the North Atlantic. There may be other colonies in the Pacific even larger than Bogoslof. There is a good deal of evidence that somewhere in the Pribilofs or in the Aleutians there is probably the largest murre colony in the world. It may be on St. George Island or Walrus Island or even on some island which has not been surveyed by an ornithologist.

The Pribilof Islands are well documented because of the various visits by scientists to the fur-seal rookeries. Immense colonies are recorded for St. Paul, Walrus and St. George Islands. In the summer of 1953, a group of expert ornithologists, Roger Tory Peterson, James Fisher, Finnur Gudmundsson and William Cottrell, visited the Pribilofs. Both Fisher and Gudmundsson were specially interested in sea-birds, and they carefully examined every murre colony they encountered. Of St. Paul they commented (Peterson and Fisher, 1955): "Roger tried to count the birds that stood shoulder to shoulder on a hundred yards of cliff, and using this sample estimated that a minimum in number of a million murres were on the ledges of St. Paul. Another group, not much smaller in number (for pairs spend little time together on the ledge), were away fishing, or floating in rafts of hundreds on the sea below the cliffs . . . " Both species of murres were present at St. Paul. The thick-billed murre " . . . hugged the rocks that offered little more than a foothold", while the common murre " . . . seemed to command the broader ledges".

On the St. George Island colony, Peterson and Fisher (1955) commented: "There seemed to be far more sea-birds on St. George than on St. Paul. It was debatable which were more numerous, the murres or the choochkies [least auklets]; both probably ran into millions. One of the men stationed at St. George once tried to estimate the number of choochkies in this great hillside colony and after sitting out there for three days, watching them come and go, decided that there were about 36,000,000. This is probably an exaggeration, but Ira Gabrielson vouches for the fact that there are millions. We did not get the impression of quite such numbers, although the murres on the northside cliffs certainly ran into millions".

The Pribilof Islands lie in the belt of overlap of the two murres. Gudmundsson, according to Peterson and Fisher (1955), thinks "that in normal seasons the common murres tend to arrive on the ledges before the thick-billed murres, and take the best places, the great, broad, flat platforms; leaving the arctic birds to secure what is left, the smaller ledges at the edge of the cliffs. Perhaps in some seasons the arrival of the common murres may be delayed, and the thick-billed murres get to the big ledges first". In any case, an extraordinary ebb and flow in proportion of the two species is evident on Walrus Island in the Pribilofs. The pendulum has swung from nearly all thick-billed murres in 1872 and 1874 to perhaps mid-way in 1880; to nearly all thick-billed in 1901; to nearly all common in 1911 and 1914; to all or nearly all thick-billed in 1940; to nearly all common in 1953 (Peterson and Fisher, 1955).

Regarding the breeding population of murres on Walrus Island, Gabrielson (1940), who visited the colony on July 7, 1940, wrote: "I tried to make an estimate of the number of murres but finally gave up after I found that even the most conservative estimate ran into the millions".

There is a large colony of common murres at Cape Mohican, Nunivak Island, off the coast of Alaska (Swarth, 1934). At St. Matthew Island, in the middle of the Bering Sea, both species breed. Hanna (1917) says of St. Matthew Island: " . . . murres are exceedingly abundant on all cliffs".

There are huge colonies on Fairway Rock (Bailey, 1943) and on the Diomedes in the middle of Bering Strait. Apparently only thick-billed murres breed on Fairway but at least a few common murres breed on the Diomedes, as Jacques (1930) recorded one from 25 specimens collected there.

Estimates of the murre populations on St. Lawrence Island were given me by Tom Cade (*in litt.*) who visited that locality in 1950. They are as follows: thick-billed murre, 100,000; common murre, 1,000.

Cade (1952) also visited Sledge Island, some 25 miles west of Nome, Alaska, in 1950. He found both species breeding there "in the high hundreds or low thousands". The common murre barely penetrates the Polar Basin from Bering Strait, with a small outpost at Point Hope, near Cape Lisburne.

It is much more difficult to estimate the murre populations in the North Pacific than in any other part of their range. The best information we have is that the colonies are immense. There are probably no more than one million of *Uria aalge californica*, with its centre of abundance on the Farallon Islands. *Uria aalge inornata* is much more numerous, with its centre of abundance perhaps in the Kuriles, where its colonies have been described as "immense". There is evidence that the most abundant form *Uria lomvia arra*, predominates in the Pribilofs, the Aleutians and perhaps the Kuriles. It is clear that the total number of murres occupying Bogoslof, St. Paul, St. George and Walrus Islands alone compares favourably with, no doubt exceeds, the total population of the eastern Canadian Arctic and West Greenland combined or the total for the eastern section of the North Atlantic. It seems certain that the total number of murres occupying the North Pacific is at least equal to the total occupying the North Atlantic, i.e., twenty millions. It is very likely higher.

Following the precedents set by James Fisher, who estimated the world population of fulmars ("I would be surprised if it were as much as two millions and would eat my hat, if I had one, if it were ten millions") and R. M. Lockley, who estimated the world population of the common puffin (fifteen million breeding adults), I am also tossing a hat into the ring.

There are approximately fifteen million thick-billed murres and one million common murres in the Polar Basin; five million thick-billed murres and five million common murres in the eastern North Atlantic; ten million thick-billed murres and half a million common murres in the western North Atlantic; and some twenty million of both species in the North Pacific, with the thick-billed murre predominating. This gives a total of some fifty-six million murres, with the thick-billed murre predominating perhaps three to one. I do not think the world population can be less than fifty million. I do not think it exceeds one hundred million.

The thick-billed murre may well be the most abundant sea-bird in the Northern Hemisphere, though it is probably exceeded in numbers in the North Atlantic by the dovekie and in the North Pacific by the least auklet.

CHAPTER VIII

Migration and Winter Distribution

As soon as the chicks leave the nest sites, both chicks and adults go out to sea. For the next several weeks they swim northwards against the currents. Thus it is that murres from Newfoundland colonies are found along the Labrador coast in September. But by the time both chicks and moulting adults can fly, their distribution with regard to the location of their colonies is rather erratic—north, south, east or west. By early winter, adults, unless prevented by ice, are likely to have returned to the vicinity of their nesting colonies.

Thus many populations of both species of murres are non-migratory. In some parts of the breeding range of thick-billed murres, the formation of surface ice or the movements of pack ice drives the murres either temporarily or for the entire winter from the vicinity of their nesting colonies. This applies especially to the birds breeding in the eastern Canadian Arctic, along the Labrador coast, and on the northwest coast of Greenland, and no doubt to those breeding in the Pacific sector of the Polar Basin, all of which must make long annual migrations. As is the case with most young birds, young murres range somewhat widely during their first winter. This may be because they have not yet acquired a traditional attachment to any particular locality.

The winter distribution of both species is confined to the off-shore zone, which may be considered to begin at the borders of the inshore zone (five miles out to sea) and extend to the edge of the continental shelf. In places the continental shelf may extend for hundreds of miles, as around Newfoundland, in the Baltic and North Seas, and around Britain. Murres do not normally occur in winter more than a few hundred miles off shore from their most southerly breeding limits. They rarely occur in the oceanic waters of the North Atlantic or the North Pacific.

Common murres have a greater tolerance for warmish waters in winter than do thick-billed murres. Common murres winter as far south as the 15°C surface temperature February isotherm, while thick-billed murres do not go beyond the 5°C isotherm (Fig. 9).

Migration and winter distribution in the Polar Basin

As previously explained, the Polar Basin is not completely ice-blocked, even in winter. Thus Clarke (1890) says of the murres of Jan Mayen: "A few remained all winter, but the main spring flight occurred on April 20, 1883". Trevor-Battye (1897) recorded murres at Spitsbergen on January 11, and Clarke (1898) saw the first one at Cape Flora, Franz Josef Land, on March 20, 1897.

The Spitsbergen population probably moves westward in winter, at least in bad ice

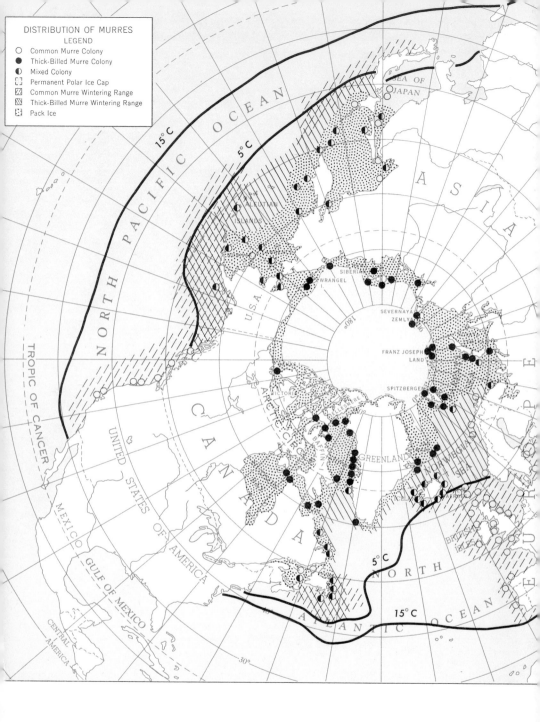

FIGURE 9. *Winter distribution of murres in relation to pack ice and the surface isotherms in February*

years. Two adults banded in Spitsbergen have been recovered in southwest Greenland in December and January, respectively. Most of the Murman coast murres apparently winter in the same off-shore waters, although a few young birds regularly move southwards along the Scandinavian coast.

There have been no winter recoveries of murres banded in Novaya Zemlya, although up to 1956 some 50,000 had been banded. This suggests that the Novaya Zemlya murres do not mingle in winter with those from the Murman coast, recoveries of which are fairly frequent. The Novaya Zemlya murres probably winter in the eastern districts of the Barents Sea, near the edge of the ice-field, which ships rarely visit. This supposition is supported by reports that murres are observed all year round at the northern tip of Novaya Zemlya by crews of aircraft (Uspenski, 1956). Individual birds, chiefly young of the preceding year, banded at Novaya Zemlya, have been recovered in March and April only to the north.

On the basis of those data, it would be correct to consider the winter migration of the European Polar Basin murres as minor movements caused by the formation of ice on the coasts. The distance of the murres from shore and the direction of their winter movements are probably directly related to the location of the edge of the ice-field and to the position of the best supply of food.

In winter, when ice conditions are particularly bad in the Polar Basin, murres are sometimes forced near land and a period of adverse winds may carry them inland to freshwater lakes and streams. Such "wrecks" have been described from Finland (Mela, 1904; Jagerskiold and Kolthoff, 1926). There are numerous instances on record where murres in the Polar Basin were trapped by quick-freezing surfaces of the sea and perished.

The birds in the Pacific sector of the Polar Basin, for instance from Wrangel and Herald Islands, must be forced out of their breeding areas by ice in winter. Perhaps some of them move westward to the ice-free Murman coast; probably most move southwards through the Bering Sea. The murres of the Kurile and Komandorski Islands and of the coast of Kamchatka, move only short distances to the south in winter; as far as the Bay of Aniua, Hokkaido, and the mouth of the Amur (Uspenski, 1956). Salomonsen (1944), writing of *Uria lomvia arra*, said: "The winter is spent in the open sea free of ice, southwards to southern Alaska and northern Japan."

Migration and winter distribution in the eastern North Atlantic

The common murres of the eastern North Atlantic are also generally non-migratory—especially the adults. Salomonsen (1944), writing of the Faeroe population, said that the adults were rather sedentary and remained in the Faeroe Sea during the winter months, being common around the islands the whole winter in fiords and off the coast, but commonest in the open sea. Young Faeroe birds, especially those of the preceding year, range more widely and have been recovered in winter as far away as Norway.

Several writers (Paris, 1921; de Paillerets, 1927) state that the majority of Norwegian birds move southwards in winter and appear in the waters of western Sweden and Denmark and along the North Sea coasts of Germany, Holland, Belgium and England

and even off the coast of France. That generalization was apparently based on a few recoveries of young birds. More recent data (Holgerson, 1951) show that the murre " . . . exceptionally migrates away from the breeding places in north Norway. Most of the birds stay along the coast or in the fiords of the northern districts." Banding records do indicate, however, that the coast of Norway is a favoured meeting place in early winter for young birds from Britain, the Faeroes, the Baltic, the Murman coast and especially from Heligoland (Vous, 1948). Murres banded at Heligoland have been recovered not only in the Bay of Biscay but northwards to central Norway and western Sweden and northeastwards to Great Britain (Stechow, 1938).

Scottish birds appear to be more or less sedentary, wintering in the seas around the British coasts. The adults sometimes make a short land visit to their traditional nesting sites in January. The young birds wander more freely and go mainly north and northeast in winter. They have been recovered as far away as the Faeroes and off the coasts of Norway and Sweden.

Murres occur in winter off the Atlantic coast of Spain, in the Mediterranean, and off the shores of Morocco and the Canaries. The various subspecies have not been identified in those localities. The extreme southern records may be those of young birds belonging to the breeding populations of the Iberian Peninsula.

Migration and winter distribution in the western North Atlantic

A considerable amount of banding was carried out in the murre colonies in eastern North America by the Canadian Wildlife Service during the years 1951-57 (Appendices A and B). In addition, Johnson (1940) reported on the recoveries from common murre colonies along the North Shore of the Gulf of St. Lawrence; Austin (1932) on those from thick-billed murre colonies along the coast of Labrador; and Salomonsen (1956) on those from the thick-billed murre colonies in West Greenland.

The total number of murres banded by the Canadian Wildlife Service was 35,810. For most population units the sample banded was rather small, although 14,000 chicks banded on Funk Island in 1956 were about 25 per cent of the young which reached the flying stage.

A total of 568 recoveries was obtained from all the Canadian Wildlife Service bandings. The recoveries of common murres (Tables 8, 9) were slightly more than two per cent, and those of thick-billed murres (Tables 10, 11) slightly more than one per cent. The comparative rates of recovery of the two species were the opposite of what would be expected, knowing that thick-billed murres form the bulk of the kill in Newfoundland. This discrepancy was probably a consequence of the fact that the sample of thick-billed murres banded was not sufficiently well distributed. The low rate of recovery precludes statistical analysis of data relating to migration and mortality of the sample. The data obtained, when interpreted qualitatively in the light of direct observations of movements, are considered to provide a reasonable indication of population dispersal.

A total of 9,320 thick-billed murre chicks was banded in West Greenland during the period 1946-57. Of those, three per cent have been recovered off Greenland and 0.4 per cent off Newfoundland.

86

Table 8: *Recoveries of common murres banded as adults in the western North Atlantic sector*

Recovered in:	Newfoundland		Labrador	
	No.	%	No.	%
Banded at:				
Labrador	—	—	—	—
Green Island	1	0.224	1	0.224
Funk Island	5	0.500	—	—
Totals:	6	0.356	1	0.059

Table 9: *Recoveries of common murres banded as chicks in the western North Atlantic sector*

Recovered in:	Newfoundland		Labrador	
	No.	%	No.	%
Banded at:				
Labrador	44	3.764	—	—
Green Island	127	2.918	2	0.046
Funk Island	272	1.801	9	0.060
Totals:	443	2.148	11	0.053

Table 10: *Recoveries of thick-billed murres banded as adults in the western North Atlantic sector*

Recovered in:	Newfoundland		Cape Dorset		West Greenland	
	No.	%	No.	%	No.	%
Banded at:						
Labrador	1	0.855	—	—	—	—
Coats Island	5	0.952	—	—	1	0.190
Digges Sound	6	0.300	—	—	—	—
Cape Hay	2	0.147	—	—	5	0.367
Totals:	14	0.339	—	—	6	0.145

The highest recoveries were in Newfoundland from young Labrador murres, both common and thick-billed. The reason seems to be that the Labrador murres arrive in Newfoundland waters in late October and remain until the following June, and thus are hunted for a long period along the northeast coast. Yet an annual kill of four per cent

Table 11: *Recoveries of thick-billed murres banded as chicks in the western North Atlantic sector*

	Recovered in: Newfoundland		Cape Dorset		West Greenland	
	No.	%	No.	%	No.	%
Banded at:						
Labrador	7	3.431	—	—	—	—
Digges Sound	39	0.486	4	0.050	4	0.050
Cape Hay	12	1.055	—	—	21	1.847
Totals:	58	0.619	4	0.042	25	0.267
West Greenland		0.4		—		3.0

Table 12: *Recoveries by years after banding*

Recoveries during year of banding	397
Recoveries during 2nd year after banding	136
Recoveries during 3rd year after banding	31
Recoveries during 4th year after banding	3
Recoveries during 5th year after banding	1
Total:	568

is not excessive. The next highest were Green Island common murres in Newfoundland and West Greenland thick-billed murres in West Greenland, each three per cent. It is also interesting that percentage recoveries in Newfoundland of Digges Sound and West Greenland thick-billed murres were comparable, while, as might be expected, approximately twice as many Cape Hay murres appeared to be shot in West Greenland as in Newfoundland.

Recoveries with respect to time elapsed after banding are given in Table 12. Because of abrasion and salt-water corrosion, bands do not usually last more than five years. Most of the recoveries were from young birds during their first winter.

Sixty-one of the 568 recoveries were outside the immediate region of Newfoundland coastal waters. Fourteen were off the Labrador coast, nine off St. Pierre, one on the Grand Banks, three in the Gulf of St. Lawrence, one (bird found dead) in Massachusetts, four off the southwest coast of Baffin Island and twenty-nine off southwest Greenland. Most murres winter far out on the off-shore zone and there would undoubtedly be more recoveries from that zone if the birds were hunted far from the coast.

The majority (497) of the recoveries were from birds shot. Twenty-nine of the banded birds were caught in salmon, herring or cod nets, 13 were found dead from oil pollution and 30 were reported "found dead" or "injured".

The bandings of common murres on Funk Island constitute the best sample obtained and warrant consideration in some detail.

Recoveries of adults were very low. From one thousand adults, only five recoveries were obtained in five years. (One adult was shot in December of the year of banding, within 75 miles of Funk Island; two in April of the second year within 20 miles; one in October of the third year within 40 miles; and one in November of the fourth year within 60 miles). Visits to the island corroborated that adult mortality was low, that bands could be expected to last for five years, and that the same adults returned to the island year after year. The evidence, even with so few recoveries, indicates that Funk Island common murre adults remain all winter off the southeast coast of Newfoundland in the general region of their traditional nesting island.

Fourteen thousand chicks were banded at Funk Island in 1956. Recoveries indicated that, immediately after leaving the island, the young swam northwards against the Labrador Current. From visual observation it is known that the young were accompanied by adults. They reached the coast of Labrador early in August and some of them stayed in that region until late November. Early in October, most of them commenced to move southwards. Five per cent of recoveries were from birds that went through the Strait of Belle Isle and were recovered during the next two months off the northwest coast of Newfoundland and elsewhere in the Gulf of St. Lawrence. The large majority returned along the northeast coast of Newfoundland, where 50 per cent of the total recoveries for that region were made during the months of October and November. During the autumn, hunters often shot four or five banded Funk Island birds in the same locality on the same date. For example, six were shot on October 8 off St. Anthony, the northern tip of Newfoundland. There were no recoveries of Funk Island murres along the northeast coast after December. A substantial number of young birds wintered off the southeast coast. The majority of winter recoveries, however, were from the south coast (Fig. 10). It appears that the Funk Island birds moved in discrete units. This may well be the case for all murre colonies.

Thirty-three common murres banded as young at Funk Island were recovered during May, June and July, most of them in nets. Their recovery localities give some indication of the summering range of young birds, although in interpreting the data it must be remembered that birds are seldom recovered in this way except on the major fishing grounds.

Thirteen of the summer recoveries were year-old birds. Three were recovered in May and June off the south coast of Newfoundland, one in June off the northwestern coast and the remainder off the southeastern coast.

Eighteen were birds of the second year. Six were recovered off the south coast of Newfoundland and off St. Pierre and five off the southeastern coast in May. Two were shot in May within 20 miles of Funk Island. Five others were recovered in June and July off Green Island.

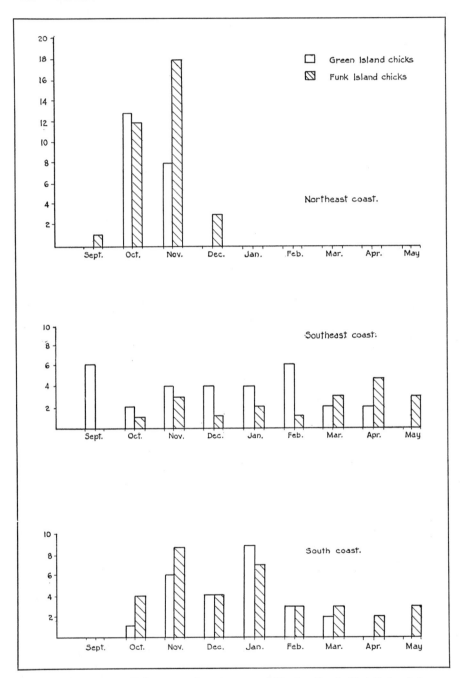

FIGURE 10. *Recoveries off the east and south coasts of Newfoundland of locally banded murre chicks, shown as percentages of total recoveries*

One bird in its third year and another in its fourth year were shot in May within ten miles of Funk Island.

Those summer records indicate that first- and second-year Funk Island common murres summer off the south and southeastern coasts of Newfoundland. In the second year some of them begin to prospect nesting colonies. In the third year they are probably breeding.

There is no conclusive evidence at what age murres first begin to breed. Johnson (1940) believes that common murres breed during their third summer. Uspenski (1956) offers evidence (return to nesting colonies) that thick-billed murres also breed during their third summer. The Funk Island recoveries suggest this and also that they return to the locality of their hatching to breed.

The recovery of adult common murres banded on Green Island was similarly low (two out of 447). Both recoveries indicated a movement northwards against the prevailing currents after leaving the colony. One was shot at St. Anthony, on the extreme northeastern coast, on July 23 of the year after banding, about one week after the "early" birds can be expected to desert the nesting island. The other was shot on October 29, three years after banding, at West Modiste, Labrador.

Most of the young birds from Green Island also went northwards after leaving the colony. The majority of the recoveries of Green Island young murres are off the southeast coast in winter. Only 15 per cent of the recoveries of Green Island murres have been off the south coast and those mainly in January. Thus it appears that after their initial movement northward, Green Island common murres, both adults and young, tend to return to winter in the general region of their nesting colony (Fig. 10).

Of eight recoveries of Green Island murres during their second summer, two were recovered off the south coast of Newfoundland and the remaining six off Green Island, Baccalieu Island and Cape St. Mary's in the immediate vicinity of nesting colonies.

A similar trend was noted in second-year birds. Seven second-year birds were recovered in the summer off Green Island and Funk Island. One was recovered off St. Anthony on July 23, about the same time that the first adults and their chicks would be expected to reach the northeast coast.

There are three third-year recoveries of Green Island murres. Two were caught off Green Island in June, the third at Rose Blanche, off the south coast, on June 14. In this latter instance a third-year bird was recovered at a considerable distance from a colony during the breeding season.

Johnson (1940) analyzed the recoveries of murres banded at Cape Whittle, on the North Shore of the Gulf of St. Lawrence, and wrote in part: "All of these birds were banded before the middle of August but none were recaptured until November. Of the six November records, two were taken on the North Shore near the same latitude in which they were banded and four had already reached eastern and southern Newfoundland waters . . . Of the two birds still remaining on the North Shore, one was taken to the west at Mingan, a distance of approximately 200 miles, and the other from Wolf Bay was taken less than 100 miles east at St. Augustine.

"Of the remaining ten banded juveniles taken during the winter months, December,

January and February, nine were in Newfoundland waters, except one taken at St. Pierre, and one off the east coast of Nova Scotia. The points of recapture for these winter records indicate a definite wintering area south and east of Newfoundland. The recovery data for ten birds banded as adults in the same breeding colonies indicate that they winter more to the east of Newfoundland but in the same waters as the young."

Recoveries of common murres banded as chicks in Labrador suggest that they arrive in Newfoundland waters in late October and remain until the following June. Most of them winter off the south and southeast coasts of Newfoundland. One was found dead in its first winter at Point Judith, Rhode Island.

Two Labrador common murres were recovered in their second summer off Green Island, two off the south coast, and another off the northeastern coast.

The single recovery of an adult thick-billed murre banded in Labrador was off the southeast coast of Newfoundland in January. The seven recoveries of juveniles indicate definitely wintering off the southeastern and southern coasts of Newfoundland. Austin (1932) mentioned five recoveries of Labrador thick-billed murres. One adult and two juveniles were recovered in winter off the southeast coast of Newfoundland. A one-year-old bird was recovered in June off the southeast coast of Newfoundland and another in August, within ten miles of the island in Labrador on which it had been banded.

Five hundred and twenty-five adult thick-billed murres were banded at Coats Island in the eastern Canadian Arctic. There have been six winter recoveries, five from the southeast coast of Newfoundland and one from West Greenland. This slightly more than one per cent recovery of adults is higher than from any other colony. It raises the interesting conjecture that the majority of the Coats Island murres may winter off Newfoundland. This is contrary to Sutton's (1932) opinion. He wrote: "As a rule the nesting Brünnich's Murres of the Southampton-Coats Island region do not move much to the southwards during the coldest months. Only when the winter is very severe, do they move to the south in finding open water where food may be obtained. It is a matter of common knowledge among the Aivilikmuit that the channel between Coats and Southampton practically never freezes, even during years when Frozen Strait to the north is frozen shut." If murres do, indeed, winter in those open waters, they are just as likely to be from the Digges Sound colonies as from Coats Island.

Murres winter in Hudson Strait, which is kept open all winter by strong tides. Constable A. P. Wright, Royal Canadian Mounted Police, stationed at Lake Harbour, Baffin Island, wrote me in 1953 that "Brünnich's Murres have been quite common along the floe-edge this winter". Perhaps most of them were from the immense colonies on Akpatok Island.

The Digges Sound thick-billed murres arrive in Newfoundland waters in November. They seem to concentrate in winter off the northeastern and southeastern coasts (Fig. 11). The only evidence of a more southerly movement was in February and March, 1957, when pack ice may have moved them southwards. In that year also there were three early May recoveries of Digges Sound murres off Newfoundland, one just barely south of the pack ice in the Strait of Belle Isle. All Digges Sound adults recovered in Newfoundland waters in winter were off the southeastern coast.

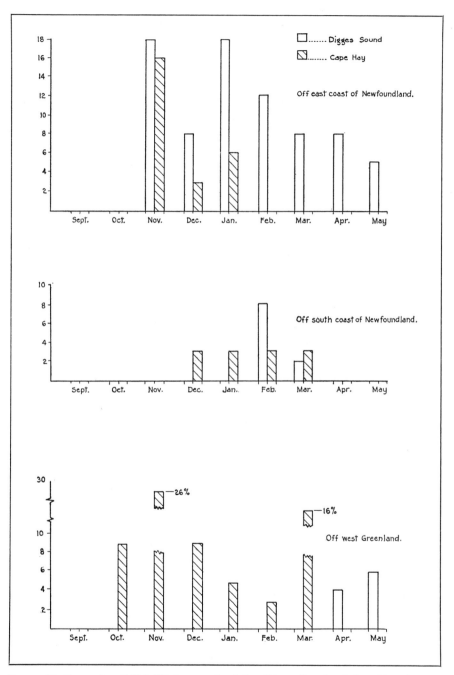

FIGURE 11. *Recoveries of thick-billed murres banded at Digges Sound and Cape Hay, shown as percentages of total recoveries*

There were three recoveries of juvenile Digges Sound murres in their second summer. All of them were found off southwestern Baffin Island, in the vicinity of Cape Dorset and in the general vicinity of their natal area. There were six recoveries of second-year Digges Sound murres. Three were in May off the east coast of Newfoundland in 1957— the bad ice year. One was in May and two in June off southwest Greenland. There were two summer recoveries of Digges Sound three-year-old birds, one in May off southwest Greenland and one in June off Cape Dorset.

Of the seven Cape Hay adult thick-billed murres recovered, five were taken off southwest Greenland between November 5 and March 18, and two in Newfoundland waters. The Newfoundland recoveries were on March 7 on the south coast and in April on the southeast coast.

Of the total of 40 Cape Hay recoveries, 26 were from southwest Greenland. The earliest recovery was at Disko, West Greenland, on October 1, the latest off the West Greenland coast on March 16.

Recoveries of murres banded as chicks at Cape Hay indicated that they arrive in Newfoundland waters in early November and winter mainly off the northeastern and southern coasts (Fig. 11). There was only one recovery from the southeastern coast of Newfoundland and that was in January. The only summer recovery from Digges Island was a bird in its first year taken off the northeastern coast of Newfoundland on June 7. This was the only summer recovery of a far northern thick-billed murre in Newfoundland waters. It very well might have been an injured, slightly oiled, or otherwise handicapped bird.

Since the majority of Cape Hay thick-billed murres and some Digges Sound thick-billed murres winter off the west coast of Greenland, it is of great interest to know that a considerable part, especially juveniles, of the West Greenland population winters off Newfoundland. So far, 37 Greenland murres (see Appendix D) have been recovered off Newfoundland. West Greenland thick-billed murres arrive in Newfoundland waters in late October or early November and remain at least throughout March. The occasional bird is recovered in April and more rarely in May. Three of the birds have been recovered in their second winter and one in its fifth winter.

Thick-billed murres winter in great numbers in the off-shore zone along the west coast of Greenland, where they are found as far north as there is open water (i.e., Egedesminde District) but are most abundant in winter in the Godthaab-Julianehaab Districts (Salomonsen, 1950). They have been recorded in winter a few times as far north as Disko Bay (Fencker, 1889), where they struggle for life in small leads in the almost continuous ice cover.

The Newfoundland region is the main wintering area for the majority of murres in the western North Atlantic (Fig. 12). Since hunting in Newfoundland normally occurs only in areas a few miles off shore, the recoveries of banded birds do not give an accurate indication of the wintering populations off Newfoundland. The wintering area off Newfoundland includes many thousand square miles of the Grand Banks region (Fig. 13).

From 1914 to 1916 and from 1919 onward the International Ice Observation and Ice Patrol Service, of the United States Coast Guard, patrolled the Newfoundland Banks

LEGEND/FIGURE 12
● THICK-BILLED MURRE COLONY

LEGEND/FIGURE 13
▥ 10-100 Birds per sq. mi.
▤ 100-1000 Birds per sq. mi.

COASTLINE
30   FMS.
50   FMS.
100   FMS.
200   FMS.
1000 FMS.

QUEBEC

ANTICOSTI I.

GULF OF
ST. LAWRENCE

MAGDALEN IS.

PRINCE
EDWARD
ISLAND

NOVA SCOTIA

N E W F O U N D L A N D

N O R T H   A T L A N T I C   O C E A N

55°

50°

45°

60°   55°   50°

FIGURE 12. *Autumn flyways of thick-billed murres in the western North Atlantic*

FIGURE 13. *Winter distribution and density of murres in the Newfoundland off-shore zone*

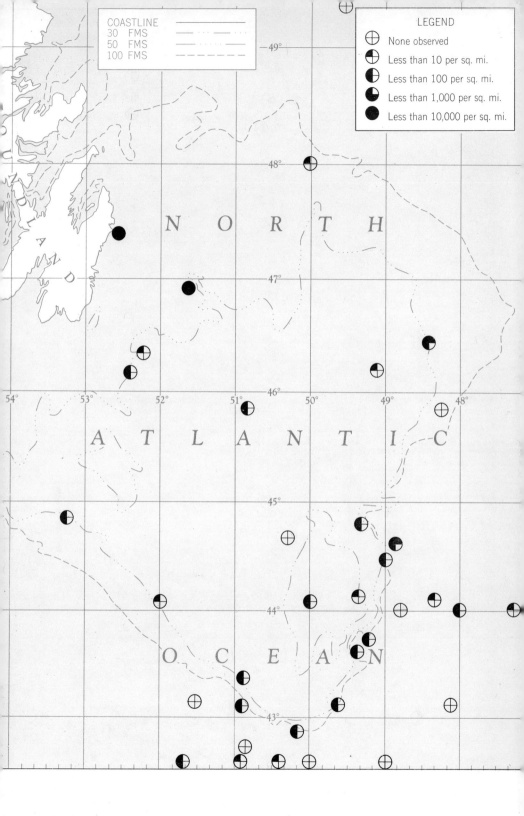

FIGURE 14. *Sample densities of murres on the Grand Banks in April*

FIGURE 15. *Sample densities of murres on the Grand Banks in May*

from June to August and from February to April for the purpose of detecting icebergs, plotting their positions, and warning ships about them. Observers on the patrol ships made detailed notes on the occurrence and abundance of sea-birds. It was thought that sea-bird numbers might indicate the presence of arctic berg-bearing waters. While there was a general coincidence between the presence of sea-birds and icebergs on the Grand Banks, it did not prove practically useful and so the patrols stopped bird-watching after 1924. I am most grateful to Captain G. Van A. Graves, Commander International Ice Patrol, for use of the data on sea-bird occurrence.

In addition, I have acquired much information on the occurrence and quantitative abundance of murres on the Grand Banks during several trips on trawlers to that region.

Murres do not reach the Grand Banks in large numbers until late in December. On December 7, 1953, a density of ten murres per square mile was recorded on the extreme northern end of the Grand Banks. No others were seen along a transect which continued southwards for nearly 300 miles.

More and more murres reach the Grand Banks in January and by early February they are spread over the entire area. They are densest on the edges of the Banks, where the turbulence of the water is greatest. On February 17, 1952, the density in several places at 46° 00′N, 52° 30′W was approximately 10,000 birds per square mile. The greatest concentrations on the Grand Banks have been found in March and April, when pack ice forces the murres wintering off the east coast of Newfoundland southwards. Those March-April concentrations are variable and occur only during bad ice years.

Murres are found on the Grand Banks in April and May (Figs. 14 and 15), but are scarce there in June. They are very rare in that area in July and August and in fact may not occur there at all during those two months. Bagenal (1950) spent from July 20 to August 4, 1950, at approximately 44° 26′N, 49° 50′W; August 8 to August 9 at 45° 30′N, 40° 00′W and from August 10 to August 17 at 44° 19′N, 49° 50′W. During those periods he kept systematic notes on all sea-birds but observed no murres. Hydrological data from the Newfoundland Fisheries Research Station indicate a continuous warming of the surface layers of the Grand Banks area during the summer months, from approximately 0° C in April to as high as 20° C in August. Those waters become progressively colder again in September.

Murres occur in winter in the off-shore zone of Nova Scotia, but apparently in small numbers. Johnson (1940) writes: "During the latter part of December, 1932, and the first part of January, 1933, I made a trip to the Tusket Islands off the southeast coast of Nova Scotia to look for the Atlantic Murre on its wintering grounds. While living on Spectacle Island, some ten miles from the main land, short trips were made with lobster fishermen to the surrounding waters, but no Atlantic Murres were observed. The Brünnich's Murre was present, but not in great numbers."

Palmer (1949) states that the common murre is a rare winter resident off the coast of Maine, that there are few definite records and no recent ones. Occasionally, individuals of either species may straggle to Long Island or even farther. Actually, murres are so rare along the New England coast that each observation is recorded in the Records of New England Birds published by the Massachusetts Audubon Society. Their rarity was demonstrated to me when, on arriving at Plum Island in the autumn of 1955, I found the entire field party of the American Ornithologists' Union with binoculars and tele-scopes trained on a single murre about a mile off shore. Table 13 is a summary by Karplus (1947) of the occurrence of the thick-billed murre, the more "abundant" win-tering species, off Massachusetts for a period of 46 years.

Table 13: *Occurrence of thick-billed murres off Massachusetts, 1896-1942*

	Date		Number	Locality
Early fall records				
	October	9, 1901	1	Essex County
	November	5, 1942	9	Plum Island
	November	7, 1938	1	Plum Island
	November	7, 1939	1	Monomoy
	November	9, 1941	1	Scituate
High counts				
	April	2, 1933	75	Plum Island
	February	4, 1934	60	Essex County
	January	28, 1922	48	Essex County
Late spring records				
	April	12, 1922	1	Nahant
	April	12, 1942	1	Manomet
	April	18, 1921	1	Salem
	April	30, 1936	1	Lynn
	May	6, 1921	1	Peabody
	May	15, 1932	1	Plum Island

Migration and distribution of murres in the North Pacific

Bailey (1943) writing on the birds of Alaska says: "The majority of Pallas's Murres winter to the southwards of the ice pack and the first arrival at Wales in the spring is during the latter part of April. My first observation was of a bird in winter dress on April 28, and they were very common on their northward migration by May 8 . . ."

Storer (1952) states that Pallas's murres are largely sedentary, but occasional indi-viduals reach Hondo and British Columbia in winter. Gabrielson and Lincoln (1959) state that in Alaska there is no evidence of any regular migration of common murres and little evidence of migration of thick-billed murres, except in the northern part of their range.

The returns in the United States Fish and Wildlife Service files show that common murres banded in Oregon tend to winter off Washington and British Columbia. Of 54 returns, 25 were retaken in Oregon (24 within two months of banding), 12 in Washing-ton, 14 in British Columbia and three in California. Concerning the Pacific form of the common murre, Storer (1952) writes: "Largely sedentary, although there seems to be a northward movement on the part of young birds of at least the Oregon population. Rare in winter to San Diego County, California."

Although more arctic waters pour out of the Polar Basin through Davis Strait and the Sea of Greenland than through Bering Strait, the North Pacific and the North Atlantic have several things in common as far as pack ice is concerned. Arctic waters and pack ice reach approximately the same limits in latitude (Fig. 9) in both. Therefore it is possible that there are wintering concentrations of murres off the Kuriles and off Japan similar to those off eastern North America. The eastern coasts of both Pacific and Atlantic oceans are free from pack ice. In both those regions the common murres winter in the same latitudes.

PART III: BREEDING BIOLOGY

CHAPTER IX

Life at Sea

For eight months or so each year, common murres inhabit a region of cold waters where often the only humans are the crews of trawlers and long-liners. Thick-billed murres inhabit the same region in winter, but are rarely found, even at that season far from the ice pack. In the southern part of the region they stay off shore, between the zone of land drainage and the deep waters beyond the continental shelf. In the northern part they remain in the shallow parts of the arctic seas that are free from ice. The entire region from the deep waters beyond the continental shelf to the edge of the ice fields is one of dynamic turbulence.

Because so much ice forms in Hudson Bay, Davis Strait and the waterways among the large Canadian islands in the Arctic, those areas become unsuitable for murres in winter. Thick-billed murres breeding in those localities migrate early in the autumn to the off-shore regions of southwestern Greenland, Labrador and western and southeastern Newfoundland. At the same time, the European populations of thick-billed murres move to the Norwegian and Barents Seas. The Pacific populations undertake a similar migration, wintering from the edge of the marine ice-field as far west as the off-shore waters of Japan.

Common murres, with greater tolerance for warmish waters, are the more sedentary. After post-breeding dispersal they move off shore, generally in a southerly or southwesterly direction, with the prevailing drift of arctic waters. Common murres do not undertake the long migrations that some individuals or populations of thick-billed murres carry out regularly. This may be because lengthy migrations, especially of the southern populations, would take them beyond the regions of cold water.

The regions in which murres winter vary sharply in temperature and salinity near the pack ice or the deep waters beyond the continental shelf. The consequent variation in water densities causes upwelling and mixing. The various nutrients and fertilizing elements in the lower layers of the ocean, even those at the bottom, are thus brought to the surface. The greatest total overturn of waters in the Northern Hemisphere occurs in spring and autumn, but turbulence in local areas may be continuous.

Although murres are strong flyers, they are rarely on the wing in severe storms. During the most inclement weather that racks the North Atlantic and North Pacific in the autumn and winter, they spend a great deal of time under water.

During autumn and winter, the only murres found within four or five miles of land, or within the zone of land drainage, are those disabled, affected by oil or carried to leeward of their normal feeding grounds by several days of continuous stormy weather.

Murres are not the only sea-birds that congregate in certain favoured regions in winter. In each region there is, in fact, a particular community of sea-birds occupying the off-shore zone. Within a community there is for each sea-bird a special biotope, where it is found in optimum numbers. For several winters, I have observed the distribution of sea-birds in Newfoundland waters (Fig. 16).

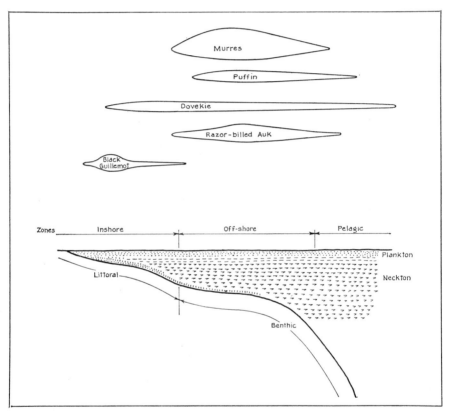

FIGURE 16. *Winter biotopes and relative densities of the alcids in Newfoundland*

The *Larus* gulls are scavengers in winter, as they are to a large extent in summer, and occur in optimum numbers in the inshore zone, close to the seashore. But in some parts of the Northern Hemisphere, the activities of man have created an artificial biotope for those gulls in the off-shore zone. Ships with their garbage, trawlers and draggers with their fish offal, encourage local populations of the gulls to forage off shore. Such is the situation on the Grand Banks of Newfoundland.

The ivory gull (*Pagophila eburnea*) is a predominant member of the off-shore avifauna in Newfoundland in February and March, when the harp seals whelp on the pack ice brought southwards by the Labrador Current. Like the *Larus* gulls, the ivory gull is a scavenger at all times, but it is more selective in procuring food. It appears reluctant to get its feathers wet and is seen most frequently on the ice, feeding on the placentae of newly born seals. Carcasses left behind by the sealers are an additional source of food.

The kittiwake (*Rissa tridactyla*) and the fulmar (*Fulmarus glacialis*) are normally pelagic in winter, roaming the high seas and feeding on plankton. They also take advantage of the artificial biotope on the Newfoundland fishing banks, where they feed on the offal discarded by trawlers. Neither the fulmar nor any of the gulls competes with the murres for food in winter.

The alcids are the dominant sea-birds in the off-shore zone of Newfoundland during the winter, as they are in all similar regions in the Northern Hemisphere. There is some competition among the alcids, especially when food is scarce, but each species, because of its size, the shape of its bill or its ability to dive, has a particular food spectrum.

It might seem that the comparatively rare razorbill (*Alca torda*), which is similar in size to the murres, would compete with them for food. Examination of stomach contents and observations of adults feeding young suggest that the food of the razorbills in summer in Newfoundland and Labrador, when food is at its optimum, is in fact similar to that of murres. But the stomach contents of razorbills taken in winter off Newfoundland were predominantly crustaceans, while those of murres contained capelin.

The black guillemot (*Cepphus grylle*) obtains most of its food in the shallow inshore or littoral zone. In addition, it is the only alcid in the North Atlantic which habitually winters in the high-arctic regions wherever there are cracks in the ice or an open patch of water remains. It therefore utilizes areas, and a supply of food, which murres do not.

The dovekie (*Plautus alle*) feeds entirely on minute crustaceans and other plankton and competes in winter only for food organisms of secondary importance to murres. The dovekie is a tremendously abundant species in the North Atlantic. But, like the black guillemot, large numbers remain in the high-arctic marine zone during the winter and utilize food which murres do not. Its ecological niche is occupied in the North Pacific by the least auklet (*Aethia pusilla*), a similarly abundant species. Neither of those small alcids is especially restricted to the off-shore zone in winter. They are more pelagic than murres and can also find food in the littoral inshore zone.

The puffin (*Fratercula arctica*) is basically an off-shore species in winter, but to some extent it also occupies the pelagic zone. Nowhere, in winter, do puffins concentrate in large numbers. Dispersed individually or in small groups over the immense off-shore zone, they seem to disappear at that time of year. Off Newfoundland, their principal food in winter is the one- and two-year-old classes of capelin and launce. They compete with murres for food in winter only occasionally.

Unlike the other alcids, murres congregate in large numbers on their feeding grounds. They are probably better divers than any of the other auks (except perhaps, the razorbill) and can therefore range more deeply in their search for food. The principal winter food of murres in Newfoundland is capelin. Competition for food with other alcids in winter occurs only when the murres' preferred food is scarce.

Soon after the adults go to sea, at the conclusion of the breeding season, post-nuptial moult begins. This moult involves simultaneous shedding of the rectrices and remiges, so that for two weeks or so adult murres are incapable of flight. During that period the chicks develop the power of flight.

The winter plumage of both species is distinct from the summer plumage in that the throat and sides of the head are white. Adults and juveniles of both species are most nearly alike in winter. The common murre can be distinguished at that time from its arctic relative by more extensive white on the sides of the head and by a narrow black line running from the eye into the white on the side of the head. In winter, the thick-billed murre's white gape marks, which are characteristic of the nuptial plumage, fade and become indistinct.

As soon as winter plumage is complete, some of the adults, presumably the older ones, begin with no apparent pause a pre-nuptial moult. This involves especially a replacement of black feathers on the throat and the sides of the head. By early February, those birds are again in full breeding plumage.

Young birds do not attain full summer plumage during the first year. Even some two-year-olds retain a great deal of white on the throat and the sides of the head in summer —a characteristic of juvenile or delayed winter plumage.

The foregoing is but a brief summary of this interesting aspect of the murre's biology. Individuals and populations vary in the timing of their moult. This may be linked with climatic conditions within their breeding ranges. The student interested in this subject is referred to Salomonsen's (1944) excellent treatise on the seasonal variations of the auks.

Although plankton does not disappear in winter even in the Polar Basin, it is not as obvious a feature of the marine environment at that time of the year as in summer.

Murres are gregarious in winter as well as during the breeding season. Although well spaced when feeding, they take off and fly in large flocks. The coherence of discrete populations is not so apparent in the spring when the young murres have not yet acquired any strong attachment for a breeding locality.

There may be advantages in gregariousness and coherence during the winter. Gregariousness provides the opportunity to share schools of fish among many instead of few. This may be important, since schools of fish usually remain at greater depths during the winter. Single murres may at times be widely scattered but they are usually within sight of one another. They quickly note the behaviour of those which have found food and are drawn to that locality.

The shrimp and other crustaceans are deprived in winter of the enormous masses of microscopic algae which flourished earlier, and depend on the reserve food they have accumulated as fat (Freuchen and Salomonsen, 1958). Those crustaceans form, so to speak, a stored depot of food for sea-birds. With the gradual decrease in the quantity of planktonic organisms in the autumn, the larger fish withdraw to spend the winter in the depths of the ocean, and likewise in November the big whales leave arctic waters. This withdrawal of the large fish, whales and even most seals leaves a greater reservoir of food for sea-birds in their more northerly wintering regions.

When food is scarce or lacking, murres soon leave for other, more productive, areas. I have watched this several times in Trinity Bay, Newfoundland, which is a rather long and narrow inlet. On March 28, 1953, for example, there were large numbers of murres in Trinity Bay, brought there by several days of strong northeasterly gales. Food appeared to be scarce and the stomachs of all murres shot by hunters were empty. On the following day, it was fairly calm and the birds began gradually to move out to sea. Small flocks flew restlessly about, alighting near others. The combined flocks would take wing and alight near still another flock. Finally, the birds had collected in a rather large and compact raft. Eventually, they moved out to sea in a steady procession.

During the winter, young birds, especially those of the first and second years, are inclined to remain on the fringes of the adult wintering grounds. They are also inclined to wander out of the off-shore zone, even to go close to land. The murres that frequent the bays and inlets of Newfoundland after northeasterly gales are predominantly juveniles, as are those most frequently wrecked on land.

During late April, while the common murres are concentrated at sea off their nesting sites, the thick-billed murres move northwards along the coast of Newfoundland. At first they may linger at the edge of the pack ice, but by the first week in May they are passing northwards along the coast of Labrador in steady flight. A similar movement in spring is recorded for the common murres in the eastern Pacific. Bailey (1948) wrote: "They winter at the edge of the pack ice and start northwards with the drifting ice, appearing off Wales in Bering Strait the latter part of April. In early May they were seen in flocks, often accompanying the migrating eider in their trek northward. They flew at great speed over the open leads, sometimes high in the air, and again dropping low".

In late spring, adults and juveniles are largely separated. Most flocks are composed of either adults in full or nearly full breeding plumage, or of juveniles. Juvenile birds from the colonies in the Canadian Arctic and Greenland are the last to leave Newfoundland waters in the spring.

CHAPTER X

The Land-Coming and Courtship

There is a tradition in Conception Bay, Newfoundland, that on St. Patrick's Day the murres of Baccalieu Island return to nest. There is a great deal of truth in this, since the local murres converge at sea some distance from their breeding colonies in late February or early March. When there is no pack ice to prevent it, they pay their first visit to the base of the cliffs about the middle of March.

In the high-arctic regions, murres congregate at the base of their nesting cliffs and even alight briefly on the ledges still covered with snow and ice. On subsequent days, a few may settle briefly on the cliffs. Four or five weeks later, they have become accustomed to the land once again and remain all night on the ledges.

In parts of Great Britain, murres sometimes return to land in January, or exceptionally, in December. They do not remain long on those visits and weeks may go by before they approach the nesting sites again. The land-coming days in the Faeroe Islands occur in March, as they do in Newfoundland.

Trevor-Battye (1897) relates that thick-billed murres return early to Spitsbergen and mentions January 11 as an arrival date. It is not clear from his account whether this date refers to land-coming or to the appearance of murres off the coast. The latter seems most likely, since murres winter in that region. Clarke (1898) saw the first murres in the spring of 1897 off Franz Josef Land on March 20. He did not see them on the cliffs until May 7 and noted that on May 16 they had gone to sea again. Clarke (1890) noted that murres remained off Jan Mayen all the winter of 1882-1883 but that the main spring flights inshore occurred on April 20, 1883. Uspenski (1956) recorded that murres first occurred at the breeding cliffs at Novaya Zemlya on May 4, 1934; May 6, 1935; April 7, 1948 and April 21, 1949. He gave three dates for their first occurrence on the cliffs ranging from April 22, 1950 to April 25, 1949, a variation of merely three days. There was also remarkable uniformity (June 9 to June 15) in the date of laying of the first eggs at Novaya Zemlya over the nine-year period.

In 1958, the first thick-billed murres arrived on the cliffs at Cape St. Mary's 17 days later than the first common murres. In the same year, the first thick-billed murres on Green Island arrived 21 days after the common murres had settled in. A similar time-lag in the arrival of thick-billed murres at mixed colonies in Newfoundland has been recorded for other years. It was also determined that the thick-billed murres in Newfoundland and Labrador consistently lay from 10 to 14 days later than common murres. The nesting phenology of murres in the large colonies where both species occur has not been carefully studied.

Uspenski (1956) recorded the first appearance of thick-billed murres in Bezymyannaya Bay on April 21, 1949. On April 24 the number of the birds had increased greatly. It had increased still further on April 25, and some of the birds had flown up to the nesting ledges (Table 14). On June 2 young birds of the preceding year appeared among the numerous birds on the water and on the ledges. Thus a definite regularity can be traced in the arrival of the birds at their nesting sites. First to appear near the nesting sites are adult birds that nested there the previous year. The second wave is composed of younger sexually-mature adults, also occupying on arrival their nesting sites of the year before. Last to appear at the cliffs are sexually-mature yearlings and some young that have not yet reached sexual maturity.

It is not known which sex is most numerous among the first arrivals at the nesting cliffs. In fact, the sex ratio in murres is not clearly understood. Krasovski (1937), using data on murres shot during the nesting period, concluded that the sex ratio was two males to one female. Kaftanovski (1951) and Uspenski (1941) obtained similar statistics in the same way. But in 1950, Uspenski (1956) captured and examined the 480 birds occupying a ledge and found that 242 were males and 238 females. The best data might be obtained by shooting murres at a season when they are not nesting. Some 1,400 murres examined in winter in Newfoundland showed no significant disparity in sex ratio. Vladimirskaya, (according to Krasovski, 1937), after killing off a flock of murres on the water in early spring, found the ratio of the sexes to be 1 : 1.

There is evidence (Uspenski, 1956) that when murres first arrive at their traditional colonies in the early spring their gonads are not fully developed. Murres first landed on the ledges at the Bezymyannaya Bay colony, Novaya Zemlya, on April 22, 1950 (Table 14). It was not until early June that collected males showed fully developed gonads.

The land-coming of murres has continued to be an exciting event for me, ever since I first saw it at Cape St. Mary's some fifteen years ago. In 1944, I arrived on March 18 at the cliffs overlooking the murre ledges. A few kittiwakes had taken up nesting sites on the cliffs but the gannet and murre ledges were unoccupied. The lightkeeper had not seen any murres near land so far that spring, although there were large concentrations about four miles off shore. On March 20, eight common murres appeared well inshore. Those may have been the vanguard, because early that morning murres appeared about one mile off and at about 9 a.m. on March 21 about 1,000 common murres had congregated at the base of the cliffs. Flocks continually arrived from far out at sea all that morning; by 11 a.m. the total aggregation at the base of the cliffs was in excess of 3,000 birds. As the morning passed, more birds gathered and they seemed to become more and more excited. The excitement eventually culminated in two forms of pre-nuptial display which I shall call "water-dances" and "joy-flights".

Water-dances are typical of most, if not all, the alcids. They are a form of communal display. Small groups begin to patter over the sea, sometimes attaining great speed with the help of their wings, but never actually taking flight. If the day is calm, the disturbed water shows intricate patterns of curving lines, loops and even figures-of-eight. Murres usually appear clumsy and cumbersome while attempting flights from the water, even under ideal conditions. In this form of display, however, there is an indefinable dancing quality about the movements. It is as though the impulse to take flight is balanced by the impulse to remain on the water. There is frequently a risk of collision with non-participants during those affairs. At the slightest likelihood of this occurring, the entire group may dive simultaneously. The dance may then continue under water with the slight variations which that medium compels. It often develops into underwater pursuits in which the white flanks of the birds show prominently as they twist and parry each other a few feet below the surface.

The flights of flocks of murres, seemingly wheeling hither and yon in joy—now up close to the cliffs, now skimming the surface of the sea—may be called joy-flights. The initial core of the flight may be only two or three birds, as in water-dancing. Others apparently flying aimlessly about at the time, swerve and join in at the tail-end of the procession until the flight may involve several hundred. Sometimes, the joy-flight flock attains an altitude of several thousand feet, which is remarkable, since murres at sea customarily fly low over the water. It wheels about with remarkable precision and at times literally dives towards the sea, levelling off at the critical moment and again soaring skywards.

At Cape St. Mary's on the land-coming day of March 21, the murres gradually thinned out late in the afternoon and went off to sea again. They were back *en masse* on the following morning, but four days passed before the first landing on the ledges was recorded. Sometimes a joy-flight would swoop close to the cliffs. As the birds flew by, one or more of them would break away and alight briefly, facing the sea and poised for instant flight. Those early landings were very brief, lasting merely a few seconds. Sometimes those early arrivals would flutter from the ledges in a beautiful, slow, butterfly-like flight and soon be lost in the milling crowd below. Thus is the initial contact made with the land.

I next visited Cape St. Mary's that spring on April 14. Joy-flights and water-dances

Table 14: *Breeding cycle of thick-bille*[1]

	1873	1933	1934
First occurrence at cliffs	—	—	May 4
First concentration at cliffs	—	—	—
First occurrence on ledges	—	—	—
First egg	June 12	June 12	June 11
Peak of egg-laying	—	—	June 12
First hatch	—	July 12	July 12
First sea-going	—	August 13	August 5
Last bird seen on cliff	—	September 20	September 9
Maximum days on ledges	—	—	—
Total days of family life	—	99	89

[1]After Uspenski (1956)

were still in progress, but by then hundreds of birds had settled on the narrow ledges, all with their backs to the sea. Not until some time in mid-May did the colony properly settle-in for the season and the birds remain on the ledges all night.

The nuptial displays of the two species of murre are similar. Thick-billed murres are more prone to joy-flights than to water-dances and their variations. I suspect that this is a natural result of the conditions in the sea in proximity to the more northerly colonies. At most of the thick-billed murre colonies a substantial amount of ice is still floating around when the birds arrive and it undoubtedly is a deterrent to surface displays. Where common murres nest on low flat islands there is no opportunity for the butterfly-like flights which require great heights to develop properly.

On May 31, 1957, the thick-billed murres at Cape Graham Moore in Baffin Bay were in the early stages of prospecting the cliffs, although the floe-edge was still some ten miles away. All that day, small groups flew high over the ice and a few individuals dropped to the cliffs from time to time as the joy-flights passed by. None of the birds remained on the cliffs longer than a minute or two. As at Cape St. Mary's, those which settled on the cliffs faced the sea and remained poised for instant flight.

Ellis (1956) was at Cape Graham Moore in the spring of 1955 when the murres had completed their prospecting of the cliffs. He wrote: "On May 16 and 17 flocks could be seen flying high over the ice towards the breeding cliff . . . returning to the water skimming just a few feet above the ice. No murres were observed at the cliff on May 19, 25 or June 6 but on June 8 . . . the murres began to arrive. Within an hour approximately 10,000 birds reached the cliffs and took up places on the ledges."

The prospecting stage was completed at Cape Hay, Lancaster Sound, by June 11, 1957. When we arrived there on that date, the cliffs were fully occupied by murres, all with their backs to the sea, and they remained there all night.

Communal displays by murres in proximity to their nesting sites probably play a part

urres at Bezymyannaya Bay, Novaya Zemlya[1]					
_1935_	_1942_	_1947_	_1948_	_1949_	_1950_
May 6	—	—	April 7	April 21	—
—	—	—	—	April 24	—
—	—	—	April 23	April 25	April 22
une 10	June 14	June 14	June 15	June 15	June 15
—	—	—	June 22	June 20	—
—	—	—	July 20	July 16	July 18
—	—	—	August 10	August 9	August 8
—	—	—	September 6	September 8	September 9
—	—	—	139	139	—
—	—	—	83	85	86

in stimulating and maintaining the breeding condition. The probable result is a synchronization of sexual rhythm among the majority of adult birds. Light intensity may be one of the factors controlling commencement of the breeding season. The proximity of the cliffs is another external factor requisite to communal display. There may be other factors which affect commencement of breeding, but at which we can merely guess at present. For instance, in bad ice years murres in the high-arctic regions may go through all the breeding preliminaries but fail to nest or do so only in small numbers.

In the course of his study on gulls, Darling (1938) made a series of observations which throw light on the social display of sea-birds. He discovered that large colonies of gulls not only begin laying earlier than small colonies but lay their eggs in a shorter period. Consequently, the larger colonies are more successful in raising young, for the greater number of birds are able to give better protection from predators. Similarly, the shorter spread of the incubation and fledging periods reduces the dangers to which the eggs and young are subject. I suspect that, in the case of murres at least, it is not the size of the colonies as such which is important with respect to survival of young, but the ages of the birds comprising the colony. The most successful murre colonies are composed of units of older birds, surrounded on the fringes by smaller numbers of inexperienced birds breeding for the first time. The earliest and most successful breeding is more or less in the centre of the units. There, experienced birds and those which choose the best nesting sites, produce the highest proportion of young.

When murres first arrive inshore, each bird remains well spaced from its neighbour. This may be called the "individual distance" and is usually one body length. Perhaps this is the minimum distance which separated it from others of its kind in the wintering concentrations. This barrier of individual distance must be broken down before the birds can establish a pair bond and thus become a part of the breeding colony.

Some authors claim that murres are paired before they return to their nesting sites. There seems to be no conclusive evidence that that is so. In fact, several weeks go by before murres at the breeding colonies have overcome the barrier of individual distance. The water-dances and simultaneous diving are apparently discontinued to avoid too close intimacy.

It is impossible for murres to avoid intimacy on the crowded ledges and so the barriers of individual distance disappear during the time of incubation and brooding. At the time the chicks are leaving the ledges the adults are again concentrated at the base of the cliffs, awaiting the young. Waves and flurries of excitement often bring them into close bodily contact, but they rarely dive to avoid it.

When murres first settle-in on the nesting cliffs, they turn their backs to the sea. On flat stacks and skerries they tend to snuggle close to rocks, boulders or any objects of that nature. Later in the season, only those with eggs close to the walls of the cliff continue to turn their backs to the sea. This habit has a definite survival value, since eggs placed close to the wall of the cliff, or sheltered by a rock, are less likely to be dislodged by panicking birds.

Observations of four pairs of thick-billed murres and six pairs of common murres banded in Newfoundland colonies showed that in the year following marking three pairs of thick-billed murres and three pairs of common murres were made up of the same individuals. Four other marked birds also returned to their sites, but with mates that were either new or had lost their bands. On Funk Island, banded common murres have been returning to the same colony, and usually to the same nest sites, for five consecutive years. Most likely they return to the same site for more years than five, but that cannot be demonstrated because beyond that time the bands are usually lost by abrasion or corrosion.

I have not been able to determine whether the male or female customarily arrives first at the potential nest site, but collection of a few specimens indicates that the first birds ✕ to arrive close inshore are males. I have observed that the males of both species are more solicitous toward the young than the females and that they spend more time brooding the egg and feeding the chick. Birds collected at a distance from the nest site during incubation and brooding are more frequently females.

There is a great deal of jostling for position on the ledges when the birds first settle-in, and it increases during the next several weeks as new arrivals attempt to find nest sites. The birds parry each other's bills, slash at each other and are generally belligerent. Later, after the birds have been on the cliffs for some time, fighting seems to be restricted to cases where there is actual interference with an occupied nest site.

If the birds are randomly distributed on the ledges, the chances that two birds of opposite sex will be nearest each other and eventually pair off are very good. It seems likely that all the males are aggressive at first, but gradually come to tolerate individuals of the opposite sex, one of which attaches herself to the particular site occupied by the male.

In one instance, a pair of banded common murres had returned to the site of their nest of the year before. For the first few days after their arrival, there was much bickering and jostling. Eventually they were observed to preen each other's head and neck and nibble at each other's bill. Mutual preening was carried on throughout the entire breeding season, even after the young were hatched.

Mutual preening and fondling, which is carried on throughout the breeding season by both species, is probably a form of behaviour which ensures the maintenance of the pair-bond during the breeding season. Until the egg is laid, the male flies off in pursuit when the female leaves the nest site. Quite frequently, they must lose each other in the milling crowd below, because they often return independently. But when an egg has been laid, one of the two always remains at the nest site unless flushed, otherwise the site would be quickly occupied by other birds. Prospecting murres which have not yet found a nest site, or others which have lost one because of a rock fall, may commandeer a temporarily vacant site.

Copulation usually takes place on the actual nest site, rarely in the water or on ice-floes. It occurs most frequently when the male flies in to the nest site and the female is in a prone position, similar to that assumed during incubation. After nest sites have been established and for at least two weeks before the egg is laid, females maintain a prone position for long periods. The earliest recorded copulation date at Cape Hay in 1957 was five days before the first egg was laid, and the latest twelve days afterwards. Thus three weeks may be considered the "copulation period". Although some birds were known to have laid two replacements before the season was over, one bird laying her last egg 26 days after loss of the first, I have watched in vain for copulation after the copulation period. The explanation may be that the spermatozoa remain viable for several weeks.

I have frequently observed promiscuous copulation at both common and thick-billed murre colonies. This occurs especially when the female is left temporarily unattended by her mate. Nørrevang (1958) observed that a female common murre in the Faeroe Islands was mounted by three different males within a single period of 20 minutes. I have made similar observations of both common and thick-billed murres and on one occasion observed an individual male thick-billed murre copulate with three different females during a period of two hours. During the copulation period, copulation may occur in "waves". It is apparent that the mere sight or sound of birds copulating has a sexually stimulating effect on the others.

During copulation, the female leans forward and elevates her rump. Her head and bill are stretched forwards and upwards. The male mounts from the side, using his wings to keep balance. The wings of the male then usually droop on either side of the female, but if the pair is on a narrow or sloping ledge he may beat his wings vigorously to keep balance.

When the male mounts, the female throws her head backwards and opens her bill wide, thus showing the brilliant yellow lining, and utters a hoarse "copulation call". Immediately after the copulation call, the head is moved forward into the plane of the body.

Copulation may take place during the first few days of incubation. At that time the female rises slightly from her egg and maintains a flattened, crouching position, while the male stands half upright on her back, his neck bent and the bill pointing upwards. Sometimes he calls loudly during copulation and sometimes remains silent.

Copulation is usually concluded by the female rising, so that the male glides off her back. In some instances, the male remains quietly on her back. In such cases, the female utters the copulation call, which usually revives the copulation movements of the male.

CHAPTER XI

Life at the Nesting Sites

Ornithologists fortunate enough to visit a very large murre colony see one of nature's great spectacles. Whether on the steep, vertical limestone cliffs of Akpatok Island or on some low basalt island in the Pribilofs, the effect is the same—an incredible, bewildering hive of birds. The view from a distance is sufficiently impressive; and at close quarters, when the noise of the birds drowns out the roar of the sea or the howling of the wind, both sight and sound are indeed overwhelming. I have spent many weeks near, or even below the cliffs of, some of the large colonies in the Canadian Arctic. The sound of a colony, especially on calm days, is like the thunder of an immense waterfall, or, more aptly perhaps, like the roar of the sea after a storm. On first contact with a large colony I have been temporarily deafened. Eventually, I became so conditioned to the clamour that I could distinguish individual sounds, and, more important, note every change in the normal tempo or tenor of the colony.

The American vernacular *murre*, the Newfoundland *turr*, and the Eskimo *akpa* presumably owe their origins to their resemblance to the calls of murres. At Akpatok Island both my Eskimo helper and I were greatly amused at the calls of a thick-billed murre which tried unsuccessfully to prevent a chick from returning to the shore. All the while the adult called "Owka-owka-owka . . .", which was clearly the Eskimo "No-no-no . . ."

Pennycuick (1956) describes four calls of the thick-billed murres at a Spitsbergen colony and the conditions under which they were used. They were a loud "arr-rr-rr-r", a sharp "uggah", a loud "rrr-haw-haw-haw-haw-haw-haw" and a low "grrr".

The copulation call of the female is distinctive. Pennycuick (1956) describes this as a "disyllabic yelp". The "arr-rr-rr-r" call, although used at other times also, is the particular call of the adults gathered at the base of the cliffs to wait for the chicks. Pennycuick's "uggah" is probably the same as my "owka".

A repetitive and apparently anxious call which I have described in my notes as "awk-awk-awk-awk-awk" is possibly similar to Pennycuick's "haw-haw-haw-haw-haw". On Akpatok Island, it often originated at night from a single bird, disturbed perhaps by a falling stone, and, in accordance with colonial behaviour, slowly spread through the entire group of birds, gradually subsiding after a half-hour or so. I particularly disliked this mirthless laughter, since the short hours of darkness were my sole opportunity for a quiet and undisturbed sleep.

A call of the adult thick-billed murre which I have not seen recorded is a rather wheezy "aowk" made during a slow butterfly flight. It was as though each beat of the wings was tearing a gasp from the bird. There was some evidence that such birds had been forcibly relieved of their nesting duties by their mates. They settled in the water in the immediate vicinity of the nest site and commenced to preen and bathe.

Towards the end of the nesting period, when the young are nearly ready to go to sea, the shrill peeping of the chicks can often be heard in a sort of "dawn chorus" for half an hour before the adults become active. Then gradually, the calls of the adults and the beating of wings build up to the accustomed overwhelming volume of sound.

A day or so before hatching, and for the next five or six days, the chick calls in a fretful cheep. Very young chicks, strayed from their parents, or accidentally knocked over the cliffs, sometimes make a wheezy cat-like sound, completely unlike their normal calls. After about seven days of age, the chick's call is a thin, quavering "wee-oo, wee-oo" which becomes shriller as the bird gets older. A particularly loud and shrill "weee-weee-weee" is made by even quite small chicks in terror. It is the call made also by chicks about to leap off the ledge and for some time after they are in the water.

The calls of thick-billed murres and common murres seem to be remarkably similar.

In crowded nesting areas of both species, the birds frequently nest so close together that they actually touch each other. Indeed murres prefer to nest close to one another, even though there may be more room elsewhere on the ledge. In such situations, a pair of murres may occupy an area no larger than one-half square foot. Krasovski (1937) considers the upper limit of nesting density to be 37 birds per square metre. In one unexploited colony examined by Uspenski (1956) the extreme density did not exceed 32 birds per square metre. In three one-square-metre plots of the densely occupied core of the common murre colony on Funk Island in 1958, there were 28, 30 and 34 birds respectively.

After pair formation, and especially once incubation has commenced, murres do not usually show aggressive behaviour towards their neighbours, but often greet them with the same ceremony they use on the arrival of their own mates. Territorial behaviour is therefore not much evident in murres after nest sites have been established, although breeding birds show aggression if approached by birds other than the neighbours to which they are accustomed.

Johnson (1941) in his study of the nesting behaviour of common murres in the Gulf of St. Lawrence, avoided use of the term "territory" and explained that activity of the breeding birds took place in three functional areas, the area of the breeding sites, the loitering grounds, and the feeding area. One might suggest a fourth functional area, namely, the display area in the sea at the base of the nesting sites where water-dances and joy-flights originate in the early spring and where the young are "captured" and led out to sea at the completion of the nesting period.

The loitering area is a very distinctive part of any murre colony. There the birds off duty may get away from the crowded nest site to rest. On steep cliffs, the loitering areas may be smooth faces of the cliff not quite suitable for nesting or even the outer fringes of the wide ledges. Rounded rocks are frequently used for loitering, as also are the very tops of the cliffs. The main loitering area on Funk Island was a smooth area of rock, some 100 feet from the main colonies close to the nesting gannets. There, many thousands of common murres spent part of the day. In addition, the two large colonies on Funk Island were each divided by a 15-foot zone or "no-man's land", which was used by approaching and loitering birds only. Loitering birds invariably face the sea and the number of birds facing the sea, especially on the cliffs, is a good indication of the progress of the nesting season. As incubation advances, more and more birds loiter. The loitering population is also increased by the addition of yearlings, some of which are exploring the colony for the first time.

Gätke (1895), in his book on Heligoland, described murres as making "endless obeisance" and all calling about nothing in particular. The large colonies seem to bubble over with continuous excitement, shown by the perpetual bobbing, bowing and shaking of heads, the mild squabbles of close neighbours, and the boisterous greetings to each new arrival. When alighting in a colony, a murre announces its arrival with loud squawks, as if to warn those on the ledges to make room for it, and it is usually received with apparently aggressive cries.

Pennycuick (1956) distinguished two kinds of bowing at the common murre colonies on Lundy in mid-April. One kind was caused by suspicion. The head was jerked down, then after a pause, jerked up again, and the bill was seldom tilted beyond the vertical. The other was noted in courtship, when two birds would stand side by side and bend down, with their bills often inclined well beyond the vertical.

Both species of murres bow continually in response to various stimuli. The presence of an observer, or any unusual happening in the colony, such as the falling of a rock or the appearance of a falcon, may result in widespread bowing. Murres bow while standing around holding fish in their bills and when congregated at the base of the cliffs while the young are fledging, as well as during the process of leading them out to sea. Bowing is apparently a movement in response to visual stimuli of some sort, since at night and on isolated ledges nodding and bobbing are infrequent and quickly die down after any disturbance has ceased. Foster et al. (1951) made the puzzling statement that on Grimsey (Iceland) the thick-billed murres do not bow, whereas the common murres do.

Perry (1940) considered bowing in the common murre to be derived from the egg-rolling movement. This is plausible enough with respect to courtship, but such an origin for an alarm movement seems unlikely.

With most birds, fighting is formal and stylized and rarely results in bodily injury—much less mortality. Such is not the case with thick-billed murres. Fights among thick-billed murres occur often, particularly in warm, calm weather, but not between recognized neighbours. It is seldom easy to tell the age, sex and status of birds seen fighting, but according to Pennycuick (1956) it appears that the most vicious fights occur when parents whose mates are brooding chicks take exception to the presence of non-breeding birds. Pennycuick describes such fights in Spitsbergen: "Two birds on the point of having a fight stretch their necks up and lay all their feathers flat, each flinching whenever the other moves. The actual fighting consists of jabbing repeatedly at the tips of each other's bills. The contestants often become very intent on this, and scramble over other birds, flapping their wings to keep their balance on the edge of the ledge, and sometimes grasping each other's bills and pulling and twisting. The fight generally ends with one bird losing its balance and falling off the cliff. In a mild fight it may fly round one circuit and land again in the same place or a little further away, but in a more serious contest its opponent immediately leaps off after it and chases it down to the water, pecking at its tail if near enough and uttering loud cries of 'arr-rr-r, arrr-rr-r'. On the water the birds continue to jab at one another, turning round and round each other and beating the water with their wings. A fight may continue for several minutes on the water; finally one bird tries to escape by diving, the other following it. The lower then usually comes up and tries to fly away, but a guillemot which has just been fighting seems wholly incapable of flight. Winner and loser alike splash along with necks outstretched, flailing the water with their wings, the loser sometimes going a hundred yards or so in this fashion".

This describes exactly the manner of fighting I have observed at most thick-billed murre colonies, except that I have frequently seen that the birds strike the water with their beaks tightly gripped together. Those fights continue with the birds grasping each other's mandibles or getting a grip on each other's wings. At Akpatok Island, fights of this sort were especially fierce and long. It seemed incredible that the birds could fight continuously for an hour or more, which they sometimes did. In fact, many of them perished from having their bills twisted or torn off. On one occasion, I found a dying bird, with its lower mandible torn off and its wings intricately twisted behind each other. The fights were so intense at Akpatok that we sometimes caught both birds in a dip net and banded them. Of six birds caught in this way and examined, three were breeding females and three were non-breeding females. This sample, suggestive as it may be, is much too small to conclude that females are more aggressive than males. I have never noted sustained fighting at colonies of common murres, either at the nest site or in the water near by. Nørrevang (1958) made a similar comment for the Faeroe Islands. Since common murres prefer to nest on wide ledges and flat stacks, where many birds, their eggs and young, might be affected by fighting, extreme belligerency could, in that species, cause great loss of life. The common murre's greater intra-specific tolerance

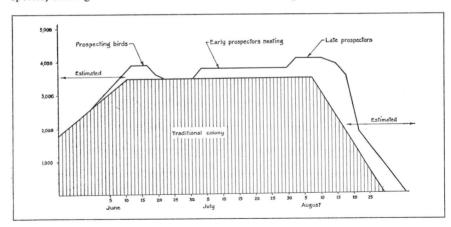

FIGURE 17. *Seasonal changes in thick-billed murre cliff populations, Cape Hay, 1957*

may well be an adaptation, through natural selection, to crowded breeding conditions.

The size of a murre colony is not static at any time, although it may be nearly so during stormy periods half-way through the breeding season.

Seasonal changes in the cliff population at Cape Hay during the summer of 1957 are illustrated in Fig. 17. Population changes, full details of which are given in Appendix C, may be summarized as follows:

1) The cliffs attained 90 per cent of their maximum population during June. This declined to about 80 per cent as some early prospectors left, perhaps temporarily.

2) After the first of July, young birds presumed to be breeding for the first time (most likely the prospectors referred to above), settled permanently on the fringes of the colony, so that the population was again at about 90 per cent of maximum.

3) After August 1, the population was further increased by another 10 per cent. The increase was assumed to consist of late prospectors, perhaps very young birds. In any case, they had no brood patches and did not attempt to nest.

4) After the middle of August, the total numbers began to dwindle as the chicks and both the breeding adults and the non-breeders went off to sea.

In the Newfoundland colonies, the birds settle down about one hour after sunset and are relatively quiet until dawn. The length of the period of inactivity depends to some extent on light intensity, since the murres at Akpatok Island commenced to settle down soon after the shadows of the cliff spread over their ledges and those at Cape Hay were relatively quiet only during the short twilight. Daily variation in the numbers of birds at the nesting sites is related to activity. On very stormy days there is less activity than on other days.

Murres were seen feeding young at Cape Hay at all times of the day except during the twilight hours. On August 18, there were three distinct peaks of feeding activity. The most noticeable was between 10 and 11 a.m.; the second between 3 and 6 p.m.; and the third, least active, period between 7 and 9 p.m.

There were usually two distinct periods of feeding activity on Akpatok Island and in Digges Sound. Since those two regions are noted for their high tides, feeding activity may be related to tidal movements. The tides were not high at Cape Hay, but both in-tide currents from Baffin Bay and out-tide currents from Barrow Strait were strong. It can be assumed that three or four times during the day, food was particularly abundant off Cape Hay. I have been unable to discern any particularly active feeding period in the Newfoundland colonies. It may be assumed therefore that diurnal activity with regard to feeding is locally dependent on oceanic phenomena, such as tides and the occurrence of schools of fish.

There is also seasonal variation in the daily activity of murres. In 1957, 50 pairs of murres were colour-banded on a certain ledge at Cape Hay and their daily activity was noted from time to time (Fig. 18). Thus it was established that early in the breeding season (June 20) a maximum number of birds was present throughout the day. At that time, laying was approaching its initial peak, copulation was frequent, and there was a tendency for both birds of the pair to remain on the ledge for long periods. Mid-way in the season (July 20), one of the pair was relieved from nest duties for a large part of the day and spent much time loitering elsewhere and at sea. After mid-August, feeding the chicks was in full swing, and both birds again spent much time on the ledge.

Pennycuick (1956) stated that no daily fluctuation was noticeable in the activity of the thick-billed murres at Spitsbergen and that it appeared that the murre's "rate of fishing

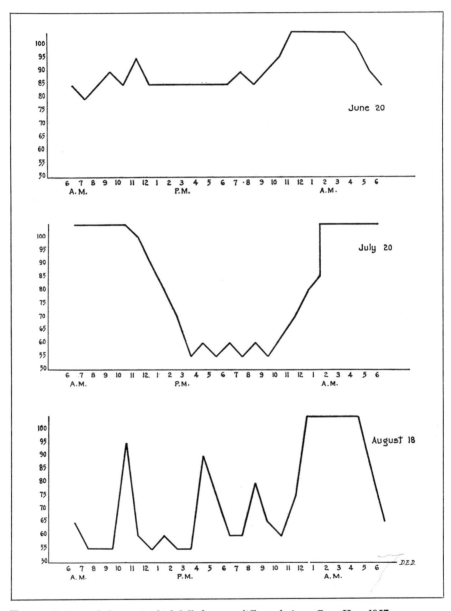

FIGURE 18. *Diurnal changes in thick-billed murre cliff populations, Cape Hay, 1957*

120

was not affected by the small diurnal variation of light intensity which occurs during the Spitsbergen summer". Uspenski (1956) also remarked that no regularity was discovered, with regard to time of day in the flights of thick-billed murres at Novaya Zemlya to their feeding grounds. I suspect that the absence of any regular pattern of feeding activity at the Polar Basin colonies is due to the lack of prominent tidal movements in that region.

As on the wintering grounds, murres associate with other sea-birds at their breeding sites. This association is comprised of birds which feed in the sea, often at great distances from land, and which have their breeding-places close to the sea, either on precipitous rocky cliffs and in the talus beneath them, or in or on the grassy and turf-covered slopes. They are principally other alcids, but the gannet (*Morus bassanus*), European cormorant (*Phalacrocorax carbo*), black-legged kittiwake (*Rissa tridactyla*) and fulmar (*Fulmarus glacialis*) are often members of this association. The *Larus* gulls breed in optimum numbers in a different biotope, often some distance from the sea. They may be considered transitional species in this association, since large colonies of murres usually have a few gulls breeding in association with them to take advantage of the opportunities for scavenging provided by the colony. For the same reason, such land-birds as the common raven (*Corvus corax*), peregrine falcon (*Falco peregrinus*), gyrfalcon (*Falco rusticolus*), and, in low lemming years, the snowy owl (*Nyctea scandiaca*) nest on the cliffs. The Russians have very aptly named such an association of sea-birds and companion species a "bazaar".

The most impressive sea-bird colonies in the Northern Hemisphere are located where there is a continuous strong flow of arctic waters, or on capes and promontories where local turbulence guarantees a constant supply of plankton and small fishes during the summer.

At no time during the year is food for sea-birds so abundant as during the nesting season. This accounts for the nesting of a great variety of sea-birds in a single locality, sometimes in fantastic numbers, without any apparent conflict over food supplies. The parts of the sea important in this regard to the members of the sea-cliff nesting association are the surface layers, and the sea-bottoms where they are not more than about 30 feet below the surface.

The petrels, kittiwakes and fulmars feed principally on macroplankton. Adapted as they are to feed on pelagic organisms, those birds can find food anywhere in the northern oceans. The macroplankton mainly consists of crustaceans and the fry of small fishes. Quite important are the shrimp-like euphausiids, the "kril" of fishermen, which at times constitute nearly the whole catch in plankton nets. They may be an inch or two in length. Generally they are colourless and transparent, but some are conspicuously red in colour. They may live near the bottom but rise to the surface for spawning in great swarms. Sometimes one may see the surface of the ocean blood-red with the dense shoals of those small shrimp. They are a favourite food for whalebone whales, as well as for sea-birds.

Murres are predominantly fish eaters (see Chapter XIV), taking fishes with an average length of 15 cm. Although macroplankton constitutes at times a part of the diet of adult murres, it does not appear to be an important part.

Each of the other alcids has its particular food spectrum. For example puffins prefer very small sprats and launce, and dovekies feed exclusively on small crustaceans. The razorbill may offer murres some competition in food in the boreal and low-arctic marine zones, to which this species is pretty much restricted. Apparently murres have the advantage, since razorbills exist only in the North Atlantic and only in relatively small numbers.

The fauna of the upper water-layers, especially the small cod, are important items in the diet of non-diving birds. Pelagic fry of cod form a substantial part of the macroplankton, but when they are 3-5 cm. long, they take to the bottom and are then available only to the divers. Gannets, and to some extent kittiwakes, dive for their food, but they do not penetrate far and are limited to the fishes in the upper layers.

Adaptation to different types of food by selection of feeding habitat is a marked characteristic of the sea-birds of the sea-cliff nesting association. The *Larus* gulls feed close inshore, scavenge along the shore-line, and prey on eggs in the murre colonies. Along the coast are found cormorants and black guillemots; a little farther out gannets, razorbills, puffins and murres; farthest out are fulmars, kittiwakes and petrels.

The impact of a sea-bird colony is felt not only in the sea but also on the cliffs, where a particularly rich and abundant growth of nitrophilous plants results from the accumulated excrement. The growth of grasses and such circumpolar northern plants as *Oxyria* and *Cochlearia* is more luxuriant there than elsewhere. This vegetation harbours an immense population of spiders, springtails, mites and insects, which in turn provide food for wheatears, snow buntings, pipits and other small passerines. A distinctive lichen on and around the less vertical sea-bird cliffs is the orange-coloured nitrophilous *Caloplaca elegans*. Being an ornithocoprophilous organism—so termed by botanists—*Caloplaca* takes advantage of the nitrogen in bird excrement. Since *Caloplaca* is phototrophic, it grows most luxuriantly on the bird cliffs facing south. When a cliff is deserted, the carpet of *Caloplaca* will survive for many years, and is a certain indication of the previous presence of a sea-bird colony. In closely packed sea-bird colonies, the nitrogen concentration is so high that all vegetation is scorched and the cliffs are completely bare and of a light greyish colour.

The different species of sea-birds occupy different nesting sites. This has been discussed by Fisher and Lockley (1954) thus: "Whether the rocks be volcanic or intrusive or extrusive or sedimentary, we are sure to find *Larus* gulls breeding on the more level ground a little way back from the tops of the cliffs—fulmars on the steeply sloping turf and among the broken rocks at the cliff edge, puffins with their burrows honeycombing the soil wherever this is exposed at the edge of the cliff or cliff buttress, Manx shearwaters or Leach's petrels in long burrows, storm petrels in short burrows and rock crevices, razorbills in cracks and crannies and on sheltered ledges, guillemots [murres] on the more open ledges or on the flattish tops of inaccessible stacks, cormorants with their nests in orderly rows along broad continuous ledges, shags in shadowy pockets and small caves and hollowed-out ledges dotted about the cliff, kittiwakes on tiny steps or finger-holds improved and enlarged by the mud-construction of their nests, tysties or black guillemots in talus and boulders at the foot of the cliff. These wild, steep frontiers between sea and land are exciting and beautiful. They probably house larger numbers of vertebrate animals, apart from fish, in a small space, than any other comparable part of the temperate world".

It is of interest to speculate to what extent there is competition for nesting sites among the members of the sea-cliff nesting association. Though each species may seem to have a preferred nesting niche, that is not always the case. For instance, gannets and murres may nest close together, as they do on Funk Island, Newfoundland, and kittiwakes and thick-billed murres occupy the same ledges, as they do at Cape Hay in the eastern Canadian Arctic and along the Murman coast.

Among Newfoundland fishermen there is a strong tradition of hatred for the gannet, which, they insist, has driven the murres away from Cape St. Mary's and Funk Island. This claim may be somewhat biased, since murres in Newfoundland are an important part of the diet of coastal residents but gannets are considered inedible. The important point is that while gannets and murres use the same habitat at Cape St. Mary's and Funk Island, there is no shortage of that kind of habitat on Funk Island or at Cape St. Mary's except on the gannet stack. Actually, a few murres, entirely surrounded by gannets, still breed on the gannet stack at Cape St. Mary's. If no gannets were nesting on its top, whose area is under 1,000 square meters, there would be room for perhaps 15,000 pairs of murres there. In 1936, after an absence of more than a century, gannets became re-established at their traditional site on Funk Island. That particular locality was occupied by a few murres at the time, although the total murre population of Funk Island in 1936 was only 10,000 pairs. Since that time, gannets have increased in number, but the murres have also increased until in 1959 they exceeded by far the total world population of gannets. I have not heard of any significant competition between gannets and murres elsewhere in their ranges. Indeed, their recent history on Funk Island suggests that they do not compete, except in a few places, for nesting space.

The case with regard to the kittiwakes is not so conclusive. At Cape Hay, Lancaster Sound, kittiwakes sometimes nested on ledges which would otherwise apparently have been occupied by murres. On June 15, 1957, additional kittiwakes arrived at the Cape Hay cliffs in tens of thousands and drove all the murres from the cliffs, except a few thousand deeply entrenched in several gullies. The kittiwake's flight was light and airy, while the murre's was direct and strong. Consequently, the murres seemed unable to get through the barrier of milling kittiwakes and remained for the most part flying back and forth some distance from the cliffs. Two days later, the majority of kittiwakes departed as unexpectedly as they had arrived and there was no apparent decrease in the nesting population of murres. In fact, a few murres successfully raised young in old or abandoned kittiwake nests.

Both common murres and kittiwakes have increased in number in the colonies at Witless Bay, Newfoundland, during the past several years. The increase in population of kittiwakes is shown by their establishment of new colonies on the cliffs of formerly unoccupied islands, while the murres have shown an increase in breeding density in their traditional colonies.

In Novaya Zemlya, according to Uspenski (1956), kittiwakes usually select the same kind of ledges and projections as do murres, but also settle in niches, small caves, and crevices in the rocks which murres do not readily occupy. Different views are held on the relations between kittiwakes and thick-billed murres in that region. Krasovski (1937) believes that in Novaya Zemlya, kittiwakes force murres from the nesting ledges. The same opinion, based on his observations in Seven Islands, is expressed by Modestov (1941). However, Kaftanovski (1951), who also worked in Seven Islands, believes that those authors greatly exaggerated the extent of harm done to murres by kittiwakes. Demme (1934) observed that in Franz Josef Land murres occupying nesting sites in spring often destroyed and threw down kittiwake nests. Finally, Belopolski, in a verbal report to Uspenski (1956), stated that in the spring of 1941 displacement of kittiwakes by increasing numbers of murres was observed on the majority of nesting ledges in Seven Islands. The murres settled in the completed or repaired nests of the kittiwakes and, after chasing away the owners, either laid their eggs in the nests or threw the nests aside and laid their eggs in the places on the ledges where the nests had been. Uspenski (1956) also stated that at Seven Islands in 1949, and in Gribovaya and Bezymyannaya Bays in Novaya Zemlya in 1950, they often saw murres chasing kittiwakes and taking over their nesting sites at the beginning of the nesting period. Those observations were supported by data which showed that in two sanctuaries the murres increased in number while the kittiwakes correspondingly decreased. The evidence, therefore, seems to indicate that although kittiwakes may frequently nest on the same ledges as murres, they are not strong competitors.

There may be much competition between the two species of murres, although in most mixed colonies differential selection of nesting sites reduces it to a minimum. On Green Island and Funk Island in Newfoundland, the nesting sites of the rather small populations of thick-billed murres are restricted to one or two steep, narrow ledges. At Baccalieu Island and at Cape St. Mary's, where thick-billed murres comprise 20 per cent or more of the total murre populations, the ledges are rather narrow, but the thick-billed murres tend to nest on the narrowest ledges rather than on the fringes of the common murre sites. In a few places the species appear to be mixed in rather haphazardly. Sergeant (1951) wrote that " . . . at Bear Island, both were associated freely together on the long, regular dolomite ledges of the high southern cliffs, in a ratio of about one *lomvia* to two *aalge*. However, on the very edge of the cliff tops *lomvia* occurred alone in a band, while on the flat tops there was a pure association of *aalge*." At Grimsey, in Iceland, accurate counts showed thick-billed murres outnumbering common murres on the steep cliffs by two to one (Foster *et al.*, 1951). This is apparently a reflection of preference for a particular ledge-type.

The situation in the Pacific is not so clear. The relative abundance of the two species on Walrus Island fluctuates in different years. Gabrielson and Lincoln (1959) document a similar fluctuation on St. Matthew Island. Cade (1952) says of the Sledge Island, Bering Sea, colony: "The two species do not segregate into separate colonies but any given nesting shelf was usually occupied by only one species at a time, and there was some evidence that with the progression of the breeding season each nesting site becomes the particular property of one species only". It seems that in the Bering Sea region, where the two species overlap in probably optimum numbers, competition for nesting sites may be acute between them.

To sum up the habitat differences, it might be said that in the North Atlantic, the common murres prefer flat places and avoid crevices, while thick-billed murres are less rigid in their choice of nest sites. Thus, in the high-arctic regions, where thick-billed murres breed alone, they occupy all types of cliff-sites.

Competition at the extreme limits of either species may be serious. Thus, Uspenski (1956) stated that at Seven Islands, off the Murman coast, competition for nesting space between thick-billed and common murres was extremely acute, and that the common murres everywhere forced the thick-billed murres to the fringes of the colonies and to the small ledges and projections that were submarginal murre nest sites. Apparently this is also the situation at Cape St. Mary's and Baccalieu Island in Newfoundland. Uspenski also claimed that the great majority of thick-billed murres at Seven Islands were unable to compete with the common murres and nested on ledges covered with a layer of earth or peat unfavourable for incubating their porous-shelled eggs. In the densely occupied colonies in Digges Sound, Hudson Bay, occupied solely by thick-billed murres, a considerable number of them nested on peat-covered stacks and ledges. It is my belief that those sites had been recently occupied, otherwise the turf would have been worn and washed away. Murres nested quite successfully there, however, since fewer eggs were lost than from the commoner bare, sloping ledges.

The only evidence to suggest intraspecific competition for nest sites was noted among thick-billed murres at Quaker Hat, Labrador, in 1952. At Quaker Hat, no sites were available except several small, narrow ledges. On each ledge were found nine or ten dead thick-billed murres which appeared to have been killed by sharp jabs on the head. The carcasses were "glued" to the ledges by the accumulation of excrement. I searched the area for carcasses but could find none other than those on the nesting ledges.

CHAPTER XII

The Egg

Murres of both species habitually lay their eggs on bare rock surfaces, not building a nest in the usual sense of the word. In a few locations, such as at Digges Sound, Hudson Bay, and along the Murman coast, thick-billed murres sometimes lay their eggs on ledges covered with peat or turf. It is believed that those are instances where competition for nesting sites is acute.

As previously mentioned, brooding birds sometimes pile up small stones under the eggs. At Cape Hay in 1957, thick-billed murres fairly frequently did that, or attempted to, with pebbles from the vicinity of their nest sites. The pebbles were picked up in the bill, brought down along the breast and dropped between the feet. A few birds were observed to move rather large pieces of rock in this manner; one piece, of rather light limestone, measured three by four by one and a half inches. There appeared to be no pattern to this behaviour. One bird shuffled along for several feet, picking up and dropping pebbles as it moved; another reached out for pebbles near it and dropped them casually around its feet. A few held pebbles for some time and then dropped them with seeming disinterest. Those observations were made on ledges where small pieces of rock were available. I have never noted a murre fly in to the nest site with a pebble or attempt to gather sea-weed or other nest material. In many cases eggs are prevented from rolling off the nest site by a few pebbles thus gathered together, which soon become cemented by sediment and excrement. They thus offer protection to the egg, which, after all, is the practical purpose of any nest. Some observers, noting this interesting behaviour, have suggested that it is an atavistic habit inherited from nest-building ancestors. It may be that because of the loss of some of the eggs through rolling from the nest site, murres have developed a secondary nest-building instinct which expresses itself in the piling of small stones around the egg. Similar behaviour is that of the Cory's shearwater (*Puffinus diomedea*), which customarily lays in burrows, but which Lockley (1942) found nesting in a cave on the Berlengas Islands off Portugal on platforms of stones, built up by the birds. Lockley said: "The stone platforms . . . as we saw them in that cave on the Berlengas might not have been planned with a conscious purpose by the builder, but they were very useful in preventing the large and rather rounded egg from rolling away".

As may be seen from Tables 15 and 16, the thick-billed murre seldom lays before the middle of June, except in Newfoundland and locally in southwest Greenland, while the common murre may lay as early as the first week in May. The time interval between laying dates for these species is due to the marine environment.

As a rule, the nesting sites of common murres are available early in the season and, in fact, most of the regions where they breed are not at all affected by ice. Along the coast of Labrador, however, the pack ice does not leave until early May and in some years even later. Both common and thick-billed murres breeding along the eastern coast of Labrador consistently lay later than murres farther south, in Newfoundland. Common murres in the Channel Islands and in Japan may lay as early as the first week in May. Mid-May seems to be the usual egg-laying date for common murres in most regions except along the coasts of Labrador and British Columbia. Bent's (1919) March 6 date for the common murre on the Farallon Islands is certainly an error.

In Newfoundland (but not along the coast of Labrador) and locally in southwest Greenland, thick-billed murres commence to lay during the first week in June; elsewhere the second and third weeks in June appear to be usual. In a few regions, such as in Franz Josef Land and Akpatok Island in Ungava Bay, thick-billed murres may not commence to lay until rather late in June. Both those regions are noted for lateness of pack ice. Actually, it is unlikely that murres in such regions consistently lay annually on the same dates, but in any one year the dates may be fairly uniform. Thus Salomonsen (1950) says of the thick-billed murres in West Greenland: "The first eggs are laid in mid-June, generally slightly earlier in Disko Bay, a few days later in Thule District, but the date is everywhere remarkably uniform, varying from 10 to 25 June." Salomonsen also gives evidence that in recent times, owing to the amelioration of climate, thick-billed murres have arrived earlier than formerly at their colonies in West Greenland.

The eggs of the murres are pyriform or pear-shaped. They vary greatly in colour. They are oftenest of light blue or light green background, with numerous patches, streaks and splashes of contrasting colours, mostly browns. Variation from the basic type of colouring is usually towards either decoloration or saturation with rusty-brown tones. The extremes, therefore, of the series are uniformly light blue eggs or eggs of light brown background with brown streaks and patches.

Experiments with common murres on Funk Island and with thick-billed murres at Cape Hay indicate that colour probably plays little part in recognition of particular eggs by individual birds.[1] Individually marked eggs were removed from the nest sites of individually-marked birds and replaced by other murres' eggs of different colours, eggs of other species and egg-shaped rocks. When birds returned to their nest sites, they invariably continued to incubate in the same location, failing to react adversely to the substitute for their own eggs. Early in the nesting period, the colours of the eggs and even the shape may be obliterated by sediment and excrement. It seems likely, however, as described elsewhere, that the great variations in the colour of the eggs act as camouflage, safeguarding them from gulls and ravens.

The pyriform shape of the murre's egg is popularly assumed to provide stability on the ledge. The notion is that a dislodged egg of this shape will rotate on its axis and

[1]More recent studies (Tschanz, B., 1959. Zur Brutbiologie der Trottellumme (Uria aalge aalge Pont.) Behaviour 14:1-100) indicate that the capacity to learn the individual characteristics of an egg may be well developed in common murres. Tschanz found that common murres have a strong inhibition against retrieving an egg of another bird, unless it closely resembles their own.

therefore rarely roll off a smooth surface. In actual fact, the greatest mortality in a murre colony is due to eggs falling off the ledges or rolling away from their proper places into crevices where they are irretrievable. The majority of the eggs fall during the first few days after they are laid. Some eggs are laid in such precarious situations that they are doomed from the beginning. The gradual accumulation of sediment and excrement assists in giving stability to the egg. Experiments in Russia (Uspenski, 1956) have shown that, although the shape of the egg and the accumulation of excrement do provide some stability, the most important stabilizer is the progressive change in the distribution of weight within the egg. As incubation proceeds, the small end of the egg becomes heavier, the large end rises and thus the radius of the curve described by the egg when disturbed is also reduced. Consequently the chance of falling is diminished (Fig. 19).

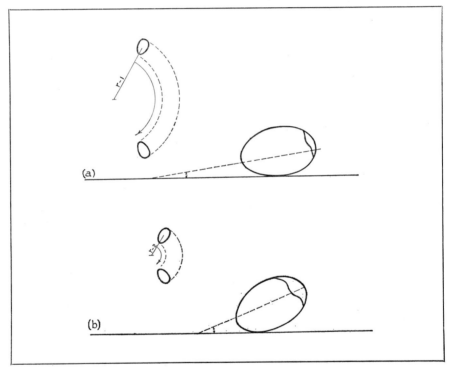

FIGURE 19. *Position of murre's egg on the nesting ledge and radius of circle described by it when pushed: (a) un-incubated egg, (b) incubated egg (from Uspenski, 1956)*

The mechanism of the phenomenon may be explained as follows: at the beginning of incubation the egg's centre of gravity, because of the small size of the air cell, is close to the large end. Gradually the embryo develops and the size of the air cell increases, causing movement of the centre of gravity towards the narrow end of the egg and a change in the position of the egg on the ledge.

Green Island, Witless Bay, Newfoundland (middle foreground) where common murres nest on the wide ledges, thick-billed murres on the narrow ledges, kittiwakes in the gulches and puffins in the turf on top

One of three large colonies of common murres on Funk Island. The foreground shows the fringes of the colony where birds breeding for the first time are not so closely packed as the more experienced ones in the core of the colony

*Part of a colony of common murres on the headland
of Indian Gulch, Funk Island, Newfoundland. The
chicks in this colony, when ready to go to sea, do
not plunge directly into the gulch.   Instead, they
follow a few adults half-way across the island to
some convenient ledge*

*A few common murres on Funk Island nest near
the gannets and even amongst them. The birds in
the middle foreground are mainly prospecting
common murres making their first contact with the
land. In the following year, they will return earlier
in the season and attempt to breed*

Cape St. Mary's, Newfoundland. The most
southerly murre colony in eastern North America.
Here, both species of murres nest with kittiwakes
in the middle foreground, and with gannets in the
right background

The sea-going of common murre chicks at sunset,
July 17, 1958, Funk Island, Newfoundland. They
have plunged into the sea from the low ledges in the
right background. As darkness approaches, each
chick, accompanied by a single adult, will swim
slowly out to sea

When cold or disturbed, murre chicks will seek shelter under the wings of any near-by adult. This photograph shows examples of the bridled phase of the common murre on Funk Island, Newfoundland

Thick-billed murres nesting on the steep and
narrow ledges of Green Island, Witless Bay,
Newfoundland. The distinctive features of this
species in the breeding season are the white gape
marks and the sharp peak of the white of the throat

The faults, pinnacles and narrow ledges of the granitic schist cliffs on Digges Island, Hudson Bay, are the nesting sites of a host of thick-billed murres. The cliffs are occupied up to a height of 800 feet. The chicks, when ready to leave, plunge directly into the sea

*Thick-billed murres nesting on isolated ledges,
Outer Gannet Island, Labrador. Large numbers of
common murres nest on this small and remote
island but they are confined to the relatively flat
central part*

A general view of the mainland thick-billed murre cliffs in Digges Sound, Hudson Bay, some of which are occupied up to 1,000 feet. The headland in the immediate foreground is now deserted possibly due to erosion

Part of the limestone cliffs occupied by thick-billed murres at Akpatok Island, Ungava Bay. The nesting ledges are on horizontal shelves some 600 feet above sea-level. The chicks, with their primaries still undeveloped, flutter outwards for a half-mile before they reach the safety of the sea

The vertical limestone cliffs near Cape Hay,
Lancaster Sound, occupied by thick-billed murres.
Parts of the cliffs are 1,500 feet in height and are
occupied right to the top. The chicks plunge directly
into the sea

*View from the land of part of the thick-billed
murre cliffs near Cape Hay, Lancaster Sound,
showing the inaccessibility of the cliffs from land
predators*

Increase in stability of the egg on the ledge towards the end of incubation is very important, as the possibility of a second laying by the birds rapidly decreases during incubation.

It has been generally assumed that the thickness of the egg-shell depends directly on the amount of mineral salts obtained by the females from their food. In the event of shortage of salts containing calcium, phosphorus and magnesium, the shells of the eggs laid become thinner. Uspenski (1956) indicated that the shells of the thick-billed murre eggs at Seven Islands (Murman coast) were only half the thickness of those on Novaya Zemlya. The diet of the murres in both places appeared to be similar. Uspenski explains the phenomenon thus. "In Novaya Zemlya the murres nest on the bare surface of rock ledges, formed by erosion of the strata and having an uneven rough-grained surface.

Table 15: *Nesting phenology of the common murre*

	Egg Date	Sea-going Date	Source
Eastern Atlantic			
Shetland Islands	—	July 12, 1946	Perry (1948)
Farne Islands	3rd week in May	—	Watt (1951)
Faeroe Islands	May 15	—	Salomonsen (1935)
St. Kilda	May 15	—	Witherby *et al.* (1941)
Wales (Skomer I.)	—	July 11, 1946	Keighley and Lockley (1947)
Yorkshire	May 14	—	Witherby *et al.* (1941)
Channel Islands	1st week in May	—	Dobson (1952)
France (Toulinguet)	May 19, 1926	—	Berthet (1947)
Western Atlantic			
Labrador	—	August 3, 1953	Tuck
Gulf of St. Lawrence	May 20	July 27, 1930	Bent (1919), H. F. Lewis (in litt.)
Newfoundland	May 22, 1952	July 14, 1952	Tuck
Eastern Pacific			
British Columbia	June 25, 1949	—	Guiguet (1950)
Washington	—	August 10, 1915	Jewett *et al.* (1953)
Oregon	June 1	—	Alex Walker (in litt.)
Santa Barbara	June 5	—	Bent (1919)
Western Pacific			
Japan	May 1	—	Austin and Kuroda (1953)

On Seven Islands the majority of murres nest on soft ground—ledges covered with a layer of peat. A small number of the Seven Island murres, as in Novaya Zemlya, lay their eggs on bare rock surfaces, but the nesting ledges of the Seven Island bird bazaars are formed of glaciated granite and have incomparably smoother surfaces, on which the possibility of mechanical damage to the eggs is much less. That fact, combined with the

Table 16: *Nesting phenology of the thick-billed murre*

	Egg Date	Sea-going Date	Source
Polar Basin			
Franz Josef Land	June 26, 1882	August 13, 1896	Clarke (1898)
Jan Mayen	June 10, 1883	August 15, 1882[1]	Clarke (1890)
Novaya Zemlya	June 10, 1935	August 5, 1934	Uspenski (1956)
Spitsbergen	—	August 14, 1864	Newton (1865)
Bear Island	—	August 20, 1948	Bertram & Lack (1933) Duffey & Sergeant (1950)
North Atlantic			
Prince Leopold Island	—	August 15, 1958	T. W. Barry (in litt.)
Lancaster Sound (C. Hay)	June 20, 1957	August 15, 1957	Tuck
Baffin Bay (C. Graham Moore)	June 22, 1954	—	Drury (in litt.)
West Greenland (Disko)	June 5,	July 27,	Salomonsen (1950)
Ungava Bay (Akpatok Island)	June 30, 1954	August 26, 1954	Tuck
Hudson Bay (Digges Island)	June 15, 1955	August 11, 1955	Tuck
Labrador (Gannet Islands)	—	August 18, 1953	Tuck
Newfoundland (Green Island)	June 4, 1952	—	Tuck
North Pacific			
Sledge Island (Bering Sea)	June 9, 1950	—	Cade (1952)

[1]There are undoubtedly annual variations in the nesting phenology, especially in the high-arctic regions. Seligman and Wilcox (1940) wrote that in 1938 most of the young at Jan Mayen were off the ledges by August 7, and the last were seen on the cliffs on August 20.

difference between Novaya Zemlya and Seven Islands in temperature conditions during the nesting period (the shell, no doubt, has some significance in temperature insulation), in all probability constitutes a reason for the greater shell thickness of the eggs of the Novaya Zemlya murres. That example once more illustrates the creative role of natural selection, and its strengthening in cases of characteristics of use to a species".

Table 17 shows the great variation in the size of murre eggs. This table suggests that the largest are those of the common murre, *Uria aalge hyperborea*, of the low-arctic region of the Polar Basin. In fact, Uspenski (1956) states that the eggs of common murres are slightly larger than those of thick-billed murres. Uspenski's measurements for the thick-billed murre eggs of Novaya Zemlya show, however, the upper extremes in both length and diameter of any eggs recorded.

There are two sources of probable bias in this table. Both Bent's and Witherby's measurements may include data from populations not at that time recognized as separate races. More important, however, would be the actual time of the season when the eggs

Table 17: *Measurements in mm. of murre eggs*

Subspecies	No. in Sample	Extremes	Average	Source
COMMON MURRE				
aalge	64	89.0 x 50.5 84.0 x 54.5 66.0 x 44.0	81.0 x 50.3	Bent (1919)
aalge	100	89.5 x 52.9 82.2 x 56.6 75.1 x 48.6 80.3 x 44.7	81.7 x 50.0	Witherby et al. (1941)
albionis	100	— —	81.5 x 49.7	Witherby et al. (1941)
californica	74	90.0 x 52.0 84.0 x 54.0 69.5 x 42.5	82.2 x 50.2	Bent (1919)
hyperborea	44	94.0 x — 74.0 x — — x 55.0 — x 46.0	84.1 x 51.4	Uspenski (1956)
hyperborea	29	— —	84.5 x 52.5	Le Roi (1911)
hyperborea	21	— —	85.6 x 51.9	Witherby (1924)
THICK-BILLED MURRE				
lomvia	41	87.0 x 53.5 67.5 x 43.0	80.0 x 50.0	Bent (1919)
lomvia	104	89.5 x 49.4 80.0 x 55.0 71.6 x 49.6 77.0 x 46.1	80.1 x 50.0	Witherby et al. (1941)
lomvia	24	— —	79.8 x 50.5	Salomonsen (1950)
lomvia	430	96.0 x — 70.0 x — — x 59.0 — x 46.0	78.9 x 51.1	Uspenski (1956)
arra	79	91.0 x 55.5 73.0 x 48.0 79.0 x 47.0	82.0 x 51.5	Bent (1919)

were collected. Uspenski (1956) showed that second and third replacement eggs were progressively smaller. Thus it may be that the eggs of the first laying of thick-billed murres are largest of all, but that they are closely approached in size by those of the northern races of the common murre, such as *hyperborea* and *inornata*.

Fifteen eggs of *aalge* weighed by Johnson (1944) ranged in weight from 83 to 117 grams and averaged 103.4 grams. Forty-four eggs of *hyperborea* weighed by Uspenski (1956) varied from 64 to 138 grams and averaged 104.73 grams. Johnson (1944) stated that an egg of *aalge* that weighed 113 grams when fresh lost 8 grams in weight in ten days of incubation. Unless the stages of incubation for all those eggs are comparable, the average weights do not mean a great deal.[1]

Incubation begins immediately after the eggs are laid. The brooding bird adjusts the egg under its brood patch with the large end in front and the small end behind. In spite of the absence of nesting material, the egg is nearly covered during incubation. A large part of it is in contact with the brood patch, the skin of which hangs down and lies closely on the top of the egg and to some extent on the sides. The egg is almost completely covered in front by the thick plumage of the abdomen and breast. Finally, the lower side of the egg does not directly touch the rock, as the egg lies on the outspread membranes of the bird's webbed feet.

Both parents share in incubation. There is some evidence that the males incubate more assiduously than the females. An incubating bird usually stands up every hour or two, flaps its wings a few times, turns the egg over on its long axis, unless it is cemented to the ledge, and sits down again. When the birds change shifts, the egg is usually transferred between the pair, literally "from foot to foot". Some eggs get firmly cemented to the ledge by excrement and sediment as incubation advances. I have observed young hatching from eggs which had been solidly fixed in position at least a week before. Occasionally, a murre lays its egg in a crack or narrow crevice in which proper incubation is impossible. Although the bird may attempt to incubate such an egg for the normal length of time or even longer, it does not hatch.

There is some difference between the brooding positions of the two species. The thick-billed murre, as a rule, broods in a prone position, the common murre in an upright position. This latter position is generally considered an adaptation to crowding. At the extreme northern limits of the range of the common murre the difference in brooding position is not so evident. At Nunarsuk Island, Labrador, common murres nesting under boulders and in small fissures incubate in a prone position, since there is no space to do otherwise.

At Cape Hay, I noted that the first birds to lay, presumably the oldest ones, incubated assiduously as soon as the eggs were laid. Those which laid for the first time late in the season, presumably birds breeding for the first or second time, incubated erratically

---

[1] Johnson (1944) showed that at one day of age, six chicks of common murres in the Gulf of St. Lawrence varied from 72 to 80 grams in weight and averaged 77 grams. Uspenski (1956) showed that the average weight on hatching of Novaya Zemlya thick-billed murres, as determined by observations over three years, was 70.33 grams, but that it fluctuated between 48 and 98 grams. It is important to know whether the eggs were first, second or third layings.

during the first five or six days. The biological significance of close incubation is extremely great for murres. Kaftanovski (1951) suggests that close incubation is the most effective means that murres have of protecting their eggs from predatory gulls. Uspenski (1956) suggests that close incubation prevents the eggs from chilling during the most critical period, which is important when the environmental temperature is low. To which I might add that close incubation also saves a large number of eggs from destruction during the normal activity of murres on a closely packed ledge.

Incubation period of common murres

Period	Reference
28 days	Tiedmann's "Anatomy und Naturgeschichte der Vogel", 1814.
A month	Selby's "British Ornithology", 1833.
Appears to last a month	Macgillivray's "History of British Birds", 1852.
30 days	Owen's "Anatomy of Vertebrates", 1866.
Fully 30 days	Saxby's "Birds of Shetland", 1874.
Nearly a month	Yarrell's "History of British Birds", 1885.

From the foregoing, it is clear that ornithologists formerly assumed the incubation period of the common murre to be four weeks or at the most a month. Evans (1891) hatched two common murre eggs in an incubator. One egg required 30 days to hatch and the other 33 days. He also placed a common murre's egg under a hen, where it hatched in 31 days. The first evidence that incubation of the common murre might be even longer than this was in Witherby *et al.* (1941), where Hortling gave a 28-33 day period for Finland and Faber a 30-35 day period for Iceland. Actually, the period appears to be quite variable, dependent perhaps on the assiduousness of the adults in incubating, but more likely on microclimatic conditions on the ledge. Uspenski (1956), from four observations, found the incubation period of the common murre on Novaya Zemlya to be 32 days in three cases and 34 days in the other.

Although Bent (1919) described the incubation period of the thick-billed murre as 28 days and Hantzsch (in Witherby *et al.*, 1941) "about one month, but longer in bad weather", other authorities gave from 30 to 35 days. Uspenski (1956) stated that of 19 eggs kept under close observation in Novaya Zemlya, two hatched on the 30th day; seven on the 32nd day; four on the 33rd day; two on the 34th day; and four on the 35th day.

The case histories of 100 marked eggs at Cape Hay indicated that the incubation period in that locality, as determined from the time the egg was laid to the time the chick emerged completely, also varied (Fig. 20). Ten per cent of the chicks emerged completely 32 days after the eggs were laid; 30 per cent, 33 days after, and 60 per cent, 34 days after. The Cape Hay data were acquired from either the observation of actual hatching or the determination of it within an hour or so. Times of laying were noted early in the morning and late in the evening. Thus there could not have been more than 12 hours error in any observation.

At Cape Hay, some chicks emerged several hours after first pecking through membrane and shell; others required nearly two days. If the membranous lining of the egg dries

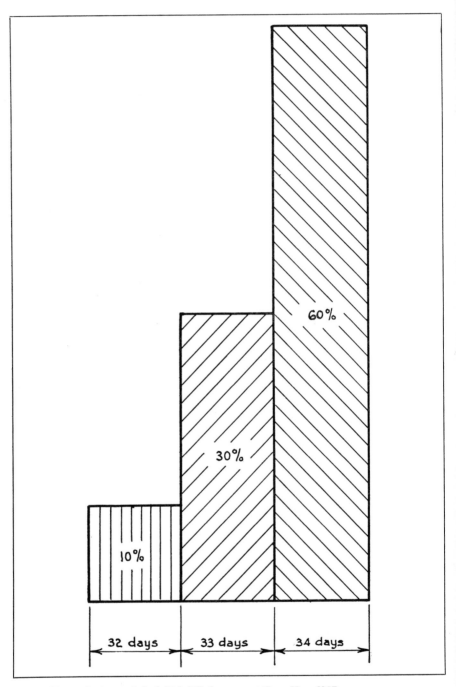

FIGURE 20. *Incubation period of thick-billed murres at Cape Hay, 1957*

out quickly, it appears to become tough and thus emergence takes longer. This appears to be proof that the length of the incubation period is influenced by microclimatic conditions at the nest site.

In a few instances the adult was noted pecking nearly all the outer covering of the shell away, thus facilitating the emergence of the chick. The assistance of the adults in bringing the chick out of the egg towards the end of incubation was also noted by Uspenski (1956), who stated that at Novaya Zemlya some of the eggs (in 1949 up to five per cent) were completely or partially deprived of their calcareous shells. Uspenski suggested that since the eggs were very porous, it was difficult for embryos to breathe in eggs plastered over with excrement and that they were able to continue development only if part or all of the calcareous shell was broken away. This condition did not, however, appear to be always involved at Cape Hay, where occasionally an apparently "clean" shell was pecked away by the adults.

More than fifty years ago, Kirkman (1912) wrote that murres "lay one egg unless robbed, when they will lay another, and if this is taken, even a third." Until recently, however, no actual effort had been made to determine statistically the ability of murres to replace lost eggs.

An experiment to determine this ability was carried out at Cape Hay, Lancaster Sound, in 1957. Some 500 pairs of thick-billed murres and their eggs were marked. Since a substantial number of eggs—nearly 20 per cent— were lost through human interference, data on only 400 pairs were analysed. Fig. 21 shows that the loss of eggs

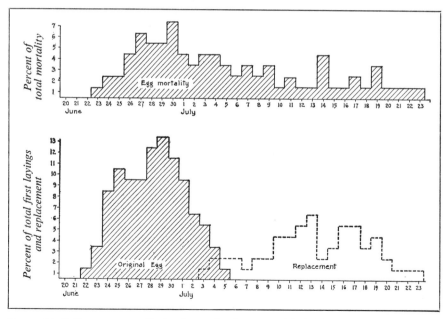

FIGURE 21. *Daily occurrence of laying, loss and replacement of thick-billed murre eggs, Cape Hay, 1957*

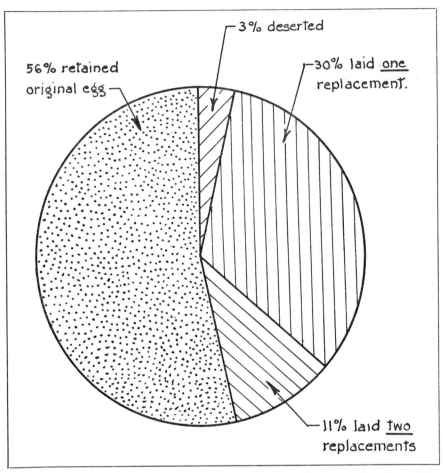

FIGURE 22. *Extent of retention of original eggs and replacement of those lost, Cape Hay, 1957*

was continuous during the entire laying period. Peak loss almost coincided with peak of first laying. Replacement eggs were laid almost throughout July. The peak replacement occurred 14 days after peak loss. It was found that 44 per cent of the sample lost at least one egg during a 32-day period. It was also found that 30 per cent laid one replacement, 11 per cent laid two replacements and three per cent deserted or did not re-lay (Fig. 22). Eighty per cent of the birds which had lost eggs replaced at least one egg.

In experiments carried out on thick-billed murres by Gorbunov (1925) and Krasovski (1937), counts of eggs taken indicated that up to 67.3 per cent would be replaced. In 1950, Uspenski (1956) collected fresh eggs daily from three areas in Novaya Zemlya. He found that as high as 77.3 per cent of the females laid a second egg (average 58.9 per cent) and that an average of 1.4 per cent of the females laid a third.

At Cape Hay in 1957, no egg which, when lost, had been incubated for five days or more, was replaced. Uspenski (1956) found that lost eggs incubated four days or more in 1949 and two days or more in 1950 were not replaced. Possibly those differences can be explained by the age distribution within the two populations.

There was also a difference between the Cape Hay and Novaya Zemlya birds in the length of time required to produce a replacement. Uspenski (1956) found that at Novaya Zemlya freshly removed eggs were replaced from 15 to 22 days later. The studies at Cape Hay showed that the period required for replacement in that locality varied from 10 to 16 days. One marked female lost her original egg and the next and laid a third (i.e. two replacements) within 26 days. The differences between the replacement periods of the Cape Hay and Novaya Zemlya birds may be due to physiological conditions related to age. The murre colonies at Novaya Zemlya have been heavily utilized for many years, while that at Cape Hay has been unmolested by humans for several centuries. Thus the Cape Hay murres may, on the average, be older birds. One would suspect that the population having the higher proportion of birds of optimum breeding age (i.e., from five years of age until senility) would have the shorter replacement period.

Loss of eggs is continual in a murre colony. Risk of loss is highest shortly after the eggs are laid, since the birds frequently lay their eggs in precarious positions. Stabilization of the egg increases with incubation and experiments at Cape Hay indicated that an egg which has survived for eight days has approximately a 70 per cent chance of hatching. Some idea of the loss of eggs may be determined from the data on 400 females at Cape Hay, mentioned above, which laid a total of 632 eggs, of which only 243 hatched. Only 60 per cent of the birds succeeded in hatching an egg.

In a common murre colony, 203 of 659 eggs were irretrievably buried in filth and water on Funk Island in 1956.

Young murres laying for the first time probably seldom, if ever, succeed in hatching their eggs. As a rule, they lay on the fringes of the colonies, in the most vulnerable locations, and are quick to desert. In addition, they lay late in the season, too late in the high-arctic regions to raise their young if they do hatch.

At Funk Island in 1953, common murres began to lay in an area on the fringes of the main colony. All the eggs were deserted. Each year thereafter more and more birds laid eggs in that section. In 1956, although most eggs were deserted when they were half incubated, the first young were produced by that group. In 1958, some 600 eggs were laid in the section and 103 young were hatched.

Loss of eggs in a murre colony is not restricted to falling off ledges. Some eggs roll into crevices and others roll too far away to be retrieved. On flat stacks, pools of water and filth act as traps for rolling eggs. However within small limits, a murre will retrieve its dislodged egg. It will also incubate an egg, not its own, which rolls into its nest site. It was previously noted that some murres place small pebbles around their eggs and thus prevent them from rolling. Those peculiar habits, considered together, are of no little importance, since any safeguard to protect the egg from destruction results in higher productivity.

Many murre eggs, especially in the High Arctic, are lost because of rock falls. The geological structure of most sea-bird colonies in those regions permits multiple fracturing and disintegration of the rock. Most of this action originates during intervals of dynamic temperature in the winter and spring. But small rocks fall and avalanches occur all summer and rock slides during the spring thaw sometimes kill adult murres and sweep away their eggs.

Of 632 eggs marked to study egg replacement at Cape Hay in 1957, 389 were lost. Of the 389 lost, 19 per cent were smashed by rock falls, eight per cent rolled into crevices, one per cent was taken by glaucous gulls and the remainder either fell off the ledges or were suspected, because of their precarious position, to have done so.

Most of the falling occurred during stormy nights. That may happen because adults are more than usually restless on such nights, but more likely because at such times the cliffs are overcrowded by non-breeding birds which otherwise would have remained at sea. I have actually watched eggs in exposed situations blown off cliffs. Such incidents are probably rare, since the egg is normally covered by one of the adults. Nevertheless in jostling and in nest relief there are brief moments when the egg is exposed and vulnerable.

Thus the total loss of eggs in a murre colony is substantial. Taking the low productivity of young birds into consideration, it is unlikely that more than 50 per cent of the eggs of birds nesting on narrow ledges hatch. A higher proportion of eggs laid on broad ledges and flat stacks can be expected to hatch.

CHAPTER XIII
The Chick

The chicks of both species spend from 18 to 25 days on the ledges before they go to sea. For some time after it has left the ledges, the young murre is unable to fly in the true sense of that word. Three weeks or more must elapse before it can make a sustained flight.

The chicks cannot properly be called nestlings, since there is no actual nest. They are ptilopaedic or hatched with a covering of down. They require frequent brooding, in contact with the brood patch for the first few days, and thereafter under a wing, until a day or two before they go to sea.

The egg loses approximately 20 per cent of its weight during the development of the embryo. About the 30th day, the yolk is almost entirely withdrawn into the abdominal cavity of the embryo. The nearly hatched chick now assumes a characteristic position in the egg; the body lies along the long axis of the egg, the feet are tucked under the body, and the egg-tooth is in contact with the shell.

From the time the chick first penetrates the membrane and the shell, two or more days may occasionally be required for it to squirm out of the egg. Occasionally, the adult assists by pecking away all or part of the hard, calcareous shell. For the first two days, the chick is rather helpless and moves feebly. By the end of the third day, the yolk sack has been completely absorbed and the chick becomes increasingly active. At that stage it feeds for the first time.

The colour of the newly hatched thick-billed murre chick is variable. The back, sides and rump may vary from light brown to pure black, but are usually cinnamon brown. Down of a lighter shade is scattered on the head and neck. The breast and abdomen are white. The down is short on the abdomen, somewhat longer on the back and sides, and reaches its greatest length (10-11 mm.) on the back of the neck. The density of the down is more or less equal over the whole body. Common murre chicks are so similar to thick-billed murre chicks that it is difficult to distinguish them until they commence to feather out. Then the common murre chicks, as a rule, show more extensive white on the sides of the head.

During the first few days of the chick's life it is brooded frequently by direct contact with the brood patch of the adult. At the age of five or six days it moves under the adult's wing, and is able to bear more and more exposure. At about that time, the brood patch of the adult begins to feather in rapidly. Chicks of that age and older often take shelter under the wing of any adult nearby. Occasionally, two, three or even four chicks crowd under the drooping wings of a single adult. This is one of the advantages of colonial nesting.

The greatest mortality of chicks results from exposure during the first six days of life. The investigations of Rolnik (1948) and Kaftanovski (1951) indicate that thermo-regulation does not begin to be stabilized until about the sixth day. Progressively, thereafter, the chick can bear more exposure. Actually, thermo-regulation is not complete until a short time before the chick is ready to go to sea.

During the first two days of its life on the ledge, the chick loses weight as the yolk sack is absorbed. Increase in weight is then fairly rapid until about the 14th day, when it decreases again because of extensive feather development. About the 17th or 18th day the chick again shows a gain in weight, but it commences to lose again a few days before entering the sea. A combination of causes probably contributes to the loss of weight before taking to the sea. Some authorities state that the adults cease feeding the chicks and thus stimulate them to leave the ledges. On numerous occasions I have watched chicks being fed on their last day on the ledges. The chicks are most active, however, when they are ready to go to sea, and probably require more food than the adults will bring. At Akpatok Island in 1954, feeding experiments with young birds hand-reared from hatching until ready to go to sea, indicated that chicks lost weight rapidly at that stage unless fed especially well (Tuck and Squires, 1955). Additional energy at that time goes into the stabilization of thermo-regulation.

Observations on chicks and adults marked with coloured dyes have revealed a number of facts about parental care. At each feeding, a chick eats one fish, the size and weight of which varies. Because of their restlessness, especially when hungry, chicks more than six or seven days of age make frequent journeys from one adult to another and often receive food from adults other than their parents. Adults which have lost their chicks, even those whose eggs are not yet hatched, sometimes feed wandering chicks. Those observations indicate that the assertions by Gorbunov (1925) and others, that parent birds feed only their own chicks and are even able to recognize their voices, must be rejected.

Plumage develops quickly on the growing chick. The tips of the upper wing-coverts appear first on the second or third day. On the third or fourth day, the tips of contour feathers appear all over the body. At two weeks of age, the chick is almost covered with developing feathers—patches of down remain only on the head, abdomen and thighs. According to Uspenski (1956), by the 18th or 20th day, at which time some of the chicks are sufficiently thermo-regulated to go to sea, the body feathers may be from 15 to 17 mm. in length, and the upper wing-coverts, 30 mm.

Chicks leave the colony for the sea at varying ages, probably depending on the location and climate of the colony. The average age of chicks going to sea at Novaya Zemlya is 20 days, at West Greenland, 21 days, and on the Murman coast, 23 days. At Cape Hay in 1957, the chicks went to sea when from 18 to 25 days of age with the majority (40 per cent) at 19 days of age. Their weights ranged from 175 to 215 grams. At Akpatok Island, in 1954, thick-billed murre chicks went to sea when between 23 and 24 days of age and weighing between 250 and 275 grams. They went to sea at Digges

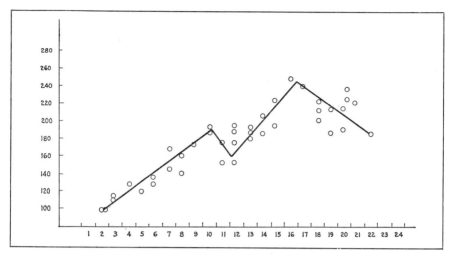

FIGURE 23. *Growth curve of common murre chicks in the Gulf of St. Lawrence in 1931 (from data in Johnson, 1944)*

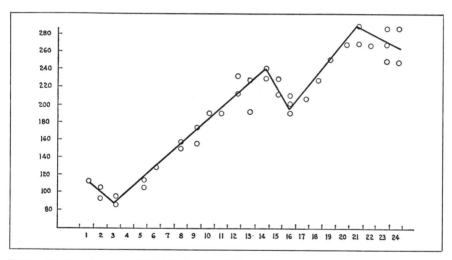

FIGURE 24. *Growth curve of thick-billed murre chicks in Ungava Bay, 1954*

Sound in 1955 when between 19 and 25 days of age and weighing between 200 and 225 grams. Kaftanovski (1951) reported that thick-billed murre chicks went to sea at Seven Islands when between 20 and 24 days of age and weighing on the average 250 grams. Fig. 23 shows the growth curve of common murre chicks in the Gulf of St. Lawrence in 1931. Fig. 24 shows the responding curve for thick-billed murre chicks in Ungava Bay in 1954.

Weights of 21-day-old chicks in different localities may vary greatly. Some of the chicks at Cape Hay in 1957, were only half as large as those at Akpatok in 1954, when they went to sea. They were similar in plumage density and feather length.

This difference in the growth of murre chicks in different localities may be explained by climate, especially air temperatures. In the lower temperatures of Cape Hay, chicks must devote a greater part of their energy to thermo-regulation than at Akpatok Island in Ungava Bay. The difference in the mean air temperatures during August at those two localities was some 25° F. Colder and shorter summers may cause an earlier descent into the sea, requiring additional expenditure of energy in accelerated feather growth.

The chick is susceptible to disease, rock falls, exposure, falls from the ledges, and predation. Mortality is highest in the first several days of the chick's life on the ledge. At Cape Hay in 1957, 44 per cent of the mortality of chicks occurred during the first days of life. Until it is three or four days of age, the chick, if knocked over on its back, is just as likely to roll outwards over the cliff edge as inwards towards safety. From six days of age onwards, not only is the chick able to bear more exposure, but it has developed the tendency to hide when danger threatens and the ability to cling to precarious positions without falling. Mortality becomes progressively less as the chicks grow. From seven days of age to the time of going to sea it totalled only seven per cent.

The mortality of thick-billed murre chicks at Cape Hay was due to the following causes:

Exposure	38%
Falling into cracks	12%
Falling off ledges	41%
Unknown	9%

Chick mortality varies with the hazards of the nest site and the weather. Low air temperatures lead both directly and indirectly to the death of chicks. Chicks left alone begin to suffer from exposure and move towards adults in search of warmth. They frequently fall off the ledges at such times. Severe rain storms washed chicks off the cliffs in Digges Sound in 1955. Rock slides killed chicks at Digges Sound, Akpatok Island and Cape Hay. Some chicks of common murres apparently suffocate during heavy rain storms on Funk Island.

Uspenski (1956) determined that the loss of chicks at Novaya Zemlya was from 20 to 40 per cent, depending on the nature of the cliffs. The daily appearance of men, or their prolonged stay on the ledges, doubled mortality. The Novaya Zemlya murres appeared to suffer more from exposure and starvation than did those at Cape Hay. In addition, in 1948, some 18 per cent of the chick mortalities at one locality in Novaya Zemlya were caused by a purulent inflammation of the subcutaneous cells of the head.

Chick mortality at Cape Hay in 1957 was only 11.5 per cent. It was small compared with the egg mortality. Comparatively high egg mortalities and low chick mortalities were also recorded for Akpatok Island in 1954 and for Digges Sound in 1955.

A reverse situation was noted at the densely populated common murre colony at Funk Island, Newfoundland, during the summer of 1956. Several heavy rain storms in early July killed approximately eight per cent of the murre chicks on each occasion.

Strong easterly winds and rain in the middle of July, 1958, caused similar mortality. The heavy mortality on those occasions was suffered by chicks well grown and nearly ready to go to sea. Very young birds being brooded at the time escaped almost entirely. The reason seemed to be that the large chicks were smothered or trampled on during the storms. During storms in July the nesting sites are extremely crowded. They are occupied by the breeding adults, the small chicks, the chicks more or less fully grown, and non-breeding birds which come in from the sea seeking shelter.

Chicks sometimes take to the sea before they are sufficiently homoiothermic. In the excitement of sea-going, the cliffs are sometimes nearly deserted by the adults, and many chicks too young to survive life in the sea jump off the cliffs to the milling adults below or follow the adults and large chicks into the sea. Some of those helpless young birds are soon picked off by gulls. Some drown and others succeed in reaching land again, where, huddled on rocks and low ledges, they perish during the night. A chick fully thermo-regulated and with feathers resistant to the water, rides high. A chick not so well developed gets water-soaked and sinks lower and lower in the water. Deaths from this cause may on some days be as high as 10 per cent of the young birds going to sea. They probably become progressively less numerous, since the excitement of sea-going is highest during its first three or four days.

If the land-coming of murres is exciting, the sea-going is even more so. For a few days before the chicks are ready to go to sea, adults congregate at the base of the cliffs and call excitedly. There are no joy-flights and water-dances such as characterized the land-coming, but the formation of a milling congestion of birds in which numbers and noise are outstanding is a feature of murres' behaviour at this time. At first such groups concentrate a little way off shore. As time goes by, the groups become larger and the birds spend more time close inshore, at the very base of the cliffs. At a densely occupied colony, thousands of adults in a compact mass gather at the base of the cliffs, calling excitedly, when the sea-going period arrives. Such early groups are probably non-breeders or birds which have lost their eggs or young, but at the critical time of sea-going they are joined by increasing numbers of breeding birds.

At Funk Island on some calm evening during the middle of July—the date of first sea-going varied by only four days during three years of observation there—adults and grown chicks walk to the sea over the low smooth rock. They have particular routes, which are used annually, each leading towards a low part of the island where the sea washes ashore. Each of the three separate nesting groups has two or more such traditional paths to the sea. Several of the routes are nearly direct, but others, because of faults in the rock or other obstacles, are long and winding.

For several days before the first sea-going, adults congregate close inshore at evening and call excitedly. An even more noticeable change takes place within the nesting colonies. A large number of adults spread out loosely from the colonies, so that they now occupy a much greater area. The nesting colonies appear to be expanding and spilling over into the sea. Adults gather at the edge of the water. If flying birds alight on the island, they do so more frequently on the borders of the colonies than in their midst.

At that stage many of the chicks, especially the large ones, wander out towards the fringes of the colonies. Some of the adults and chicks then begin a slow procession towards the sea. The gross appearance of the colony changes again as the loitering birds on the fringes either join the procession or rush towards the sea to call anxiously. The birds at the head of the procession may hesitate for a short time on reaching the sea, but more frequently they plunge directly into the water or permit a wave to wash them off. They join the excited throng a few feet off shore.

There appears to be no competition between the adults of Funk Island for possession of chicks at sea. Just before darkness sets in, the processions towards the sea have ceased. More and more single adults leave the inshore concentration and return to the island. The remaining adults and chicks now move farther out to sea. Here and there can be seen a single adult and chick, separated from the others. They work farther and farther out to sea. By early morning they are scattered, each chick with a single adult, several miles from the island. Very rarely do two adults accompany a chick to sea at Funk Island, and if so, there is no evidence that both adults remain with the chick.

Each evening thereafter, unless it is stormy, adults and chicks wend their way towards the sea and the same sequence of events occurs. At Funk Island, the greatest number of birds leaves the island on the third or fourth day of sea-going. After that, for several weeks, smaller numbers leave each evening. Eventually the island is deserted.

Numerous chicks not fully developed and too young to survive away from land, join in the sea-going. They come from the fringes of the nesting colony, which is mostly deserted by adults at that time. Some of those young birds follow the others into the water. Most of them quickly become water-soaked and drown. Those which reach shore again invariably die from exposure on their way back to the colony.

Some of the very young birds at the edge of the sea are surrounded by adults, seemingly to prevent their entering the water, and just before dark they follow the adults back to the nesting colonies. On their way back to the colony many of those very young ones cannot overcome the obstacles they surmounted on their way downward. They perish during the night. In spite of such losses, adult protection at the sea edge may very well save a large number of the chicks which tend to go to sea prematurely. Nørrevang (1958) noted similar behaviour by the cliff-nesting common murres in the Faeroes. He wrote: "Also other young on the ledge showed unease, but the parent birds seemed to prevent them from coming to the edge by standing on the edge with the back turned to the sea, a most unusual position, the birds normally standing breast to the sea".

The sea-going of common murre chicks from cliffs is different from that described for Funk Island, where they literally walk off into the water. At the time of the sea-going of both species, the chicks' primaries are not yet developed, but they must make their plunge into the sea, sometimes from great heights. Kay (1947) describes the sea-going of common murre chicks from the cliffs in Shetland:

"On July 31, 1946, at the famous bird-cliffs at Noss, in the Shetland Islands ... birds started coming off the cliffs at 8 p.m., the peak was at 10 p.m. and the flight lasted for another hour ... The large majority of these young birds flew down each accompanied by one parent, the youngster flying from three to six feet in advance of, or to the side of the adult. Both alighted on the water ... then immediately rushed towards each other, the parent calling loudly and excitedly, evidently fully aware of the danger in separation. Both birds now swam leisurely towards the open sea, the young bird very close to its parent's side. A few of the young ones were accompanied on their flight by two adults, presumably both parents . . . A number came down alone . . . "

Nørrevang (1958) describes a similar flight of common murre chicks at the Faeroe Islands. Several times he watched the actual flight from the ledges and remarked that one of the parents followed the chick as it leapt from the ledge. Nørrevang also noted that the young were never seen to leave the ledge alone.

The sea-going of thick-billed murre chicks differs from that of common murre chicks mainly in frequent competition between the adults for possession of a chick.

I have seen thick-billed murre chicks leaving the breeding cliffs at three large colonies. The most impressive was at Akpatok Island, where the ledges were some 500 feet above our camp and the chicks had to make a half-mile "flight" to reach the sea.

The first sea-going on Akpatok Island in 1955 occurred at dusk on the evening of August 26. At the start of sea-going, as many as seven adults accompanied a single chick on its outward flight, the chick calling shrilly, first plunging downward, then levelling out somewhat, beating its wings furiously. Invariably, one adult would be close to the chick, the others spread out in V-formation close behind. Frequently the adults used a beautiful, slow, butterfly-like flight, during which their wings arched over their backs, nearly touching. The group splashed into the water close together. Immediately other adults already in the water, or those flying around, closed in and all surrounded the chick. The chick was jostled, apparently pecked at and "hounded" continuously. It frequently dived, and then most or all of the adults dived simultaneously. Occasionally, all the adults took flight, leaving the chick alone for a time. Soon the same adults or others returned. Eventually all but a few lost interest or moved off to join the party surrounding another newly-arrived chick. Finally, a single adult remained with the chick and both went out to sea.

As the sea-going continued, the last chicks leaving the ledges were accompanied by single adults or even made the flight alone. Most of the adults were now concentrated in the water.

During the next few days chicks were taken as far as 20 miles to sea for experimental purposes and released. Always they were joined by a group of adults and the same sequence of mobbing and eventual leading away by a single adult took place. Sometimes we released a chick when there was no adult nearby. It was amazing how quickly adults flying some distance away were attracted by the shrill cries of the chick in the water and gathered around it.

Fisher and Lockley (1954) described this mobbing of chicks in the water: "The arrival of the chick upon the water excites the whole group of adults in the immediate vicinity . . . They surround it when it comes to the surface, and they may even make mock attacks, forcing it to submerge for a moment . . . The incident ends in the youngster swimming close to the adult which most persistently answers its calls, and it is led away to sea."

The sea-going occurs most often in the twilight hours of evening, but late in the season the last chicks may leave the cliffs at any time of the day. At Cape Hay in 1957, the sea-going was at its peak during the twilight hours of midnight. Salomonsen (1951) said that the young leave the Greenland colonies also during the night and Cullen (1954) reported a peak of chicks flying during the dusky hours around midnight at Jan Mayen.

There is a great danger to the chicks from predatory gulls during their flight to the sea. Gulls are abundant then, since their own young are on the wing. In addition, migrating hawks and owls are attracted to the colonies at that time. At Akpatok Island in 1954, the number of predators during the sea-going period was nearly double what it had been earlier in the summer (Fig. 25). Chicks which go to sea prematurely and would

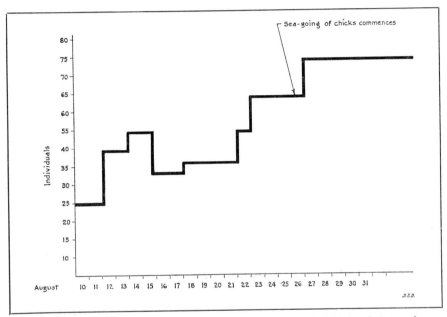

FIGURE 25. *Changes in murre predator numbers at Akpatok Island, 1954, in relation to the sea-going of murre chicks*

soon perish in any case are preyed upon more frequently than active homoiothermic chicks. Clarke (1898) describes such an instance at Spitsbergen: "The looms began to come down from the cliffs at Cape Flora on the 13th of August, and the descent lasted until August 24th. Several old birds came down with one young one; indeed, I have seen as many as five accompany it. It is a bold flight to take, for the cliffs where they are cradled are from 600 to 800 feet above sea-level, and the young birds are not able to sustain their own weight during so long an essay, but gradually come lower and lower until they strike with a heavy thud on the floe or land. Some quickly recover themselves and hurry away as fast as they can to the open water, while others are harried by Burgomasters (*Larus glaucus*); and those that are killed afford food for the bears."

Most murre colonies are so situated that the young can glide directly into the sea.

At Akpatok Island, however, between one of the colonies and the sea there was a grassy meadow half a mile in width. Even though the nest ledges were some 500 feet above sea level, very few of the chicks failed to glide directly into the sea.

The habit of going to sea during the twilight hours of evening has definite survival value in that the semi-darkness affords protection from the marauding gulls. Very rarely does a gull attempt to capture a chick surrounded by excited adult murres. There is greater danger to the chick when it is finally led away from the vicinity of the cliffs by the single adult, but as a rule that is done during the darkest part of the night.

Most observers have commented that the parent accompanies the chick to sea. That is probably rare. In fact, many of the colour-banded adults return to the colony after

---

Table 18: *Annual increment of thick-billed murres at Cape Hay, 1957*

A *June 11 to July 23*
   Sample of 400 pairs produced 632 eggs, of which 324 were lost.
   Therefore, eggs produced per pair: 1.58
   And, loss of eggs during period A: 51.3%

B *July 24 to August 20*
   Sample of 1,200 eggs produced 812 chicks.
   Therefore, loss of eggs during period B: 32.3%
   812 chicks produced 719 chicks going to sea

C Therefore, loss of chicks: 11.5%

The increment at the time of sea-going can thus be calculated as follows:
   : 1.58 less 51.3% (A) or .71
   : .71 less 32.3% (B) or .47
   : .47 less 11.5% (C) or .41
   : *41 chicks going to sea per 100 pairs*

---

their chick has gone. Perry (1944) noted: " . . . Once down from the cliffs, the chick stays well out to sea, though one or both parents continue to return to the nesting ledge for as long as a fortnight after the departure of the chick".

Colour-marking at the common murre colony on Funk Island and at the thick-billed murre colony at Cape Hay also indicated that the chick was accompanied to sea rarely, if at all, by one of its parents. In both localities unmarked adults were seen with colour-marked chicks and colour-banded adults returned alone to the nesting sites as long as two weeks afterwards. At Digges Sound the chick often alighted on the water in the centre of as many as 10,000 milling adults. At Cape Hay in 1957 nearly 60 per cent of the adults were without eggs or chicks when the sea-going period arrived. Such unattached birds were in the great majority at the base of the cliffs at that time. It seems therefore that if the chick is accompanied to sea by one of its parents, it is purely by

163

chance. Collection of adults accompanying chicks at sea indicated that either sex may care for the young at that stage. Care of the flightless chick at sea, like communal brooding and feeding, is an example of the contribution of socialized behaviour to the survival of the young.

Table 18 indicates that the annual increment at Cape Hay in 1957 was 41 chicks going to sea per 100 pairs of adults. At Cape Hay in 1957, marked adults, marked eggs and marked chicks were observed in selected sample areas in an attempt to assess productivity of the colony. Percentages of eggs hatched and chicks fledged at each site are given in Table 19.

Table 19: *Hatching and phenology of thick-billed murres at Cape Hay, from July 24, 1957*

Site No.	Type	Date of hatching of 1st egg	Date of sea-going of 1st chick	% eggs hatched	% chicks fledged
A	Sub-marginal	July 30	August 18	62	77
B	Marginal	July 30	August 19	70	79
C	Marginal	July 30	August 19	60	91
D	Optimum	July 27	August 17	75	87
E	Optimum	July 28	August 18	75	93
F	Optimum	July 28	August 16	72	88
G	Optimum	July 28	August 16	60	88
H	Optimum	July 28	August 17	51	82
I	Optimum	July 27	August 18	75	96
J	Optimum	July 24	August 15	63	86
K	Improved	July 31	August 19	74	96
L	Experimental	August 1	August 19	75	99
			Average	67.66	88.50

PART IV: FACTORS AFFECTING POPULATIONS

CHAPTER XIV

Food and Feeding Habits

Murres obtain their food from the sea by diving and "flying" under water. Their short tails, short wings and feet specially placed, proportioned and developed, permit rapid sub-aqueous flight.

Some idea of the freedom of murres under water is given by Trevor-Battye (1897), who described the diving ability of thick-billed murres at Spitsbergen: "They dive very deeply and far, often going almost perpendicularly down by the side of a floe, which would be some ten feet or so in thickness and perhaps six or seven yards across, and reappearing on exactly the opposite side." There is some disagreement on the depths to which murres may pursue their food. They have been caught occasionally off Newfoundland on longline trawls set at 40 fathoms (Tuck and Squires, 1955). Although the fishes which are their principal food penetrate to greater depths than that, especially in the winter, murres obtain most of their food in comparatively shallow water and especially on the edges of deep troughs where vertical water-circulation brings the fishes to the upper water-layers.

Murres digest their food very rapidly. Rarely can undigested fishes be found in their stomachs. However, most stomachs contain identifiable fish otoliths, various bone fragments and the chitinous remnants of crustaceans. Direct observations of feeding and the determination of food items dropped at the nesting sites add to the knowledge of their food.

The polar cod (*Boreogadus saida*), which rarely grows longer than seven inches, is the most important fish in the diet of murres in the colder waters. Trevor-Battye (1897) wrote that, except for one taken from a char's throat, the only specimens of this fish taken by him in Spitsbergen were dropped by murres which he deliberately shot for that purpose. Uspenski (1956) found that polar cod occurred in 57.46 per cent of stomachs of adult thick-billed murres examined at Novaya Zemlya in 1947 and in 70.8 per cent of stomachs of chicks (Table 20). Polar cod formed 34.5 per cent of food items brought to the thick-billed murre chicks at Akpatok Island in 1954 (Table 23), approximately 50 per cent of food items of thick-billed murre chicks at Digges Sound in 1955, and 90 per cent of food items of thick-billed murre chicks at Cape Hay in 1957. Since polar cod are fairly abundant along the Labrador coast and in the deep troughs of the large inlets along the east coast of Newfoundland, they probably form a substantial part of the winter diet of murres in that region also.

The first- and second-year classes of Atlantic cod (*Gadus callarias* and *Gadus morrhua*), or codlings up to seven inches in length, sometimes form a substantial part of the diet of murres in regions where other fish of similar size are not abundant. According to Uspenski (1956), Atlantic cod occurred in 20.2 per cent of stomachs of adult thick-billed murres examined at Novaya Zemlya from 1942 to 1950 and in 27.03 per cent of stomachs of chicks (Table 21). In 1948, Atlantic cod formed 51.6 per cent of the food of the adults and 70.6 per cent of the food of the chicks at Novaya Zemlya. The variation in importance of Atlantic and polar cod as food items for thick-billed murres at Novaya Zemlya is a reflection of the varying abundance of those two species at particular localities. That in turn is a product of the changes in water temperature occasioned

Table 20: *Stomach analyses of thick-billed murres, Novaya Zemlya, 1947*

Occurrence of food items in stomachs

	Adults		Chicks	
	No.	%	No.	%
Fish				
Gadus morrhua	126	47.1	—	—
Boreogadus saida	154	57.46	17	70.8
Mallotus villosus	4	1.49	—	—
Clupea harengus	2	0.75	6	25.0
Ammodytes tobianus	3	1.12	1	4.2
Myoxocephalus	1	0.37	—	—
Gymnelis viridis	2	0.75	—	—
Crustaceans				
Sclerocrangon	—	—	1	4.2
Euthemisto sp.	—	—	1	4.2
Polychaets				
Nereis sp.	1	0.37	1	4.2

by influxes of Atlantic water into the polar regions. The recent abundance of Atlantic cod along the west coast of Greenland is an example, though now it is reportedly retreating from the more northerly localities. It is a rare species in Ungava Bay (Dunbar and Hildebrand, 1952). The only indication of its presence near Akpatok Island, Ungava Bay, in 1954, was the presence of otoliths in the stomachs of several adult thick-billed murres (Tuck and Squires, 1955).

Uspenski (1956) records haddock (*Gadus (Melanogrammus) aeglefinus*) taken by adult thick-billed murres and brought to their chicks at Novaya Zemlya in 1949 and 1950 only. Like Atlantic cod, haddock therefore is not a dependable source of food for Novaya Zemlya murres. Taning (1930) also records haddock as well as *Gadus merlangus*, a related inshore species, in the food of murres in Iceland.

Table 21: *Stomach analyses of thick-billed murres, Novaya Zemlya,*
1942 and 1947-1950

Occurrence of food items in stomachs

	Adults		Chicks	
	No.	*%*	*No.*	*%*
Fish				
Gadus morrhua	238	20.2	10	27.03
Gadus (Melanogrammus) aeglefinus	41	3.48	—	—
Boreogadus saida	554	47.02	19	51.35
Mallotus villosus	12	1.01	—	—
Clupea harengus	6	0.49	10	27.03
Ammodytes tobianus	33	2.79	3	8.11
Icelus bicornis	31	2.63	—	—
Myoxocephalus sp.	33	2.79	—	—
Gymnocanthus sp.	8	0.66	—	—
Lumpenus maculatus	29	2.47	—	—
Gymnelis viridis	4	0.33	—	—
Pleuronectidae	47	3.97	—	—
Pisces (unidentified)	81	6.88	—	—
Lycodes sp.	4	0.33	—	—
Crustaceans	35	2.95	2	5.41
Polychaets	48	4.05	1	2.7
Molluscs	6	0.49	—	—
Aquatic plants	6	0.49	—	—
Pebbles	430	36.5	6	16.22

The launce or sand eel (*Ammodytes* sp.) is an important food of murres in shallow-water regions. Adult launce rarely grow longer than seven inches and therefore all age classes are taken. *Ammodytes americanus* is the principal food in summer of both species of murres at the Gannet Island, Labrador. Its European counterpart, *Ammodytes tobianus*, comprised from 80.3 to 86.1 per cent of the food of both species on the Murman coast (Kaftanovski, 1938).

Capelin (*Mallotus villosus*) is a low-arctic fish which in recent years has been extending its range northwards, presumably in response to amelioration of the marine environment. Freuchen and Salomonsen (1958) relate that capelin have recently occurred in considerable numbers at Thule, northwest Greenland, where they were hitherto unknown. Capelin were formerly considered an off-shore species which came inshore

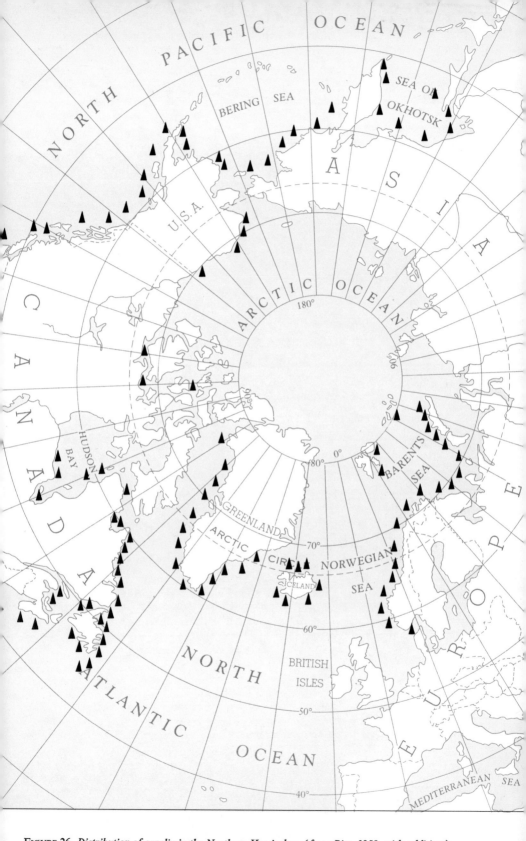

FIGURE 26. *Distribution of capelin in the Northern Hemisphere (from Pitt, 1958, with additions)*

during July and August to spawn and then retreated again to deep waters. Recent research (Pitt, 1958) shows that capelin also spawn on the fishing banks off Newfoundland as far as 200 miles off shore and are therefore more plentiful than was realized. They are found off shore in winter in great schools and consequently are very important to murres as a winter food. Although polar cod, small Atlantic cod and haddock have been found in the stomachs of murres wintering in Newfoundland, the great majority contained capelin almost exclusively (Table 22). Capelin also are the principal food of both adults and their chicks during the summer in Newfoundland.

Krasovski (1937) found that capelin comprised 18 per cent of the food of thick-billed murres at Novaya Zemlya in 1933. More recently, capelin have probably not been so abundant at Novaya Zemlya, since Uspenski (1956) found that they comprised less than one per cent of the total foods taken by murres in that locality from 1942 to 1950. They were not recorded at all during 1948. Similar fluctuations in the numbers of capelin taken by murres at other localities have been recorded. Dunbar and Hildebrand (1952) recovered only three specimens in Ungava Bay during their marine investigations in that locality from 1947 to 1949. Capelin comprised 1.4 per cent of the food brought to thick-billed murre chicks at Akpatok Island in 1954. In the following year, they com-

Table 22: *Stomach contents of wintering murres off Newfoundland*

	Thick-billed murres	Common murres
Number of stomachs examined	(614)	(44)
Percentage occurrence of items in other than empty stomachs		
Mallotus villosus	93.1%	91.7%
Gadus callarias	4.1%	3.9%
Melanogrammus aeglefinus	1.8%	3.1%
Other	1.0%	1.3%

prised nearly 50 per cent of the food brought to the chicks at Digges Island in Hudson Bay. Since capelin have such a wide distribution (Fig. 26), they undoubtedly form a large part of the diet of murres during migration and in winter, but they are not a dependable supply of food for chicks in the more northerly regions.

Small herrings are heavily utilized by murres in certain regions. Salomonsen (1935) states that *Clupea sprattus* is the principal food of common murres and their chicks in the Faeroes. Kaftanovsky (1938) found that *Clupea harengus* comprised up to 16.2 per cent of the food of thick-billed murres on the Murman coast.

The fishes mentioned above are the most important ones for murres. Murres will, however, take almost any fish up to seven inches in length, as Tables 21 and 23 show, and in the case of the eel-like blennies, fish of notably greater lengths are eaten. The food of breeding murres includes a substantial amount of bottom fishes. This can be explained by the adults foraging near shore at times during the breeding season. For example, at Akpatok Island in 1954, blennies formed 19.8 per cent of the food brought to the chicks, the mailed sculpin (*Triglops pingeli*), 26.69 per cent, and the small Greenland halibut (*Reinhardtius hippoglossoides*), not elsewhere recorded in their diet, 6.67 per cent.

Table 24 shows that there was a good deal of fluctuation in the food species brought to the murre chicks at Akpatok Island in 1954. It will be seen that polar cod had a high incidence of occurrence during the first few days, that decreased towards the end of the period, while the mailed sculpin showed a low incidence at the beginning of the period that increased towards the end. The percentage occurrence of blennies remained fairly constant and this was also true of other species. The arctic squid percentages fluctuated more than other species, but this may have been in consequence of their variable habits

Table 23: *Percentages of fishes and invertebrates in sample of thick-billed murre food to young, August 9-28, 1954, Akpatok Island*

Species	English name	Number of individuals	Percentage of total
FISHES			
Mallotus villosus	Capelin	38	1.40
Myctophidae	Lantern fish	2	0.07
Boregadus sp.	Arctic cod	931	34.50
Eumesogrammus praecisus			
Lumpenus lumpretaeformis			
Lumpenus maculatus			
Lumpenus fabricii	Blennies	536	19.84
Lumpenus medius			
Gymnelis viridis			
Gymnelis stigma			
Ammodytes americanus	Launce	36	1.33
Sebastes marinus	Redfish	1	0.04
Icelus bicornis	Two-pronged sculpin	4	0.15
Triglops pingeli	Mailed sculpin	721	26.69
Myoxocephalus scorpioides	Arctic sculpin	2	0.07
Gymnocanthus tricuspis	Stag-horn sculpin	1	0.04
Eumicrotremus spinosus	Spiny lumpfish	24	0.89
Liparis tunicatus	"Sea-snails"	45	1.66
Liparis koefoedi			
Reinhardtius hippoglossoides	Greenland halibut	180	6.67
Unidentified fish remains	——	9	0.33
Total fish:		2,530	93.70

of schooling. Generally, it was observed that a high incidence of mailed sculpins was accompanied by a low incidence of blennies, so it would appear that the blennies were selected against. Since blennies are probably easy to obtain and comparatively bulky, they may provide bulk when mailed sculpins are not available. On the other hand, most of the mailed sculpins were gravid and may have been selected because they were sluggish and easily caught, rather than because they were preferred.

No little variety of invertebrates has been recorded as food of murres. Twelve species of invertebrates were brought to the thick-billed murre chicks (Table 23) at Akpatok Island in 1954, yet in total they accounted for less than one per cent of the volume of food brought. Crustaceans were found in the stomachs of only two chicks at Novaya Zemlya in 1942 and from 1947 to 1950. Since certain forms of plankton are locally abundant during the summer months, they form an important part of the food of the

Table 23—continued

Species	English name	Number of individuals	Percentage of total
INVERTEBRATES			
Annelida			
Eunoë nodosa	——	1	0.04
Nereis sp.	Sand-worm	2	0.07
Amphipoda			
Gammarus sp.	——	1	0.04
Gammarus wilkitskii	——	1	0.04
Anonyx nugax	——	2	0.07
Decapoda			
Pandalus montagui	Shrimp	7	0.26
Lebbeus polaris			
Lebbeus groenlandicus	——	32	1.19
Spirontocaris spinus			
Argis dentata	——	55	2.04
Mollusca			
Gonatus fabricii	Arctic squid	70	2.59
Onchidiopsis glacialis	——	1	0.04
Total invertebrates:		172	6.30

Table 24: *Daily occurrences (in percentages) of principal fishes and invertebrates in thick-billed murre food to young August 9-28, 1954, Akpatok Island*

	Mal-lotus	Boreo-gadus	Blen-nies	Ammo-dytes	Triglops	Rein-hardtius	Argis	Gona-tus	Others
Aug. 9	...	53.8	20.5	...	10.3	5.1	2.6	7.7	....
Aug. 10	...	46.3	25.4	...	23.9	....	...	1.5	2.9
Aug. 11	1.6	40.4	24.2	1.6	17.8	6.5	...	3.2	4.7
Aug. 12	0.8	46.5	18.1	...	18.1	3.9	2.4	4.7	5.5
Aug. 13	...	42.2	13.2	...	23.7	13.2	5.3	...	2.4
Aug. 14	4.8	30.2	25.6	1.2	24.4	6.6	1.2	1.8	4.2
Aug. 15	...	29.5	20.5	1.0	30.5	7.2	1.9	3.3	6.1
Aug. 16	0.4	42.3	17.8	1.6	26.4	4.7	0.8	2.3	3.7
Aug. 17	1.2	36.1	12.7	0.3	26.8	4.6	2.5	1.5	14.3
Aug. 18	3.0	26.1	15.3	0.5	32.5	7.9	3.9	2.0	8.8
Aug. 19	2.3	30.9	22.1	0.9	29.5	3.7	3.7	2.3	4.6
Aug. 20	0.6	32.1	22.4	3.2	22.4	10.9	1.9	0.6	5.9
Aug. 21	2.9	30.3	13.6	...	32.0	7.8	2.0	2.0	9.4
Aug. 22	...	34.2	15.3	0.6	24.2	8.9	1.9	8.9	6.0
Aug. 23	3.0	30.8	18.8	3.0	24.1	9.8	1.5	2.3	6.7
Aug. 24				Birds not fishing—very stormy					
Aug. 25	1.4	32.7	20.6	3.7	23.4	8.0	2.3	3.7	4.2
Aug. 26	...	33.3	16.3	2.3	30.2	8.5	1.6	...	7.8
Aug. 27	3.1	28.1	3.1	3.1	53.2	6.3	...	...	3.1
Aug. 28	...	30.8	16.9	3.1	37.0	7.7	...	...	4.5

adults at that season. Uspenski (1956) states that the red colour of murre excrement in the spring at Novaya Zemlya indicated a predominance of small crustaceans in their diet at that time. Hartley and Fisher (1936) found no fish in the stomachs of four adult thick-billed murres collected at the foot of a glacier in west Spitsbergen. All four contained *Thysonoessa inermis* in numbers and two also contained a prawn, *Spirontocaris gaimardii*. In late July, adult murres at the Gannet Island, Labrador, have been observed consuming large quantities of the pteropod, *Clione limacinalis*. At that time the ledges and the loitering areas on the cliffs are stained purple with their excrement. Several species of crustaceans became locally abundant during early August in Digges Sound in 1955 and in Lancaster Sound in 1957. Immediately the adult murre excrement showed a distinctive purplish tinge.

It is important to consider what differences, if any, exist between the foods of thick-billed and common murres. If there were a distinct food spectrum for each species, it would suggest that their populations, especially in the regions of overlap, are controlled by the availability of particular foods rather than by competition for nesting sites or by differential nesting chronology. The present evidence indicates that there is no distinct food spectrum for each species. Their foods appear to be whatever small fishes occur. Polar cod, capelin, launce, small Atlantic cod, and herring predominate. All those fish "school" and may be abundant locally. Macroplankton is important to adults only in the summer months. The food of chicks is almost exclusively fish. Experiments at

Akpatok Island in 1954 (Tuck and Squires, 1955) indicated that murre chicks fed on crustaceans alone gradually lost weight and eventually perished. Their excrement was composed of undigested chitin and became progressively solider.

Kaftanovski (Table 25) suggested that there might be some difference between the diets of the two species at Seven Islands; that common murres showed a preference for launce and thick-billed murres for herring and capelin. That conclusion does not agree with our present knowledge of murre foods in other regions. Thus, herring is the most important food for common murres in the Faeroes, launce the most important for both species in Newfoundland. But polar cod is most abundant in the high-arctic region and capelin and herring are most abundant in the low-arctic, and the diet of birds from individual colonies, regardless of their specific identity, shows a high incidence of the species of fish abundant near the colony. Until much more quantitative work has been

Table 25: *The food of murres at Seven Islands (after Kaftanovski, 1938)*

Percentage and incidence of occurrence of items in stomachs

	Common Murre	Thick-billed Murre
Ammodytes tobias	86.1% (31)	80.3% (156)
Clupea harengus	8.3% (3)	16.2% (32)
Mallotus villosus	—	3.0% (6)
Gymnocanthus tricuspis	2.8% (1)	—
Gadidae	2.8% (1)	0.5% (1)

done in regions where the two species overlap in large numbers, it must be concluded that there is little difference in the foods of thick-billed and common murres.

It has long been a matter of speculation how sea-birds acquire water for their needs. Sea water is known to be toxic to man and most other mammals because of its high salt content. Some authors have stated that sea-birds drink sea water (Murphy, 1936), while others have maintained that they can exist wholly on water obtained from their food (Smith, 1953). Recent research by Schmidt-Nielson and Fange (1958) on the function of the nasal or salt gland of the brown pelican (*Pelecanus occidentalis*) shows that the salt gland can excrete a highly concentrated solution of sodium chloride. The excretory capacity of this gland permits sea-birds to tolerate ingestion of sea-water because the salt is excreted in a concentration higher than in sea-water. Quantitatively, the role of the salt gland in the elimination of sodium chloride is greater than that of the kidney. According to Technau (1936), the salt glands of murres are well developed. There seems no doubt that this gland performs the same function for murres as it does for the brown pelican.

Early in the nesting season, adult murres forage in large groups. As incubation progresses and the young hatch, more and more adults may be observed foraging singly. At a large colony, except during stormy weather and at dark, there is a continuous stream of small flocks and individual birds flying to and from the cliffs. At Akpatok Island, thick-billed murres foraged in an area not more than ten miles in radius from the colonies, with the greatest concentrations from one to five miles off shore. Thus the two colonies on that island, some 30 miles apart, were separated by a ten-mile stretch of coastal water from which murres were virtually absent. The presence of murre colonies in that region could not be detected until the observer came within ten miles of a colony.

The Digges Sound murres feed in two distinct areas. One is situated between Ivugivik and Mansel Island, some 15 miles from the nearest colony, and the other is a similar distance away in Hudson Strait towards Sugluk. Both areas are rather shallow but near deep troughs. The resulting turbulence creates conditions especially favourable for fish.

Adults sometimes bring fish to the nesting sites a week or more before the young are hatched. On those occasions, they remain for long periods merely holding the fish in their bills, or playing with it by placing it at their feet and fondling it. Occasionally, they swallow it but they never, apparently, give it to their mates. Nørrevang (1958) records an instance of a common murre on the Faeroes incubating an egg while holding a fish in its bill.

Rarely do adult murres bring more than one fish at a time to the chick. Normally, the fish is held lengthwise, with the tail overhanging the bird's bill and the head of the fish well down in the bird's gullet. Holding the head of the fish down in the gullet permits softening and partial digestion of the heads of such fish as sculpins, some species of which have rather spiny heads. The heads of the mailed sculpins in particular, would, if undigested, seem likely to offer some difficulty to the chicks. The adults often retained the fish, moreover, for a considerable period, sometimes as long as one hour, before presenting them to the chicks. This may be biologically important, as the tough heads were then found to be softened or partially digested. In fact, most of the fish presented to the chicks are headless or nearly so.

Selous (1905) whimsically describes the feeding of the common murre chick at the Shetlands: "The chick, when a very substantial fish is brought in for him, is asleep under the mother's wing, and both parents seem averse to disturbing him. The one with the fish seems quite embarassed. He approaches, stands still, looks at his partner for advice, shuffles about, turns this way and that, and several times bending his head gives a choked and muffled *jodel*, for his mouth is almost too full to speak. Still the chick sleeps on, and still the parents seem to doubt the advisability of waking him. At length, however, they admit it to be necessary. The father shuffles up into his usual position, the mother rises by slow and reluctant stages, as though apologetically, and finally stirs the chick several times with her bill till at last he rouses. Then, in a moment, he busks up, and, seizing the large fish, swallows it in a whole-hearted gulp."

When the chick is very young, it may not eat more than once a day. Later, it is fed two or three times a day, sometimes oftener. Each feeding consists of a single fish, which is sometimes actually longer than the chick itself. Fish up to 15 cm. in length are eagerly taken by hungry chicks scarcely one week old. The chicks go through prolonged contortions while swallowing. If the fish is especially large, they remain inert with eyes closed as the fish is being digested, while ripples of muscular reaction pass over their bodies. Experiments with marked birds show that frequently adults other than the parents feed the chicks.

Experiments at Akpatok Island in 1954 (Tuck and Squires, 1955) showed that at two weeks of age the thick-billed murre chick required at least 100 grams of food daily. During its life on the ledge, the chick required 13.4 grams of food to make one gram of body weight. The Akpatok Island chicks put on approximately 150 grams of body weight while on the ledges and consumed approximately 2,000 grams of food each in three weeks. In other words, they required roughly half their weight in food daily, and tripled their weight in three weeks.

The weight of murre chicks at three weeks of age varies greatly at the different colonies (Figs. 23 and 24). It has been suggested that such differences in body weight may be due to the greater energy requirements of chicks in higher latitudes. Uspenski (1956) showed that the Novaya Zemlya chicks varied in weight in different years and presumed that the difference in their rates of growth could be explained by the difference in climatic conditions. He stated, however, that the daily food requirement of the thick-billed murre chick at Novaya Zemlya was from 30 to 45 grams. He also suggested that the daily intake of food of the adult was 100 grams. The investigations at Akpatok Island (Tuck and Squires, 1955) indicated that the daily intake of the adult may be roughly one-quarter of its body weight. This is also true of both species of murres on their wintering grounds off Newfoundland. It is likely, then, that there is less food available for murres in the high-arctic regions.

Uspenski (1956) calculated that two million thick-billed murres and their annual increment utilized 25,000 metric tons of food during their four months' stay at Novaya Zemlya. Our studies indicated that murres consumed approximately twice that amount in the Ungava Bay area. The total amount of plankton and fish consumed by murres annually must be substantial.

That sea-birds utilize tremendous amounts of plankton and fish is now more generally realized. A recent study of the food of the rather small Cape penguin (*Spheniscus demersus*) in South Africa by Davies (1956) indicates that 5,000 penguins consume approximately 2,000 tons of fish annually. At that rate, two million of them would consume 800,000 tons annually.

The only fish of any commercial significance which murres utilize are herrings and the young of Atlantic cod. Both are highly exploited in the North Atlantic and yet after a long history of commercialization show no indication of lower populations. Like all the fish murres use for food, both are prolific. A female Atlantic cod, for example, 39 or 40 inches long, may be expected to produce about 3,000,000 eggs yearly, and larger fish produce more eggs in proportion (Bigelow and Schroeder, 1953).

In exchange for food taken from the seas, murres contribute to the waters the nutrients in their excrement and eventually those in their carcasses. The situation may be summed up by saying that murres, like other sea-birds of the region, form a link in the intricate ecology of the northern seas.

CHAPTER XV

Disease and Weather

To exist in such tremendous numbers as they do, species such as the murres, with an annual increment rarely exceeding 25 per cent, must have, once they are fully grown, a comparatively long life expectancy. Atkinson (1949) wrote: "Chancey and casual though the whole nesting economy did look, it worked. And after all, the ordinary foolish guillemot was in even worse case—single-brooded, laying but one egg and that easily knocked from its precarious ledge, its young watched over by black-backs, itself the prey of winter storms and ship's oil waste—yet no one had suggested that its hordes diminished. Such birds *must* have a long breeding life".

One would expect, therefore, that factors such as disease and inclement weather which sometimes limit numbers of other species of birds, would be of less importance with respect to murres.

There is one recorded instance of a possible epizootic in murres, although the precise cause was not definitely established. Jewett *et al.* (1953) wrote: "On May 15-16, 1942, many hundreds of dead murres washed ashore on the ocean beaches of Gray Harbour and Pacific counties. No oil was found on their plumage and the cause of death was not determined." Jewett counted the birds along several stretches of beach near Copalis, where he found they averaged 149 murres to the mile.

Murres living in the more southerly latitudes are apparently more heavily parasitized than those in the High Arctic. Uspenski (1956) states that in spite of the densely populated and filthy state of the colonies in Novaya Zemlya, the murres there are not heavily parasitized. He explains this by the relatively small variety of their food and the low summer air temperatures, which are unfavourable for the development of parasitic eggs in the external environment or ectoparasites on the birds themselves. Belopoloskaya (1947) recorded six species of endoparasites and three of ectoparasites infesting murres breeding along the warmer Murman coast. Markov (1937), in a general list of murre parasites, records eleven species of endoparasites and five of ectoparasites.

At Novaya Zemlya in 1948 (only at the Bezymyannaya Bay colony) 18 per cent of the murre chicks died from a purulent inflammation of the subcutaneous cells of the head (Uspenski, 1956). A sudden enlargement of the head was observed, usually before the age of ten days. Within two or three days the skin became covered with open sores, the swelling subsided, but pus formed a crust sticking the down together. Death of the chicks followed and no case of recovery was noted.

Rapid freezing of the surface waters in the arctic regions takes a toll of wintering murres. Adverse weather during the ledge life of the chicks also results in mortality. For example, Uspenski (1956) recorded a mortality of 68.8 per cent of chicks at Novaya Zemlya in 1948 as a result of extreme cold weather.

On the wet and stormy night of July 10, 1956, approximately eight per cent of the common murre chicks on Funk Island perished overnight. Eighty-eight per cent of them were ten days of age or more and too large to be brooded by the adults during the storm. It seemed likely that they were smothered. It is not likely that continuous adverse weather would have progressively affected the Funk Island chicks in that way, because the deaths of a number of growing chicks would have relieved pressure in the over-crowded colony. In this instance, however, weather was a factor limiting the productivity of the colony. A similar mortality occurred on Funk Island during a heavy rain-storm on July 14, 1958. Again, the deaths were nearly all of chicks half-grown and older.

Fisher and Lockley (1954) state that after late springs and in hard weather in the Arctic some, or even all, local populations of sea-birds may fail to breed. "In our opinion", they write, "these non-breeding years in the Arctic are simply due to bad weather closing down the food supply". It has been reported that in bad or late springs, the ice fails to break up along the east coast of Baffin Island and the sea-birds traditionally nesting in that area are unable to find food within foraging range of their breeding colonies. Wynne-Edwards (1952), referring to the fulmar colony at Cape Searle, Baffin Island, in 1950, said; "I . . . feel satisfied that it exceeds a lower limit of 200,000, though it may not be as high as half a million birds". Yet, after the late spring of 1953, Watson (1957) did not think there were more than 25,000 fulmars at Cape Searle in late May, although they were abundant in Davis Strait. Ice cover was still extensive during Watson's visit, no eggs were seen and none of the five females collected was in breeding condition.

Similar conditions occur in some years on the east coast of Greenland, especially from Scoresby Sound northwards, and at Spitsbergen, although the present climatic ameliora-tion seems to make conditions in that area more reliable. Manniche (1910) noted a large non-breeding population in northeast Greenland in 1907, a bad ice year, but not in 1908, when conditions were more favourable. Bertram, Lack and Roberts (1934) found a number of bird species non-breeding at Scoresby Sound in 1933, although other species were "clearly unaffected". Bird and Bird (1940) write of 1938 as a "complete non-breeding year" for all the birds in northeast Greenland except the passerines.

According to Bertram and Lack (1933), C. T. Dalgerty observed a similar phenome-non at Edge Island, Spitsbergen, in the late season of 1927, as did Captain J. H. McNeile in 1932 in a part of Spitsbergen worked by Dalgerty in 1931, when conditions were normal.

Bertram and Lack (1933) record the result of a late season on Bear Island in 1932. In that year, the sea ice did not disappear until the first week in June, apparently two months later than usual. Among the sea-birds, the following proportions failed to breed: herring gull, 67 per cent; great black-backed gull, 94 per cent; glaucous gull, 60 per cent; kittiwake, 70 per cent and murres (both species), 75 per cent.

Regarding the apparently abnormal behaviour of sea-birds at Bear Island in 1932, Bertram and Lack commented that it was clear that so large a non-breeding population was exceptional. No previous visitors to Bear Island had mentioned such an occurrence and the Rev. F. C. R. Jourdain had informed them that there was nothing comparable in 1921.

Sea-birds, unlike land-birds, have no shelter from storms. Regardless of their ability to survive in storms on the open ocean, or to move to parts of the ocean where conditions are less turbulent, storms are hazards which take their toll.

Reagan (1910) recorded the effect of a storm on a sea-bird colony in the North Pacific: "On August 28, and for some days following that date, a severe storm swept the Pacific coast of Washington. At that time of the year the nestlings on the bird island were just about to fly. Some had already gone to the water, and those that were still on the rocks were blown into the pounding surf by the raging wind. When the storm abated the coast was strewn with dead birds. In walking a quarter of a mile, I picked up 58 dead birds and half that number of crippled and half-drowned ones. The gulls suffered least for they had taken to the water some weeks before and were able to reach places of safety. Many cormorants perished, nearly all of the Puffins and California Murres. A half hundred thousand birds must have perished".

When a storm of wind and rain occurs during the sea-going period, the losses of murre chicks are often great. The adults are especially restless during storms and the half-grown young are washed or blown off the cliffs. Such a storm occurred in Digges Sound on the night of August 11, 1955. Approximately 700 chicks were found dead in a small cove on the following morning. Hundreds of others had managed to climb back to low ledges along the cliffs, where they were found huddled together for warmth—but dead, nevertheless. It was impossible to obtain a precise count of the dead chicks after that storm, since ocean currents had undoubtedly removed most of the casualties. The beaches at either end of the cliffs were strewn with dead chicks. The loss was seemingly highest on the most exposed nesting ledges. The total mortality certainly ran to many thousands.

On a very stormy day in August, 1954, the thick-billed murres on Akpatok Island did not leave the cliffs to feed their young (Tuck and Squires, 1955). A wind and rain storm occurred at Akpatok Island just after sea-going had started. The chicks did not leave the cliffs during the storm, but hundreds of those which had gone to sea were washed back, half-drowned or dead. A heavy rain and wind storm occurred at Cape Hay during the peak of the sea-going period in 1957. The beaches of the coves near by were strewn with dead nestlings. Ocean currents had carried away many other casualties.

Freuchen and Salomonsen (1958) describe the mortality of murres in West Greenland caught in a freeze-up: "When ice forms in the fjords in December or January, the murres concentrate in areas of open water that are produced by winds or currents . . . Sometimes the open spot freezes up, and the birds then fly around until they find another patch of open water. When the cold increases and the fjords become completely covered with ice, and the coastal waters far out to sea as well, the murres in the fjords are usually badly off. They keep flying around in flocks searching for open water and then eventually fall down on the ice, exhausted or stricken with panic at not being able to find water. Some-times they stray in over the land, where they soon succumb and are found dead or dying, often far from the sea. Such catastrophes, which may hit many thousands of murres, usually happen in January, when a considerable drop in the temperature and a resulting sudden freeze-up of large expanses of water is most likely to take place".

Salomonsen (1935) states that the common murres wintering around the Faeroes are sometimes washed ashore after storms. Baxter and Rintoul (1953), commenting on the occurrence of murres in Scotland, wrote: "There can be no doubt that numbers winter in the seas around our shores, as after every storm they are cast up dead". According to Austin and Kuroda (1953), murres are frequently cast ashore by winter gales in Japan where they perish on the beaches.

Wrecks of murres

The occurrence of sea-birds inland, especially during or after storms, is not infrequent in maritime regions. It rarely involves such truly oceanic birds as kittiwakes and fulmars. It frequently involves Leach's petrels, dovekies and murres concentrated near the coast before the storm. Tropical sea-birds from the Gulf of Mexico are sometimes found inland along the coastal regions of the Atlantic States after hurricanes. At the moment of writing this account, hundreds of laughing gulls and black skimmers, never before recorded for Newfoundland, are being found dead or dying along the coast after the passage of Hurricane Helene. The U.S. Coastguard, which carries out "on the spot" research of hurricanes off the Florida coast, reports that sea-birds frequently occupy the "eye of the hurricane", its calm low-pressure centre. In that event, sea-birds may be carried by "drift" in the direction in which the hurricane is travelling.

In Britain, the dovekie seems to be especially vulnerable to autumn storms and there are many accounts of their wrecks along the British coast and sometimes far inland. Sergeant (1952) summarized the dovekie wrecks of 1948-51 in Britain and explained that during the 1948-49 wrecks there were strong northeasterly gales along the coast and during the 1950-51 wrecks, "deep troughs of low pressure moving regularly from the Grand Banks areas".

The Leach's petrel is the sea-bird most commonly wrecked on land in Newfoundland. Hundreds of petrels may be involved in each wreck. Such disasters occur only along the southeast coast and may reach as far inland as Gander. The most recent wrecks of Leach's petrels in Newfoundland occurred on October 13-14, 1947; October 4-5, 1948; April 28-29, 1951; October 13-14, 1952; October 5-6, 1953; October 12-13, 1953; November 2-3, 1953; October 7-11, 1954; November 12-13, 1954; October 8-10, 1955 and October 13-14, 1955. Most petrel wrecks in Newfoundland occur during the first two weeks in October. This is a period when air masses moving rapidly from the north-west and southwest over the North American continent meet off the southeast coast of Newfoundland. This meeting of air masses invariably results in northeast gales. If the gales reach 50 m.p.h. and a bird is flying in the same direction at 30 m.p.h., the bird is carried southwestward at 80 m.p.h. If it is flying in the opposite direction, it is still carried southwestward at 20 m.p.h. It is likely that travelling low pressure areas account for most of the petrel wrecks along the southeast coast of Newfoundland. The wreck of October 13, 1955, followed a different pattern, in that a low pressure area recurved off the southeast coast of Newfoundland, forming a "pocket" which enveloped the petrels and brought them to land. The story is as follows:

A low pressure area formed over Hudson Bay on October 10, 1955. It moved rapidly southeast, accompanied by strong northwest winds to the rear and had centred over Newfoundland by early morning of the following day. On October 12, the low moved in a somewhat easterly direction out over the Atlantic. On the early morning of October 13, it was centred about 250 miles northeast of Holyrood, Conception Bay, and at about noon it began to recurve westward, the winds meanwhile becoming stronger. In the afternoon of October 13, Leach's petrels were reported in fairly large numbers close inshore along the southeast coast of Newfoundland, especially off Holyrood. Later that evening, the low continued its recurve, but now in a somewhat southeasterly direction. The winds intensified until at 5 a.m., October 14, they had reached hurricane force. Meanwhile, thousands of the petrels which had been close inshore at Holyrood on the evening of October 13 now appeared on the land. They seemed to be attracted by the asphalt highway or by the lights of automobiles. Hundreds were run over by vehicles and in a few instances petrels flew through the open windows of cars. The petrels, which are oceanic birds, had been "wrapped around" by the recurving low pressure area off the southeast coast of Newfoundland and brought inshore, where, as the winds increased, they had little "sea-room" in which to manoeuvre. Templeman (1945) described what may have been a similar incident at Holyrood in the early summer of 1941: "On June 16, 1941, at Holyrood we counted along a quarter of mile of beach 151 recently killed Leach's Petrels. A local fisherman reported seeing large numbers of these petrels on June 13 when there was a strong NE wind blowing onshore on this beach. Before dark on this date there were a number of patches of these petrels a short distance from the shore. These petrels were possibly washed in by the sea while sleeping or blown on shore by the strong wind and being unable to get off were killed by the seas beating on the shore".

Murres have never been known to be wrecked on the southeast coast of Newfoundland in October. This is because common murres are concentrated at that time of the year off the northeast coast and thick-billed murres have not yet reached Newfoundland waters in significant numbers. Occasionally, common murres in some numbers have been recorded wrecked from Grand Lake. It is likely that they came from the long inlet of White Bay, some 40 miles northeast. A combination of a long, narrow inlet and strong gales funnelling up that inlet is a natural setting for a murre wreck.

The most extensive murre wreck recorded for eastern North America occurred in December, 1896. During that month, thick-billed murres were found in rivers and lakes as far south as South Carolina and as far inland as Indiana. Fleming (1907) summarizes this unusual invasion and others from 1890 to 1904. He concluded that the murres involved originated in Hudson Bay, which had frozen over and forced them overland in search of food. He said: "Coming south, in Hudson Bay, the murres were caught between the moving and shore ice, and being cut off from their food supply, had no

FIGURE 27. *Weather pattern which caused a wreck of murres at Quebec, Montreal and Toronto on November 27-28, 1950*

alternative but to migrate". A glance at Fleming's map will show that those flights more likely originated in the Gulf of St. Lawrence or perhaps along the New England coast. Murre wrecks in eastern North America have sometimes been described as "eruptive emigrations". Even recently, Snyder (1957) stated: "Occasionally the eastern population undergoes an eruptive emigration in late autumn or early winter and scatters to the Great Lakes region and far into the continental interior. The best evidence available suggests that those flights originate from the Gulf of St. Lawrence and do not involve birds from the Canadian Arctic". The facts are that the "eastern population" of thick-billed murres totals merely a few hundred individuals and that the thick-billed murres in the Gulf of St. Lawrence during the autumn and early winter are not only from the Canadian Arctic but from West Greenland as well. That only thick-billed murres are involved in those wrecks may be explained by the relative scarcity of common murres in the Gulf of St. Lawrence at that time of the year.[1]

During the night of November 27-28, 1950, strong northeasterly gales brought thick-billed murres to the city of Quebec. The first records were for the morning of November 28 from within a radius of 20 miles from the city. Mr. J. G. Coote, President of La Société Provancher d'Histoire Naturelle du Canada, wrote me: "They flew around for a few days and finally were found one after another on the beaches in a dying condition". About 1,000 reached Montreal (J. D. Cleghorn, in litt.) and they were reported from as far southwest as Toronto.

A rather simple meteorological event accounted for this so-called "eruptive emigration". On November 23, a high pressure area centered over Hudson Bay began to move southeast. About the same time a low pressure area originating southwest of the Great Lakes began to travel northeast. On the morning of November 26 the two weather systems were in close proximity in the Gulf of St. Lawrence. The result was north-easterly winds funnelling up the St. Lawrence Valley (Fig. 27), which reached a maximum of 56 m.p.h. at Quebec City between 5.00 and 6.00 a.m. that morning.

The murres involved in this wreck were almost certainly not "picked up" by the north-easterly airflow. As pointed out in a similar situation with Leach's petrels in Newfoundland, any attempt to fly into the wind would cause them to "drift" southwesterly. It is likely that there was a large concentration of murres in the Gulf of St. Lawrence at that time but not all of them were brought to land and wrecked. Those which remained for the most part in the water were safe. It is likely that those which were eventually carried into the comparatively narrow entrance of the St. Lawrence River away from their normal food supplies became increasingly restless, spent more time in the air and consequently "drifted" more, until finally they were over land.

Murres stranded inland in this way may survive for several weeks, perhaps, if they can obtain food. Harry Lumsden examined two which had been caught in a gill net in Consecon Lake in Prince Edward County, Ontario, on November 28, 1950. One contained 39 and the other 48 small perch from 2 to 2½ inches in length. Fleming (1907)

[1]With an increase of the common murre population, the chances are greater. Thus on January 31, 1959, a common murre which had been banded on Funk Island in 1956 was captured on Seneca Lake, New York.

CHAPTER XVI

Man

The history of utilization of murres by man is documented in Chapter 19. The present chapter is concerned with the effect of human utilization and of another factor for which man is responsible—oil pollution of the seas.

In many cases, the history of human utilization shows excessive harvesting with no safeguards to maintain a regular stock of older birds. The story in the New World, especially in the Gulf of St. Lawrence and at the Farallon Islands in the Pacific is especially shameful. The only murre colonies commercially exploited today are in Russian territory, where efforts are being made to harvest them scientifically.

Fortunately for this account, Russian scientists have been making regular censuses of their most heavily utilized murre bazaars. Their statistics assist us in evaluating the effect of utilization.

Exploitation of the Cape Tchernetski, Novaya Zemlya, bazaar commenced in 1930 and was undertaken mainly by a local organization. In 1942, the colony was estimated to contain more than 200,000 murres and an economic expedition began to exploit the bazaar. From 30,000 to 40,000 eggs and as many as 8,000 adults were taken in some years. By 1950, the bazaar contained only 55,000 murres; the most easily accessible ledges were rarely occupied and in some places entirely deserted.

For a long time the murre bazaars in Bezymyannaya Bay, Novaya Zemlya, were the centres of regular exploitation. Krasovski (1937) stated that murre eggs were collected in considerable numbers there before 1922 and exported to Norway. From 1922 to 1928, the bazaars supplied mainly the needs of the local inhabitants, although during those years there were destructive raids by foreigners (Portenko, 1931). After 1928, large scale exploitation of the Bezymyannaya Bay bazaars became regularized and was carried out both by local workers' organizations and by economic expeditions. In some years, more than 250,000 eggs were collected. The utilization was too heavy, as the following statistics indicate:

In 1933, the murre population at Bezymyannaya Bay was 1,644,503 (Krasovski, 1937). This total included 116,557 in the northern and 1,510,946 in the southern bazaar. A census made by L. O. Belopolski in 1942 revealed that the bazaars had dwindled to a breeding population of 600,000; 100,000 in the northern and 500,000 in the southern bazaar. Another census, in 1948, revealed that in the intervening six years the breeding population had dwindled to 290,000. The Soviet Government then protected the region completely. A census taken in 1950 recorded 371,000, a recovery of more than 25 per cent.

In 1927 and 1928, a local workers' organization began to exploit the Pukhovy Bay murre bazaars. In some years as many as 100,000 eggs were collected. The Moresverprom Economic Expedition in 1936 was even more thorough and collected 120,000. According to estimates made by Gorbunov, the bazaar probably contained one million murres in 1923. In 1942, Belopolski placed the population at 300,000. In 1950, Uspenski determined that the population had dwindled to 121,000. Once again, too systematic and intensive exploitation had had a detrimental effect.

Sauchikha and Cape Lilye are two of the few places in Novaya Zemlya where thick-billed murres nest on level areas. Those localities are close to settlements and they have been extensively exploited for many years. In 1925, Gorbunov estimated that 200,000 murres were breeding there. Subsequent counts by other observers showed that in 1930, the population had dwindled to 30,000. In 1938, it had dwindled to 20,000 and finally, in 1950, to about 1,000.

The results of a quarter century of exploitation of the Novaya Zemlya bazaars by local workers' organizations and economic expeditions are now causing concern in Russia. Murres in large areas are totally protected until their numbers recover to near their former levels. Russian research has shown that little harm is done to a colony if the murres are harvested scientifically.

In 25 years the populations of Novaya Zemlya murre bazaars dwindled some 50 per cent. A similar situation occurred on the Farallon Islands off California in the last century, where eggs were collected for six weeks each year. Between 1850 and 1880 the population had decreased by two-thirds. Towards the end of the century, the Farallon murres had been reduced in number to such an extent that traffic in eggs was stopped by the United States Government.

The Gulf of St. Lawrence was another area where there was a heavy traffic in murres' eggs in the last century. Johnson (1940) calculated that in the middle of the last century the "Halifax Eggers" may have harvested as many as 750,000 eggs annually from the colonies along the North Shore. By the end of the century the colonies were all but exterminated. In spite of complete protection since 1920, they have not returned to their former size.

It might be suggested that the Gulf of St. Lawrence murre colonies failed to recover because they had reached too low a level—a point beyond which recovery of such highly colonial birds was impossible. That even an extremely low population of murres can recover if given the opportunity to do so, is illustrated by the history of the Baltic Sea population. In consequence of persecution, the Baltic population was reduced to 20 birds at most in 1880. As a result of total protection they had increased to some 15,000 sixty years later. The failure of the Gulf of St. Lawrence colonies to increase in size after protection was extended was likely a result of change in the marine environment that caused a submarginal condition for murres. This is dealt with in more detail in the following chapter.

Salomonsen (1951) provides statistics to show what over-utilization has done to the murre colonies in West Greenland. The colonies there are close to settlements and have been harvested annually without regard for the future welfare of the breeding birds. A very large murre colony on Sagdleq Island was estimated in 1921 to contain 500,000 pairs of thick-billed murres. In 1949, R. B. Hansen considered that the population had decreased to half that size, "owing to persecution". A colony in Sermilinguaq Fjord in Sukkertoppen District contained probably more than 100,000 pairs in 1925. In 1946, Salomonsen estimated that there were only about 5,000 pairs breeding there.

In other parts of the Old World, at St. Kilda, the Faeroes and Iceland, where the right to utilize the colonies is the heritage of the inhabitants, fowling has a long tradition. It has been carried out with every consideration for the future welfare of the natural resource. Although utilization has been fairly heavy, sea-bird populations do not appear to have decreased in those areas in historical times.

Murres, then, cannot maintain their numbers when subjected to sudden and excessive human exploitation. This has been shown by the sharp decline in the murre populations in the New World during the rather brief period of excessive commercial egging. It is shown in more recent times by the sharp decline in the Russian populations in consequence of the uncontrolled activity of the economic expeditions. The history of traditional fowling elsewhere in the Old World indicates that murres are able to tolerate utilization and maintain stable numbers if sufficient breeding stock of older birds is maintained.

Apart from the planned utilization of eggs and birds, man also kills large numbers unintentionally. Newfoundland fishermen regularly catch murres on baited hooks and in nets. Five per cent of all recoveries in Newfoundland have been from trawls and nets. Jewett et al. (1953) record that murres " . . . are occasionally snagged on trolling hooks of the salmon fishermen near Dungeness". But the greatest single cause of mortality on the murre wintering grounds is not use by man for food but wanton and careless pollution of the seas by oil.

Oil pollution is serious wherever there is marine transportation, but is especially so off Newfoundland, where many great-circle routes of ocean-going vessels converge. Most traffic routed from Northern Europe, the Mediterranean and Africa to Halifax, the Great Lakes and New England ports, converges south of Cape Race on the Grand Banks of Newfoundland, and the more northerly shipping route during the summer months passes through the Strait of Belle Isle into the Gulf of St. Lawrence (Fig. 28).

Oil dumped south and east of Newfoundland is carried toward the coast by prevailing winds and currents. There is an infamous onshore current setting towards Cape Race which has caused hundreds of shipwrecks during the past three centuries. The same current brings oil slicks toward the coast and thousands of dead and dying murres and other sea-birds are found along the shores of both sides of the Avalon Peninsula in autumn, winter and early spring.

A second area of heavy mortality to sea-birds by oil pollution along the coast of Newfoundland is on the north side of Bonavista Bay, southwards from Cape Freels. A third such area is along the Newfoundland side of the Strait of Belle Isle. Although mortality of sea-birds along the Newfoundland coast as a result of oil pollution is continuous, it is most serious in winter, when eider ducks concentrate inshore and murres off shore.

Tables 26 and 27 show the mortality of sea-birds resulting from oil pollution in areas

189

Table 26: *Mortality of sea-birds per lineal mile caused by oil pollution along measured parts of the western beaches of the Avalon Peninsula, Newfoundland, March 12, 1956*

Locality:	St. Brides	Patrick's Cove	Angels Cove	Ship Cove	Point Verde	Barra-choix
Length of beach examined	.75 mi.	.125 mi.	.125 mi.	.125 mi.	.5 mi.	.125 mi.
SPECIES						
Thick-billed murre	69.3	464	456	208	152	416
Common murre	1.3	—	8	—	4	—
Dovekie	9.3	—	8	8	14	—
Black guillemot	1.3	8	—	—	4	8
Puffin	—	—	—	—	4	8
Kittiwake	2.6	—	32	—	2	8
Herring gull	1.3	16	—	—	—	—
Great black-backed gull	—	—	8	—	—	—
Eider duck	1.3	—	—	—	—	—
Oldsquaw duck	1.3	8	—	—	6	—
Common loon	—	—	8	—	—	—

along the western side of the Avalon Peninsula investigated during early March, 1956. To obtain a reasonably accurate inventory of the daily mortality in that region, all birds were removed as the sections were examined each day. It will be noted that 11 species of birds were killed and that the kill of thick-billed murres was as high as 464 per lineal mile of coast. That species was the most seriously affected. It made up from 79 to 96 per cent of all birds found dead as a result of oil pollution.

On April 15, 1957, I examined a two-mile stretch of coast near Cape Ballard, on the eastern coast of the Avalon Peninsula. Forty dying or dead murres were picked up along the shore. On the following day, 42 recently dead or dying murres were found. Many disabled birds could be seen off shore, some of them dead and floating belly up. Others were still active and trying to clean the oil from their feathers. At the same time, dead murres were reported along a 90-mile stretch of coastline from Cape Race to Cape St. Francis. Even if the density at Cape Ballard were several times the average for the part of the coast where the murres were being driven ashore, the results indicated that the number destroyed daily along that section of the coast was more than 1,000.

Each year I received letters and telegrams informing me of similar mortality to sea-birds from the vicinity of Cape Freels and from that part of the coast of the Strait of Belle Isle centring around Flower's Cove. Large parts of the coast are uninhabited and the effects of oil pollution there are never recorded.

Possibly murres are attracted to oil slicks because they mistake them for schools of

Table 27: *Proportional mortality (in per cent) of sea-birds caused by oil pollution along the Cape Shore of the Avalon Peninsula, Newfoundland, on March 12, 1956.*

Locality:	St. Bride's	Patrick's Cove	Angels Cove	Ship Cove	Point Verde	Barra-choix
Length of beach examined	.75 mi.	.125 mi.	.125 mi.	.125 mi.	.5 mi.	.125 mi.
SPECIES						
Thick-billed murre	79	93	86	96	82	94
Common murre	1.5	—	2	—	2	—
Dovekie	10.5	—	2	4	8	—
Black guillemot	1.5	2	—	—	2	2
Puffin	—	—	—	—	2	2
Kittiwake	3	—	6	—	1	2
Herring gull	1.5	3	—	—	—	—
Great black-backed gull	—	—	2	—	—	—
Common eider	1.5	—	—	—	—	—
Oldsquaw duck	1.5	2	—	—	3	—
Common loon	—	—	2	—	—	—

small fish. Observers watching schooling fish from cliffs and from aircraft have noted the similarity of schools near the surface to oil patches.

All species of sea-birds around the coast of Newfoundland are more or less affected by oil pollution. Next to murres, the eider ducks suffer most heavily. Since the ducks concentrate closer to shore than do murres, they are not affected continuously but they die by thousands when gales drive viscous masses of oil close to the beaches. In recent years, far more murres—and possibly eider ducks—have been killed annually off the coast of Newfoundland by oil than have been utilized for food.

There are accounts of mortality of murres caused by oil pollution from the Murman coast, the coast of Scandinavia, Britain, Japan and practically all regions where murres concentrate off shore. To summarize them seems unnecessary but it may be useful to record that they exist and that oil pollution of sea-birds and especially of murres is of increasing concern throughout the Northern Hemisphere.

Aldrich (1938) commented on the loss of California murres as a result of oil pollution. Jewett *et al.* (1953) wrote: "Murres were abundant on the Clallam County (Washington) beach between July 31 and August 4, 1951, most of them . . . in breeding plumage . . . the plumage of nearly all had been polluted somewhat by oil, and they apparently came to shore in a vain attempt to clean their feathers, some perching on driftwood working over their plumage until knocked off by the surf".

The late Peter Freuchen commented on several occasions on the destruction of murres along the northwest coast of Greenland since the construction of the United States base at Thule. Fisher (1956) wrote: "Of all the auks, the common guillemot seems to be the hardest hit by 'oiling'; which may be the most important single factor behind the widely observed decrease of all Britain's auks ... in the present century".

Sea-birds heavily smeared with oil on the wings cannot fly or dive and slowly starve to death. Most dead murres found weigh far less than normal. Oiled murres attempt to clean their feathers by preening and as a result their digestive tracts are often full of oil and oil sludge. A small spot of oil on the belly is often sufficient to kill the murre. A patch merely an inch in diameter destroys the insulating air pockets, so that the bird dies of exposure of vital organs to the chilling effect of the sea.

Dr. A. Vedel Taning, Director of the Danish Fisheries and Marine Institute at Copenhagen, made the following comment in a Swedish natural history journal (Sveriges Natur. nr. 5, 1952):

"When one examines the fine oil-impregnated down under the microscope it is understandable that all insulation is destroyed. The bird's natural and necessary warmth protection has been lost and the bird freezes ... Its natural powers are often decreased so it must swim to land. In severe cases the bird dies before it reaches land. I have seen Razorbills and Murres far out at sea, so soaked with water that they could keep only their head and neck above the surface. Without doubt far out to sea masses of birds have sunk to the bottom without having been observed, so that those which reach land and are observed are perhaps only a fractional part of the number that have really perished".

In 1953, the British Ministry of Transport published the findings of the Committee on the Prevention of Pollution of the Sea by Oil. This committee was comprised of officials of the General Council of British Shipping, oil companies, the Admiralty and various scientists. The committee found that with few exceptions the oil on dead sea-birds was residual fuel oil.

As long ago as 1926, the United States Bureau of Mines showed that fuel oils become viscous emulsions when agitated by sea water and continue to float on the surface for months. The report said in part: "Asphaltic fuel oils when agitated with salt water form emulsions consisting of oil, water and air. These emulsions are very viscous and adhesive and resemble a heavy grease much more than the original oils. The specific gravities of the emulsions are greater than the original oils, but still less than salt water, consequently they continue to float on the surface ..."

A report on the Second Session of the League of Nations Committee of Experts, dated October 26, 1935, shows how very far oil on the surface of the sea may drift. Experiments made at sea by the United States in 1926-1927 showed that within a period of 72 hours (after which the experiment was discontinued) a discharge of oil was traced 90 miles from its origin.[1] The Faculty of Science at the Egyptian University produced evidence to show that oil was detected on the surface of the Red Sea 500 miles away from the point of discharge.

[1] Report to the Secretary of State by the Inter-departmental Committee, March 13, 1926   (Department of State, U.S.A.)

FIGURE 28. *The main shipping routes in the North Atlantic in relation to the chief centres of oil pollution of murres in Newfoundland*

The evidence submitted by the United Kingdom to the League of Nations Committee of Experts was to the effect that fuel oils are very stable and do not appear to alter in composition or in physical properties with the passage of time; there may be slow oxidation, but it is so slow as almost to defy detection. The oils are not volatile at ordinary temperatures, and if discharged at sea they float and keep on floating almost indefinitely. In the course of time the oil disperses into an emulsoid film which becomes invisible to the human eye. Experiments carried out in 1926-27 showed that oil floated on water in experimental tanks for nearly 18 months until the water had disappeared through seepage and evaporation.

As a result of evidence submitted to the Committee on the Prevention of Pollution of the Sea by Oil, the conclusion was reached that prohibition of the discharge of oil within a prescribed zone is no more than a palliative, since some oils persist indefinitely when discharged into the sea. More drastic methods are necessary.

Pollution of the sea by oil occurs in various ways. The most serious and widespread is the practice of flushing oil tanks while at sea. Tankers which have delivered cargoes of oil must clean sludge and waste oil from their tanks before taking on new cargoes. To save time, the practice of flushing tanks with salt water while at sea has become widespread.

Secondary sources of pollution are the dumping of "burnt" crankcase oil and the pumping of oily wastes from bilges. Coastal as well as ocean shipping is at fault in that respect. The dumping of oil and oily wastes in Canadian coastal and inland waters is now forbidden by law. Since much of the damage is done by oil dumped outside the narrow strip of territorial water, the regulations have so far failed to reach the root of the problem. Canada is party to an international convention which forbids the dumping of oil within 50 miles of the coast of member countries, but only eleven nations had ratified this treaty up to 1958. Many of the most important shipping nations, such as the United States, Portugal and Spain (whose ships make extensive use of the Grand Banks), have ignored the problem on the high seas and their ships may continue to dump oil anywhere except in their own territorial waters.

Broadly speaking, there are only two ways of keeping oil out of the sea: by discharging all oily residues ashore, or by the separation of tank washings and the consumption of the recovered oil in the ship. Until all nations concerned agree to those measures, oil pollution and its inevitable fouling of beaches and destruction of murres and other seabirds will continue and will almost certainly become more serious.

CHAPTER XVII

Changes in the Environment

It is now well recognized that there has been a pronounced change in the climate of the Northern Hemisphere in recent times. Primarily, this change has taken the form of an upward swing of temperatures since 1885 and particularly since 1920 (Hare, 1955). The chief characteristics of the change have been summarized by Ahlmann (1953), Willet (1950), Lysgaard (1950) and others. This climatic change has been reflected by changes in populations of murres.

The most impressive effects of this warming of the high latitudes have been a thinning of the cold surface layer of the Arctic Ocean, a general retreat of low-level glaciers, and a retreat of arctic sea ice (Hare, 1955).

The warm Atlantic waters brought northward by the Gulf Stream regulate the climate of the North Atlantic regions. The North Atlantic Drift originates in mid-Atlantic, northeast of the Grand Banks of Newfoundland. Its branches carry warm Atlantic waters northwards to the coasts of southern Greenland and northern Iceland and as far east in the European Arctic as the Murman coast. Any amelioration of climate in the Northern Hemisphere would, then, be most pronounced in those regions influenced by the North Atlantic Drift.

The recent trend towards a milder climate in the arctic regions is most strikingly apparent in the greater ease of navigation in the Polar Basin. In 1932, for example, a ship (the *Knipowitsch*) sailed around Franz Josef Land for the first time in history. In 1953, the Russian ice-breaker *Sadko* reached 82° 41′N—the most northerly point ever reached by a surface ship under its own power. In 1942, the Royal Canadian Mounted Police Ship, the *St. Roch*, navigated the Northwest Passage and in 1944 repeated that feat.

In recent years, codfish have been slowly advancing up the West Greenland coast. In 1913, the total catch was only five tons; today the codfish industry is a major one in West Greenland. According to Brun (1957), "Greenland is now the home of a modern fishing and fish-processing industry competing with the best in the world market."

In the past there have been eras of striking warmth in the Arctic. Perhaps one of the most interesting was the period about 1,000 years ago which permitted the Vikings to colonize Greenland and visit North America five centuries before it was "discovered" by Columbus. According to Icelandic records, a subsequent deterioration in climate took place between 1200 and 1300 or a little later.

The longest climatic records, those from Holland, date from the beginning of the 18th century. They show that the winters became colder from the first half of the 18th century to the beginning of the 19th, and have since grown warmer.

A summary of the records from Norway and Spitsbergen from 1836 to 1938 shows that a temperature change in recent years was by far the largest of any in that century. The recent climatic amelioration in Finland has lengthened the period of vegetative growth and affected the forest and agricultural economy.

A climatological study of Russia shows that the winters grew warmer from about the latter part of the 19th century and that this was especially noticeable at such far northern stations as Kola, Archangel and Leningrad.

Meteorological records for Canada are not as complete as those for Europe. The best are from Toronto for 1830 and subsequent years. Toronto's average winter temperatures have increased approximately 3.3°F. since 1870. Montreal's winter temperatures have increased 2.5°F. since 1880. The winter temperature on the coast of British Columbia has risen approximately 1.5°F. in the course of the past 35 years.

The waters pouring out from Hudson Strait and Davis Strait converge off Cape Chidley, forming the Labrador Current, which flows along the coast of Labrador and the eastern coast of Newfoundland, finally dissipating in the Gulf Stream at the edge of the Grand Banks. Any sustained influx of Atlantic waters or other ameliorating influences in the eastern Canadian Arctic, especially in Hudson and Davis Straits, would thus indirectly affect the climate of Labrador and Newfoundland. I now propose to show that this has occurred.

Fig. 29 shows the mean January temperature for St. John's, Newfoundland, from 1872 to 1956 and (for comparison) the mean January temperatures for Cape Race and Belle Isle, Newfoundland, from 1920 onwards. January records were chosen as an index of climatic change, as any lessening (or thinning) of arctic waters brought to the east coast of Newfoundland by the Labrador Current would be reflected during the winter, when the waters give up the heat absorbed during the warm months of the year.

The St. John's mean January temperatures[1] show a comparatively mild period from 1872 to 1902, with the warmest interval 1886 to 1900. After two decades of abnormally cold temperature, an upward swing began in 1927. This trend was most pronounced in 1937, when the temperatures at Belle Isle (Fig. 29), fully exposed to the Labrador Current, began to rise rapidly. The trend has been maintained ever since, the highest mean January temperature (34.4° F) on record being noted at St. John's in 1956.[1]

Salomonsen (1948) summarized the effect of this recent climatic change on the bird-life of Greenland, the Faeroes and Denmark. Gudmundsson (1951) did the same for

[1]There are no January statistics for St. John's for the years from 1909 to 1914 or for 1927, 1930 and 1931. There are also a few gaps in the Cape Race and Belle Isle records. The statistics were adjusted to allow for this as Hare (1952) shows that the St. John's mean January temperature (computed for 50 years) is 12°F higher than that of Belle Isle (computed for 75 years) and 2°F lower than that of Cape Race (computed for 19 years). Since 1942, weather records have been kept at Torbay, five miles from St. John's. There is a 46-month interval when records were kept at St. John's and Torbay. These showed that Torbay temperatures were, on the average, 0.08°F lower than those of St. John's. In Fig. 29 the Torbay temperatures have been adjusted to represent St. John's temperatures for the period when the latter were lacking.

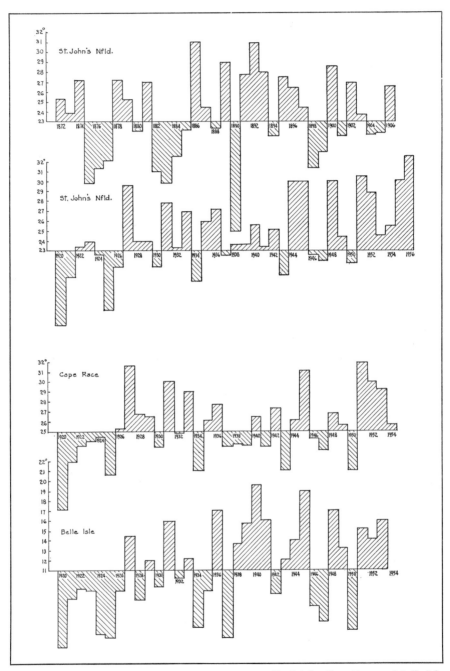

FIGURE 29. *Comparative mean January temperatures at St. John's, Cape Race and Belle Isle, Newfoundland*

198

Iceland. A more recent paper (Nørrevang, 1955) has gone into great detail on the changes in the bird-life of the Faeroes caused by the climatic changes in the North Atlantic area.

As sea-birds depend on a marine environment, changes in that environment are likely to be reflected by changing populations of sea-birds. I now propose to show that there have been changes in the Labrador Current (which affects the coast of Labrador and the east coast of Newfoundland), at least since 1936.

The best proof of changes in the marine habitat has reference to catches of fish and marine mammals. From such records and also from Templeman and Fleming (1953) we learn that several economically important marine species have increased greatly in abundance since 1936.

The presence of mackerel (*Scomber scombrus*) in commercial quantities off the east coast of Newfoundland since the mid-forties is an indication of a more favourable marine environment in that area. The export figures for mackerel indicate less than 200,000 pounds per year for the earliest figures available, 1856 to 1868; about 300,000 to 400,000, 1870-72; and 700,000 to 800,000 in 1879-80. Less than 5,000 pounds were exported in each of the years 1883, 1884, 1885, 1891 and 1897, and there were no further exports until 1936. The export of mackerel did not rise to 200,000 pounds again until 1945, after which it increased rapidly and ranged between two million and four million pounds from 1947 to 1952. Templeman and Fleming (1953) in commenting on the present mackerel fishery, stated: "The recent increase in mackerel appears to be an increase in population presumably due to a recent warm period, the east coast being during cold periods a too-low-temperature environment for the success of this species."

Although changes in catches of mackerel reflect the recent change in the marine environment of the east coast of Newfoundland, there have been many other "warm" water species occurring there recently in increasing numbers, among them billfish (*Scomberesox saurus*) and basking sharks (*Cetorhinus maximus*). Both those species

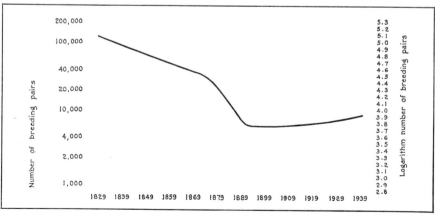

FIGURE 30. *Changes in breeding populations of gannets in the Gulf of St. Lawrence, 1829-1939* (*from Fisher and Vevers, 1944*)

were so rare before 1936 that for a time thereafter their occurrence caused much comment in the local press.

Using mackerel catch as a yardstick of significant changes in the marine environment in the Newfoundland region, it will be noted that conditions in that region were unfavourable from about 1880 until about 1936. During the period 1880-1919 there was also a decrease of murres in the Gulf of St. Lawrence and along the eastern Labrador coast and of gannets in the Gulf of St. Lawrence (Fig. 30).

The evidence for a period of climatic amelioration previous to the 1880's in West Greenland and in Spitsbergen is well documented. Dunbar (1954) has also documented the probable changes in the Ungava Bay region for that period. He writes: "The presence of Atlantic cod in Ognac Lake, a saltwater lake on the shore of Frobisher Bay, may also

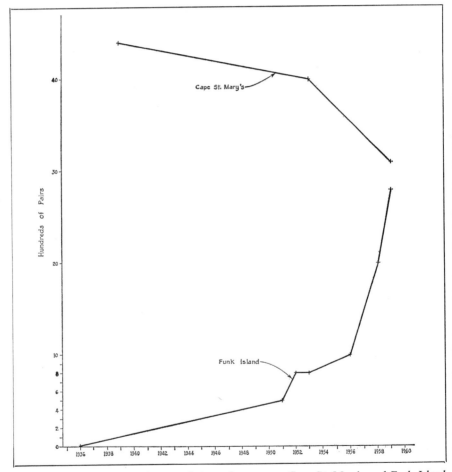

FIGURE 31. *Changes in breeding populations of gannets at Cape St. Mary's and Funk Island, Newfoundland, 1936-59*

be relevant to this matter. The locality lies over one hundred miles from the northern-most present occurrence of the cod, Resolution Island, and the cod is not found in the waters of Frobisher Bay itself. The Ognac Lake cod must therefore have reached the lake during a former period of warmer climate. The 1880 period is the most likely, for the lake is very small and the survival of an isolated cod population in so confined a habitat for longer periods of time is not probable."

Significant changes have occurred in the sea-bird populations off the eastern coast of Labrador and eastern Newfoundland during the past two decades. One of the most interesting and best known is the increase in breeding populations of gannets (*Morus bassanus*) at Funk Island off the southeast coast of Newfoundland (Fig. 31).

According to the old records, gannets were present in large numbers on Funk Island when it was visited by Jacques Cartier in 1534. More recent visitors to the island, Peter Stuvitz in 1841 and Professor J. W. Milne in 1874, do not mention gannets, and Lucas (1888) stated that there were no gannets on Funk Island in 1887. Wynne-Edwards (1935) saw none on his visit on June 29, 1934.

On July 20, 1936, Gilliard (1937) reported that seven pairs had become re-established at Funk Island. As that year coincided with the occurrence in large numbers on the east coast of Newfoundland of mackerel, on which gannets feed to a large extent, the sub-sequent history of the Funk Island gannetry is important.

Peters and Burleigh (1951) recorded 200 pairs of gannets breeding on Funk Island on July 5, 1945. I estimated approximately 500 pairs on July 10, 1951, at least 800 pairs on July 9, 1952, and about the same number on July 11, 1953. A precise count on July 15, 1956, by D. H. Pimlott and myself revealed that there were 1,204 occupied gannet nests on Funk Island. On July 13, 1958, I estimated about 2,000 occupied nests. On July 14, 1959, James Fisher and I found 2,013 nests with either egg or young and evidence that 755 other nests had been built but were empty; thus a maximum of 2,768 nests may have been occupied.

The Baccalieu Island gannetry (also on the southeast coast of Newfoundland) is an old one, but specific accounts of its early history are lacking. According to Templeman (1945) there is evidence that a colony existed there several centuries ago. Lucas (1888), however, saw no gannets there on July 21, 1887, nor did Wynne-Edwards in 1934. Peters (1942) found 200 pairs breeding on Baccalieu Island on July 24, 1941. In July 1959, Roger Tory Peterson counted 208 occupied nests.

Wynne-Edwards (1935) estimated that gannets first came to Cape St. Mary's between 1877 and 1883, about the time Funk Island and Baccalieu were deserted. Davies and Keynes (1948) estimated that the Cape St. Mary's gannet colony in 1939 numbered 4,394 pairs, plus or minus 369. In July, 1953, I estimated that the Cape St. Mary's gannetry did not exceed 4,000 occupied nests. On July 18, 1959, James Fisher and I counted 3,136 occupied nests at this colony.

Austin (1932) spent three summers, 1926 to 1928, exploring the Labrador coast. During that period he did not record a single gannet north of the Strait of Belle Isle. During exploration of the Labrador coast in 1950, 1951 and 1952, I encountered small groups of gannets (mostly sub-adults) as far north each year as Nachvak. The occasional gannet sighted within recent years in Hudson and Davis Straits, and indeed as far north as Lancaster Sound, thus does not necessarily come from Iceland, as has been assumed.

Changes in the marine environment of eastern North America have thus been paralleled by changes in occurrence of many species, notably mackerel and gannets. At the close of the last century, great fears were held for the survival of the indigenous populations of birds. Changes in numbers of murres are well known, although they have been recorded in less detail. It was because of population changes that in 1916 both species of

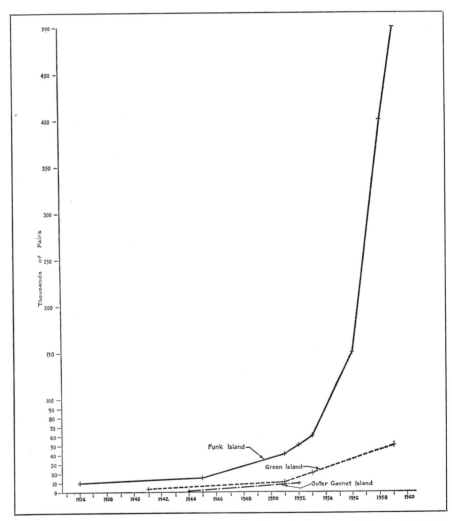

FIGURE 32. *Recent changes in breeding populations of common murre colonies situated in the Labrador Current*

murres were classified as non-game birds in the Migratory Birds Treaty between Canada and the United States.

The known fluctuations of the common murre populations on Funk Island (Fig. 32) are given in Table 5. The increase was gradual between 1936 and 1952 and more rapid from then onwards.

The Baccalieu Island murre colony increased from "1,000 pairs, possibly less . . ." (Johnson, 1940) in 1934 to an estimated 5,000 pairs on June 24, 1941 and decreased to 2,500 pairs in 1959. Another murre colony on the southeast coast of Newfoundland, at Green Island, showed a progressive increase from 1941 to 1959 (Fig. 32). The single murre colony on the south coast of Newfoundland, at Cape St. Mary's, decreased from an estimated 5,000 pairs in 1934 to 2,500 in 1942 and had not recovered by 1959.

At the Gannet Islands, Labrador, the increase in murre populations has also been progressive (Fig. 32).

The situation is very different in the Gulf of St. Lawrence, where the murre colonies never fully recovered from a crash decline which probably occurred in the 1880's. Johnson (1940) gives evidence to indicate that the colonies in that region at one time may have supported 375,000 birds.

Most of the colonies along the north shore of the Gulf were made migratory bird sanctuaries in 1925 and for the next ten years showed a slight increase; but during the past two decades they have remained static. The total population of murres in 1955 was less than 13,000. Apparently a crash decline with no subsequent recovery took place at Anticosti Island. In 1861, A. E. Verill (1865) found murres "in large numbers along the eastern and northern shores of Anticosti." Brewster (1883) "saw none at the eastern end of the island." Dr. H. F. Lewis recorded merely 220 individuals at Anticosti on June 9, 1940.

It will be noted that although a very marked decrease occurred in the murre populations along the Labrador coast, in Newfoundland, and in the Gulf of St. Lawrence in the latter part of the nineteenth century, the recovery has been significant only since 1936 and only in those areas influenced by the Labrador Current, i.e., on the eastern coast of Newfoundland and Labrador. The great decrease has long been blamed on commercial egg utilization, which was certainly excessive, but it may well be that a climatic change unfavourable to the murres was also important. Since the increases in breeding murre populations along coasts directly affected by the Labrador Current have coincided with changes in the marine environment brought about by recent climatic amelioration, it is not unreasonable to suppose that the preceding decreases were partly in response to climatic deterioration with its associated ecological changes.

In at least one region in Europe murres are probably more abundant today than they have previously been in historical times. That is in the Baltic Sea, where as previously noted, the population in 1880 was 20 birds and in the early 1940's about 15,000. A spread away from the main colony on Bornholm to other localities was noticeable in 1936 when they were recorded breeding on Graesholm (Salomonsen, 1943). It is striking that this was the same year that increase was first documented in Newfoundland.

Graesholm is now set aside by the Danish Government as a bird sanctuary. Erik Peterson informed me that at least 500 murres bred in Graesholm in 1956.

Changes in the marine environment may affect murre populations over an extensive area. Changes in the terrestrial habitat, brought about by various types of erosion, have less profound effects, but may be of much importance in local distribution.

The largest murre colony in the eastern Canadian Arctic, at Digges Sound, is situated on cliffs of granitic schist, as are most of the colonies along the Labrador coast and in Newfoundland. That type of formation does not provide many extensive flat ledges, but weathers unevenly into outcrops and pinnacles. Erosion by the sea on such formations forms numerous coves and gulches and probably provides more new nesting sites than it destroys.

Great changes in land formation have occurred at some of the traditional sites within historic times. Johnson (1940), writing of the murres in colonies on the Magdalen Islands said: "Dr. Lewis informed me in 1933 that there are two rather large groups of murres on the north island of the bird rock group, but that this island being made of soft rock, is disintegrating rapidly and is expected to be lost within a period of ten years as a nesting site for these birds."

Turner (1885) reported thick-billed murres breeding abundantly "at Cape Mugford", Labrador. Murres do not breed in that region at present, nor are there any likely-looking areas where they might breed. If Turner's report is correct, the explanation of their disappearance must be that the nesting ledges have eroded away.

The first mention of murres in considerable numbers along the eastern coast of Labrador was by Packard (1891), who described in glowing terms the murre colony on Tinker's Island. No murres now nest on Tinker's Island, nor do the shelves and ledges which Packard described in 1864 now exist.

In Great Britain, a murre colony in Sussex was destroyed by a fall of rocks in 1879; another, which was formerly quite large, on the chalk cliffs between Dover and St. Margaret's Bay, has also been deserted as a result of rock falls. The colonies on Akpatok Island in Ungava Bay, at Cape Hay in Lancaster Sound, and on Prince Leopold Island are on limestone formations. At Akpatok Island in 1954, tremendous rock falls removed entire sections of the cliffs, destroying nesting sites and even killing many adults. Similar falls with similar results occurred in Digges Sound in the summer of 1955 and at Cape Hay in the summer of 1957. T. W. Barry reported rock falls on Prince Leopold Island in 1958 and saw numerous murre carcasses, apparently crushed by the falling rock.

Certain cliff faces on the mainland of Digges Sound, on the western side of Akpa Cove, showed evidence of former occupation, especially the extensive growth of nitrophilous lichens. Natives at Ivugivik confirmed that murres had nested there within their memory.

Murres have also deserted part of the cliff at Cape Graham Moore. Katharine Scherman (1956) gives the Eskimo reasons for that desertion, told her by Panipookoochoo:

"Now I will speak. Once the akpas nested on a steep cliff near here. People were killed climbing this terrible cliff to get the akpas and their eggs. After many years the akpas had a meeting together. Too many people were killed climbing the cliffs, they said. The next time a man was killed they would move to an easier cliff. That summer a man climbed the terrible cliff and fell off and was killed. So the akpas moved to the Akpa Cliff, where they now live, and where men can get their eggs without danger. There, I have spoken."

Close examination of the deserted cliff faces at Digges Sound and Cape Graham Moore shows that the former nesting sites have been nearly eroded away.

Many of the colonies in the Pribilofs and Aleutians are located on basalt. Such geological formations are prone to great changes in consequence of erosion by the sea and weathering. Perhaps the most dynamic changes occur in the arctic regions where heavy frosts, followed in the spring by rapid thaws, precipitate avalanches which sometimes take away the entire face of a cliff.

Bent (1919) describes destruction of the nesting habitat of thick-billed murres in the Bering Sea, and the remarkable tendency of the species to return to their traditional nesting site on Bogoslof Island, 70 miles northwest of Unalaska:

"Considering the wonderful volcanic performance of this interesting island, it is surprising that murres still resort to it as a breeding ground, for at each of its frequent eruptions many thousands of these poor birds have been killed; but still the 'foolish guillemots', as they have been called, return to it again the next season. The violent eruptions of the summer of 1910 threw up enough material to join together the three little islands forming the Bogoslof group. In 1911 the volcano subsided and the towering peaks of Castle Rock, from 200 to 300 feet high, were literally covered with nesting murres. I could hardly hazard a guess as to how many hundred thousand murres were breeding on this and on other portions of the island."

CHAPTER XVIII

Predation

I have not found proof that any marine mammal in the Northern Hemisphere preys on sea-birds, even irregularly, although it is likely that the omnivorous killer whale (*Grampus orca*) may do so. There appears to be no counterpart in the Northern Hemisphere to the sea-leopard (*Hydruga leptonyx*) which preys almost exclusively on penguins in the Antarctic. Bryant (1888) offers rather flimsy circumstantial evidence ("Mr. Emerson has seen young sea lions with their muzzles slobbered with eggs") that young sea lions (*Zalophus californianus*) eat murre eggs on the Farallon Islands.

On at least two occasions a large cod (*Gadus callarias*) caught on the Grand Banks had an entire murre in its stomach. Legendre (1926) records an instance when a murre was taken by *Lophius piscatorius*. On one occasion at the Gannet Islands, Labrador, I saw large sculpins rise to the surface and gulp down at least three murre chicks which were swimming in shallow water. Those are probably unusual incidents.

Bryant (1888) recorded one other rather unusual predator of murre eggs on the Farallon Islands: ". . . the island mule . . . found that eggs make an agreeable variation in his diet. He hunts nests very assiduously, growing fat and sleek in the breeding season."

The only land mammal which preys on murres to any considerable extent is the arctic fox (*Alopex lagopus*). It is well documented that arctic foxes take the eggs of dovekies and eider ducks, among others, but their ability to utilize murres or their eggs is largely restricted by the inaccessibility of their nesting sites. It seems possible that the cliff-nesting habit of thick-billed murres has evolved in response to the hazard presented by foxes. Arctic foxes are able to prey upon living murres only on the fringes of a colony accessible from land, and thus are principally scavengers.

Braestrup (1941) points out an ecological difference between the coastal foxes in Greenland and the lemming foxes which occur only in the northern sections of East Greenland. The coastal foxes live on sea-birds and other forms of marine life and are largely sedentary.

On islands having large populations of foxes, such as the Pribilofs and the Komandorskie Islands, most of the food of foxes is obtained by beach-combing. Barabash-Nikiforov (1938) has published quantitative data on the food of foxes on one of the Komandorskie Islands. He showed that sea-birds, mostly obtained as carcasses, were the principal food item of the foxes on that island, comprising 39.5 per cent in volume. Sea-birds are also preferred to any other food item by foxes in the Pribilofs (Osgood *et al.*, 1915).

206

Müller (1906) suggests that foxes are able to catch live sea-birds in winter. He often observed from tracks leading away from the shore that a fox had carried an eider or a murre still able to flap its wings. It is likely that in such instances the birds were partially incapacitated through injury, in which case the fox would be acting as a scavenger. I have captured sea-birds myself under such circumstances. Freuchen and Salomonsen (1958), referring to the fate of the murres caught in a freeze-up in West Greenland wrote; "The murres that fall to the ice are always doomed. They are unable to rise from such a flat plane, and within a short time are attacked by ravens, gyrfalcons, or arctic foxes."

The scavenging ability of the arctic fox is ably summed up by Müller (1906), who described their behaviour in South Greenland, noting that they carried away the food items which they did not consume on the spot and buried them separately: ". . . an egg here, a fish there, a crab in the third place, a piece of skin in a fourth, etc., and he always knows how to find it again with an astonishing precision, even if covered with a deep layer of snow". Braestrup (1941) writes: "In regions where the foxes are chiefly dependent on bird cliffs the storing of food for the winter seems to play an important role, which is quite natural considering that the foxes have access to a very rich food supply for a limited part of the year."

Several writers (Hayes, 1867; Gibson, 1922; Pederson, 1931; Freuchen and Salomonsen, 1958) have referred to stores or caches of sea-bird eggs made by the foxes in Greenland. Those were mainly the eggs of the dovekie, which are laid in loose rubble and scree and are therefore accessible for fox predation.

During our studies on Akpatok Island in the summer of 1954, we found a maximum of fourteen foxes living off one of the murre colonies. The murre ledges in that locality were inaccessible to the foxes, but they found more than enough birds killed or injured by rock falls. Later in the season, young birds fell off the cliffs and the foxes buried the carcasses or cached them in crevices and holes at the base of the cliff.

The murre colonies in Digges Sound are inaccessible to foxes from the top and do not have a shore where the foxes can utilize dead or injured birds. Consequently, arctic foxes were very rare in the vicinity of the cliffs in 1955.

At Cape Hay in 1957, we found several unoccupied dens near the murre colony and noted that the murres nested in a number of places which would have been easily accessible to foxes. We did not, however, see a fox in the vicinity of the Cape Hay colony during the breeding season. This may have been because lemmings were numerous on other parts of the island. There is no habitat suitable for lemmings near Cape Hay. Foxes were quite abundant elsewhere on Bylot Island that year, wherever lemmings were plentiful.

It seems likely that at Cape Hay murres are preyed upon by foxes and thus serve as an alternate food item when populations of lemmings are low. At Akpatok, accidentally killed murres are the principal food item for a small population of foxes. Dead adults and chicks can be found at each murre colony in autumn. In some cases they fall into the sea and are washed up elsewhere on beaches, where they are utilized by foxes. Thus, directly or indirectly, each murre colony in the Arctic is important to foxes. The raven (*Corvus corax*) takes eggs and possibly young of murres, but, like the fox, it is primarily a scavenger and feeds mostly on fallen chicks and birds killed accidentally. Ravens occasionally nest on murre cliffs, but they are early nesters and their young are fledged while the murres are still laying. The egg stealing propensities of ravens should not be underrated, but since they patrol only the tops of the cliffs, their opportunities are limited.

I have examined numerous scats of the snowy owl (*Nyctea scandiaca*) and found in them remnants of both chick and adult murres. I have never observed a snowy owl capture an active murre. Perhaps the snowy owl, also, is mainly a scavenger, feeding on fallen chicks and injured birds.

I have noted the rough-legged hawk (*Buteo lagopus*), goshawk (*Accipiter gentilis*), peregrine falcon (*Falco peregrinus*) and gyrfalcon (*Falco rusticolus*) preying on murres at one time or another. Those birds are highly territorial and nest far apart, even when they nest in large sea-bird colonies. In 1954, three pairs of peregrine falcons nested at approximately one-mile intervals along the three miles of the southern murre colony on Akpatok Island. As far as could be determined, the falcons fed exclusively on murres injured by falling rocks, which they captured from the scree bordering the colony. The peregrine falcon was not recorded breeding in the large loomeries at Digges Sound or Cape Hay, where injured birds fell directly into the sea.

A peculiar relationship between murres and nesting peregrine falcons was noted at Akpatok Island. The murres which nested in the immediate vicinity of the peregrines' nests, some of which were scarcely ten feet away, were completely accustomed to the predators' presence, while murres nesting a quarter of a mile away would flush from their ledges when the peregrines approached. Because the peregrines respected each other's territories, there was a hiatus of about one-quarter of a mile between any two peregrine nests which was not disturbed by them. When a gyrfalcon or a rough-legged hawk cruised by the cliff (none nested on the cliff itself), adult peregrines, one from each of the nearest nests, combined to drive it from the immediate vicinity.

Even an injured murre is not easy prey for a peregrine or a gyrfalcon. I have observed falcon and murre cartwheeling along the beach in a welter of blood and feathers for nearly a mile before the murre was subdued. More often than not the murre reached the water and escaped.

The *Larus* gulls are predators at times, but more often scavengers. Since one of each pair of murres is nearly always in attendance at the nest site, the gulls usually have to content themselves with fallen eggs and chicks.

Human interference sometimes creates an unnatural opportunity for gulls to take unattended eggs and chicks. Ray (1904) writes thus of the gulls on the Farallon Islands: "From my own observations I do not think that in a battle royal the gull with its hooked bill has any advantage over the murre with its stiletto-like weapon, but succeeds in its high-handed robbery by better control of wing and foot and overwhelming numbers. The gulls swoop down when the murres have been flushed from their eggs and secure the booty, or a number by harassing a single bird simultaneously from all sides start the egg rolling. It is amusing to see a bob-tailed, erect, soldier-like murre with an egg between its legs and a single swaggering gull endeavouring to secure it. Every time the gull cranes its neck forward for the egg the murre also bends with a vicious snap of the bill, which the gull is wise to dodge; and thus the birds will keep salaaming, like two polite Japanese, until another gull comes to aid its fellow or, unaided, the bird gives up the attempt." Johnson (1940) confirms this relationship when he notes that predation by great black-backed gulls (*Larus marinus*) on the murre colonies in the Gulf of St. Lawrence was extensive only if the murres were molested by human interference. Kaeding (1905) makes the same point for the western gull (*Larus occidentalis*), saying: " . . . for, while the human eggers took only the fresh eggs, they disturbed the whole colony of murres and the gulls took everything in sight."

Johnson (1938), who studied the relationship of the great black-backed gull to common murres in small colonies in the Gulf of St. Lawrence, arrived at several conclusions:

a. On islands where both species are nesting out in the open, the gulls take a certain percentage of the eggs regardless of disturbance.

b. If the murres are disturbed, the damage may be anything up to complete loss of the murre colony.

c. On islands where the two birds are found nesting and the murres are protected by being down in crevices, caves, or faults in the rocks, the gulls are not likely to get many of the murre eggs.

d. On large islands where the gulls are nesting at some distance from the murres, disturbing the gulls does not appear to affect the murres as long as they are never visited by man.

The most numerous predatory gull at thick-billed murre colonies in the Polar Basin and the North Atlantic is the glaucous gull (*Larus hyperboreus*). Concerning the association of glaucous gulls with other sea-birds in West Greenland, Salomonsen (1951) says: "Of the 91 Glaucous Gull colonies in Disko Bay in 1946, 49 were Glaucous Gulls only, 25 associated with other gulls (Iceland and Kittiwakes) and 17 with gulls as well as with other sea-birds." Glaucous gulls quite frequently are associated with thick-billed murres. They are reported to breed at each of the 44 Novaya Zemlya murre colonies. The ratio of glaucous gulls to thick-billed murres, on cliffs where they breed together, may be rather small. Uspenski (1956) gives three comparative ratios of glaucous gulls to murres for the Bezymyannaya Bay bazaars in 1950. They were 120 : 240,000; 84 : 120,000; and 0 : 11,000.

In the eastern Canadian Arctic the ratio of glaucous gulls to thick-billed murres nesting in the same colonies is even lower, and amazingly consistent.

At Akpatok Island in 1954, there was one pair of glaucous gulls to approximately 100,000 murres. There the gulls fed on dropped fish, fallen chicks and adults accidentally killed. The gulls hunted chicks assiduously during the sea-going period, which, however, commenced at twilight, so that their predation at that time was limited not only in time but also to unattended chicks. Murres recognize gulls on the water as enemies, and during the sea-going period they sometimes combine to drive them away.

At Digges Sound, most of the glaucous gulls nested at least seven miles from the murre cliffs and rarely visited them. At the cliffs, the ratio of breeding glaucous gulls to thick-billed murres was one pair to 100,000. The glaucous gulls nesting with the murres in Digges Sound most frequently fed on injured adults or fallen chicks in the water but sometimes obtained whole eggs which rolled down the grassy slopes. One gull nest-site, where there were two half-fledged young, contained the remnants of 320 murre eggs. Calculations based on data obtained at that nest and three others indicate that a pair of glaucous gulls and three offspring might utilize as many as 800 murre eggs and chicks during a breeding season.

In 1957, glaucous gulls were widely distributed in small discrete colonies in Navy Board Inlet and Lancaster Sound. The ratio on the murre cliffs at Cape Hay was also one pair of glaucous gulls to 100,000 thick-billed murres. At Cape Hay, the gulls scarcely bothered the murres. Instead, they fed almost exclusively at the floe-edge and, later, along the coast, on remains of marine mammals, which were very abundant in that region. A study of a large number of glaucous gull nests in that region revealed that the eggs of murres were a very minor item in their diet—in fact, there was no evidence of eggs at most nests. The gulls fed, however, on carcasses of murres floating in the sea and brought back remnants of the carcasses to the young.

When other food is available, gulls do not appear to prey heavily on sea-bird eggs or chicks. In 1956, only four pairs of herring gulls (*Larus argentatus*) and three pairs of great black-backed gulls nested on Funk Island, in association with some 300,000 common murres. During an eleven-day period in July, 1956, I did not note a single instance of a gull taking either a murre's egg or a chick, although hundreds of "misplaced" eggs and temporarily lost chicks were completely exposed. Instead, both species of gulls fed exclusively on squid and capelin, which were abundant off shore. Gulls appear unable to affect the population of a murre colony to any serious extent except when human interference provides unnatural opportunities.

Murre colonies contain such great numbers of birds, well protected by their location on inaccessible ledges, that predation is not an important factor controlling their populations.

PART V: ECONOMICS

CHAPTER XIX
Murres and Men

Colonies of murres have been a source of food and material for clothing in many parts of the world. The history of their utilization includes examples of ruthless exploitation on the one hand and orderly harvesting on the other. Murres and their eggs were food for the early explorers of the Arctic, briefly provided a base for commercial enterprise in the Gulf of St. Lawrence, and served for several centuries as a staple item in the diet of the Faeroes.

Like nearly all undertakings which provide for the welfare of those who depend on the sea for existence, the taking of murres and their eggs is fraught with danger. It is basically a young man's undertaking. Youth, in demonstrating prowess, has little regard for life and limb. Lives have been lost by falls from murre cliffs while egging, by hunting accidents and in storms while hunting in the winter.

Students of early Canadian history may recall that the ring-leaders of Henry Hudson's mutinous crew were attacked and mortally injured by Eskimos when they landed at the murre colonies in Digges Sound to "replenish their supplies". William Baffin, on his fourth voyage, anchored at Digges Island on July 29, 1615, and on the following day, while passing through Digges Sound, wrote in his log: ". . . for in this place is the greatest quantities of these fowle that in few places else the like is to be seen" (Markham, 1881). Thus were charted for future explorers, as an important source of food, the largest colonies in the Canadian Arctic.

The whaling captains who last saw the Franklin expedition told how, at the entrance of Lancaster Sound, the Franklin ships were "salting down" sea-birds—probably murres from Cape Graham Moore. The accounts of early arctic explorers and marooned whalers describe many instances in which starvation was averted by eating murres. Nesting murres can be captured without using ammunition; this has made them an important and inexpensive source of food. Some of the murre colonies in the eastern Canadian Arctic are recorded for the first and sometimes the only time in the accounts of explorers engaged in the search for Sir John Franklin and his ill-fated expedition. Admiral Sir F. Leopold M'Clintock, who was very prominently associated with that search, wrote: ". . . our loom soup[1] is incomparable; more like hare soup than any other, but richer,

---

[1]M'Clintock's recipe for loom (i.e., murre) soup:
Take 8 looms, skin and take off the two white lumps near the tail; clean and split them into pieces, wash them well, also the livers. Put them into a large saucepan, and cover them well with water, and boil for four or five hours.
An hour before serving up, put in ½ lb. of bacon cut up small; season with pepper and salt, 2 table-

darker, and better adapted to our climate, our appetites, and consequently to our tastes".

In just as serious a vein, F. G. Jackson, "marooned" at Cape Flora, Franz Josef Land in 1896, described how he shot 1,617 murres and thought wistfully, as he sat on a buttress and shot 98 flying murres out of a hundred, about the Norfolk pheasant-shooting he was missing.

Primitive or isolated peoples everywhere depend on wild animals for much of their food. Wherever a wild animal is important in the economy of a people, its capture and use become part of the tradition of that people.

Before guns and ammunition were available to the Eskimos of the Canadian Arctic, they used murres and their eggs wherever they could be obtained. The possession of guns and ammunition now assures the Eskimo a supply of meat without the necessity of living in the vicinity of the rugged sea-bird cliffs. Historical accounts based on Henry Hudson's experiences show that, in 1610, Eskimos concentrated on or near the large murre colonies in Digges Sound, Hudson Bay. Those colonies are now visited only once or twice a year by the few Eskimos of Ivugivik, who use perhaps a thousand eggs and several hundred nesting birds annually. Ammunition is too precious to waste on birds as small as murres. Seals and other large mammals yield more meat at less cost. For the Eskimos of Hudson Bay, the murre cliffs in Digges Sound and on Coats Island now provide only an occasional delicacy, rather than a staple diet.

Along the murre cliffs at Cape Hay are the remains of stone enclosures in which murres were cached. They are pyramidal in shape and approximately 30 feet square at the base. Each could hold four to five thousand adult birds. Some distance beyond the brow of the cliffs are the remains of about twenty stone dwellings in rather good condition. Murres must have been a very important food for the people who lived there. But centuries have passed since then and only vague, half-forgotten legends regarding life at Cape Hay remain with the Eskimos now living at Pond Inlet and Arctic Bay, the most northerly Eskimo tribe in Canada. They claim that the natives at Cape Hay were the Toonijuk—the prehistoric people, who, they say, were living in the land when the Eskimos came. I spoke to many of the Pond Inlet people and could not find a single person who had ever visited the Cape Hay murre cliffs in summer.

Eskimos formerly lived on Akpatok Island, but not within the memory of those now living in Ungava Bay. In 1956, remnants of camp sites deeply covered by sand were found in a meadow at the base of the southern murre colony. The few visits now made to Akpatok Island by the natives of Payne Bay and Cape Hopes Advance are only in search for walrus.

And so it is with the other known murre colonies in the Canadian Arctic. Eskimos do not live near them and rarely if ever utilize the birds or their eggs. Some hunting of murres in the early spring and autumn is done by the natives of southwestern Baffin Island and at Padloping and Pangnirtung on the east coast, but it is insignificant. In

spoons of Harvey Sauce, a little Cayenne pepper, half a wineglass of lemon juice, a tablespoon of ground allspice, and a few clove; thicken with 4 tablespoons of flour mixed in cold water, then stir gradually into the soup.

Add ½ pint of wine, after which let it boil for a few minutes. The result will be 4 quarts of rich soup.

brief, the murre colonies in the Canadian Arctic are now almost completely unexploited.

Historical accounts show that the aborigines of Newfoundland, the Beothucks, used sea-bird eggs for food and their skins for articles of clothing. The so-called "Liverpool Manuscript" from the archives of the First Earl of Liverpool, one-time chairman of the Committee for Trade and Plantations, dated 1792, has recently come to light. One account in this manuscript is as follows: "McDonald said that he and four other men were on Funk Island to get birds' eggs there; from whence they saw two canoes, each rowing twenty-four paddles on a side and containing upwards of 100 of the native savages of Newfoundland." Since it is now known that the Beothucks had war canoes which usually could carry no more than eight or ten persons, it seems likely that they made special canoes to reach this outermost island, with its enormous supply of sea-birds and eggs.

Jacques Cartier, who discovered Funk Island in 1534, Sir Humphrey Gilbert, and many other early explorers visited Funk Island and collected eggs, although it is likely that the main object of their attention was the great auk.

Murres and their eggs were harvested on Funk Island and along the eastern coast of Labrador by fishermen until about two decades ago. At one time as many as 1,000 ships were engaged in the Labrador fishery. As a matter of course the ships stopped off at Funk Island to collect meat and eggs and visited the colonies on the coast of Labrador for the same purpose later in the season. Both eggs and birds were salted and were sometimes the main item of summer's meat in the fishermen's diet, apart from fish.

It is likely that all Newfoundland sea-birds were used by the residents of the island during its early history. An early account of the use of the common murre (Anspach, 1819) may illustrate: "These are called Baccalo birds and have ever been considered as of sufficient importance to mariners, particularly in foggy weather, by giving them notice of their approach to the coast even as far as the banks, as to deserve some special protection of government against the attempts of bird and egg hunters. Notwithstanding the proclamations issued from time to time by the Governors of Newfoundland, for that particular object, it has not infrequently happened that, tempted by the vast profit produced by the sale of those birds, of their eggs and of their feathers, and regardless of the extreme dangers which attended the attempt, some daring individuals contrived by means of ropes, poles, and wires to make a general sweep of the eggs as well as the birds with long poles, or by covering with nets the chasms in the rock where the birds are nesting; these frightened by the firing of muskets, or by very loud hallooing, fly up and are caught in the net."

With the cessation of the Labrador fisheries and the inevitable changes in the economy of Newfoundland, the desire or need for sea-bird eggs for food dwindled.

Before 1949, when Newfoundland became a province of Canada, murres were shot in the winter, salted and sold commercially. The sale of canned "turr" supported a minor industry. Since 1949, in conformity with the laws of Canada, utilization of murres has been restricted to personal use for food in remote and isolated localities only. It was estimated in 1949 that approximately 200,000 murres were shot annually for food in Newfoundland. In consequence of a more favourable economic situation since confederation with Canada, only half that number are now shot annually.

Murres occur in Newfoundland coastal waters at the only slack period of the year; the fishing gear has been stacked away for another year and the proper season for cutting firewood has not quite arrived. Other game birds being scarce, turr hunting became an annual recreation for the young men, providing at the same time much needed meat. Turr hunting in Newfoundland is never without its dangers, since the birds are most abundant in the bays during the stormy northeasterlies, when only small boats can be used. Many adventurous tales associated with this hunt are still in the making in Newfoundland folklore.

The Murre Rocks near Cape Mecatina in the Gulf of St. Lawrence formerly supported a famous colony. There, in 1833, a boat was loaded with 2,500 eggs in a few hours (Audubon, 1844). The eggs were collected "in astonishing quantities" and "sent to distant markets", where they were sold at from one to three cents each (Coues, 1861; Bryant, 1861). Johnson (1940) estimated that the "Halifax Eggers" harvested as many as 750,000 murre eggs from the North Shore of the Gulf of St. Lawrence in a single season. The "Halifax Eggers" and the "Yankee Fishermen" sometimes came to blows over the right to pillage the murre colonies in that region. One account (Tucker, 1839) is as follows:

"On the Mecatina Isles, situated in the Gulf of St. Lawrence, and near the Labrador coast, immense flocks of sea-fowl throng, during the warm season, to deposit their eggs. The fishermen not infrequently gather these eggs by hogsheads, and they become an article of traffic. The fishermen from Nova Scotia have long claimed these birds as their own, and until Yankee enterprise cut in for a share, they enjoyed the whole of the plunder. Disputes often arose between the Yankee and Nova Scotian fishermen as to the possession of these treasures, and on one occasion the dispute rose so high, that the 'blue noses' as the Nova Scotians are called by Yankee fishermen, fortified themselves with (King's arguments), fire-arms, and determined to prevent the Yankee from carrying off the eggs. But Yankee cunning is sometimes a match for any arguments. They knew that these islands were usually covered in a dense fog in the morning. They accordingly waited off shore in their vessels, until the 'blue noses' had gathered together large quantities of eggs upon the shore, ready for packing, as was their custom, intending on the following day to pack their eggs in casks already provided, and take them aboard their vessels. When the morning came, and the fogs had begun to clear up, the 'blue noses' found the Yankee had been there before them and carried off all their eggs. The affair gave rise to some belligerent operations, but finally resulted in an agreement of the parties not to deny to each other a reciprocity in the matter of eggs. And thus the storm blew over, without involving two great countries in war."

The colonies along the North Shore were also utilized by the local inhabitants. When Brewster (1883) first saw Perroquet Island, in 1881, murres were nesting plentifully, but a week later "the colony had been practically annihilated by Indians".

The common murre was formerly taken in substantial numbers, especially at the Farallon Islands. The exploits of the eggers there have been described by Heerman (1859), Baird, Brewer and Ridgway (1884), Bryant (1888), Ray (1904) and others.

The work was done by teams of twelve or fifteen men, who divided the island into sections and hunted systematically every other day—breaking every egg they could find the first day, so as to ensure the freshness of those gathered the next. Each man wore a blouse-like "egg shirt", made from a cotton flour sack drawn tightly around his waist, and capable of holding some 200 eggs. The first party of eggers to take possession each year held their position against all comers and once even defied federal government officers sent to remove them.

The season commenced on July 1 and lasted for six weeks. During that period, immense numbers of eggs were gathered. In 1854, the Farallon Egg Company, organized to supply the San Francisco market, sold more than 500,000, all from a single island, where, according to eggers, not more than one egg in six had been gathered. Between 1850 and 1856, according to Bryant, from three to four million murre eggs were shipped from the islands—an average annual harvest of about 600,000 eggs. Thirty years later, the number had dropped to one-third. Towards the end of the century commercial egging had so reduced the colonies that the traffic was stopped (Bent, 1919). With the signing of the Migratory Birds Treaty between Canada and the United States in 1916, it became illegal to exploit sea-bird colonies in North America.

Many writers, including Peter Simon Pallas, who first described the Pacific form of the thick-billed murre, have stated that the murre is the great egg-bird of the North Pacific, utilized alike by Aleuts and Eskimos, and the only important economic sea-fowl of the Bering Sea. There are few statistical accounts of the extent of utilization in that region, but Elliott (1880) describes one instance of the utilization on Walrus Island: "On the occasion of one visit . . . July 5, 1872 . . . six men loaded a badarrah at Walrus Inlet, capable of carrying four tons, exclusive of our crew, down to the water edge with eggs in less than three working hours."

The murre colonies in the Kuriles are immense and most of them are situated on flat sites and therefore quite accessible. The adults are herded into "pounds", constructed of high fish nets. Gizenko (1955) recorded that, in 1948, 111,464 eggs were sold from a single colony (Seal Island), while the total utilization, including local consumption from that particular colony, probably totalled 150,000 eggs.

In former times, exploitation of the large sea-bird colonies in Iceland was of much more importance to the inhabitants that it is today. The species most heavily utilized were the common and thick-billed murres, the puffin, the razorbill, the kittiwake, the fulmar and the gannet. The adults of all of those species and the eggs of most of them were taken for human consumption. The mechanization and industrialization of the Iceland fisheries, which began shortly before the beginning of the present century, has so affected the economy of Iceland that exploitation of the sea-bird colonies has now been discontinued in many places.

The murre colonies in Iceland are the property of individual farms or of communities. The Icelanders have long been aware of the need to maintain a breeding population and consequently practise moderate exploitation. They collect eggs only once in each place so that replacements have an opportunity to hatch. They do not take murre chicks at all.

The murre cliffs in Iceland are generally difficult of access, so that fowling is hazardous.

The fowlers are lowered over the cliffs, where they snare the adults with a noose of fine wire or twine attached to a long pole. In some localities, rafts with horse-hair nooses set on them are moored at the base of the cliffs. The birds get entangled in the nooses and are thus captured. Some birds are shot, although in most regions the people do not permit shooting near the nesting colonies. The Icelanders cure their catches for winter by smoke-drying or salting in brine.

The official statistics of Iceland do not record the quantity of eggs utilized, but data on the numbers of adults taken are available. In 1912, 112,234 adult murres were taken, but in 1939, only 19,290. This represents a decline in the sea-bird industry of Iceland, rather than in the sea-bird populations (Gudmundsson, *in litt.*).

Apart from the eider duck, the thick-billed murre is the most important bird in the economy of Greenlanders (Salomonsen, 1950). The flesh and the eggs are taken and the skins with feathers are used for blankets and capes or *tingmiaq*. The feathers are used for down-coverlets or sold to trading companies. No organized fowling takes place in Greenland, except perhaps in the Thule District, where the murres are cached uncleaned and eaten raw during the winter.

A large number of murres are shot each winter along the coast of southwest Greenland, usually from kayaks. In order not to disturb the flocks too much, the primitive bird arrow is still used in some places in preference to a gun. The annual kill has increased from about 70,000 in 1850, to about 100,000 in 1900 and 200,000 in more recent times (Salomonsen, 1950). Egg collecting takes place where the breeding cliffs are accessible but is important only in the Upernavik District, where about 10,000 eggs are taken annually.

The eggs of murres are used to a notable extent in Russia. On October 7, 1942, the Soviet War News published in London carried this news item:

"A school children's expedition to the Arctic has just returned to Murmansk. Accompanied by a group of workers, thirty senior pupils hunted game and collected guillemot murre eggs. The nests were found in abundance on the rocky coast. The children set out last spring, and spent two months of their summer holidays in the Arctic.

"To reach the eggs they had to be lowered by ropes from the top of the cliffs. They braved rain, mist and snowfall, and brought back 35,000 game-birds and 160,000 guillemot eggs for the Murmansk hospitals".

For many years the murre colonies in Novaya Zemlya have been centres of heavy exploitation. The colonies in Pukhovy Bay, especially, have a long history of utilization. Sadovski (1910) states that at the beginning of the twentieth century, Norwegians took large numbers of murre eggs from Pukhovy Bay, the yolks of which were used in soap-making. According to Gorbunov (1925), Norwegians regularly harvested the Pukhovy Bay colonies until 1922, when further collecting was prohibited by Russia. From 1927 onwards local workers' organizations systematically utilized the Pukhovy Bay colonies. In some years economic expeditions collected 100,000 eggs or more there in a season. In 1936, the Morzverprom Economic Expedition collected 120,000 eggs in Pukhovy Bay.

After 1928, large-scale exploitation of the Bezymyannaya Bay colonies was carried out by both economic expeditions and local workers' organizations. In 1933, 342,500 eggs were collected there and in 1934, 200,250. Eggs from other regions in Novaya Zemlya were also utilized. Between July 2 and July 14, 1935, 12 men gathered 300,000 murre eggs from Novaya Zemlya for sale in Archangel.

The Novaya Zemlya murre colonies are considered by the Russians of such economic importance that, in 1933, S. R. Krasovski, chief of the Ornithological Party of the Novaya Zemlya Scientific and Economic Expedition of the All-Union Arctic Institute set up special biological projects, the aim of which was to determine the possibilities of economic exploitation and the organization of a regular industry. Some of the scientific reports, especially the more recent ones, have been drawn on to compile this monograph.

The eggs of the common murre have traditionally been collected for domestic use in many coastal regions of the Old World. The colonies in Orkney, Shetland and the Faeroe Islands and at St. Kilda all have long, interesting histories of utilization. At St. Kilda, the eggs were being used when Martin (1698) visited the island. During their three weeks' stay in 1697, Martin's party was provided daily with 18 murre eggs per man. He wrote: "We had the curiosity . . . to make a Calcule of Eggs bestowed upon those of our Boat, and the Stewart's Birlin, or Galley, the whole amounted to sixteen thousand eggs; and without all doubt the Inhabitants, who were triple our Number, consumed many more Eggs and Fowls than we could". At St. Kilda in 1829, Mackenzie saw on two occasions, 17 and 14 basketfuls of eggs taken from a single colony, each basketful holding about 400 eggs (Mackenzie, 1905). About 1902, the "take" in a favourable season was 6,000 eggs (Wiglesworth, 1903). The traditional fowling at St. Kilda came to an end in 1930, when the inhabitants were evacuated and moved to the mainland.

Along parts of the British coast, utilization has varied from locality to locality and according to the commercial value of the eggs. At St. Abb's head in 1846 murre eggs were sold at a penny each. Eggs collected at Steep Holme were used by sugar refineries in Bristol (Lewis, 1936). Cordeaux (1884) described how in 1844 four gangs of climbers took 130,000 eggs, mostly of murres, in 52 days from the Bempton cliffs. They were sent to Leeds, where the albumen was used in the manufacture of patent leather.

In the Faeroes, as in Iceland, the right to take murre eggs at the best sites on the cliffs usually belongs to certain land-owners and is often hereditary. This right is guarded jealously, but may be delegated temporarily to others. The owner may rent it to a neighbour or permit a specified number of days' catching in return for other services.

Apart from its economic importance, fowling in the Faeroes provides the recreational and mental stimulus which belongs to all kinds of hunting and adventurous occupations. In spite of the discomfort and dangers of days and nights on open ledges or in cramped dug-outs on the cliffs, and the loss of life which occurs nearly every year, fowling in the Faeroes is regarded still as the most exciting of all summer tasks. Its economic necessity has by virtue of long centuries of usage become part of the national life of the Faeroes, affecting folk-lore and customs, and providing outlets for the sporting instinct inherent in the people. The Faeroese guidebook, "Faeroerne Natur og Folk", suggests that its importance to Faeroese culture has been in no way diminished by the influence of modern civilization.

The puffin is unquestionably the most valuable item of food among the Faeroe sea-birds, and in a good year the total catch for the islands must be 400,000 to 500,000 puffins (Williamson, 1945). But a large number of murre eggs are also gathered, as many as 80,000 a week. Most of the eggs are preserved in a "water-glass" mixture of salt water and peat ash. Eggs and potatoes form a staple winter meal on the islands. Some of the murre eggs are exported; others provide a colourful tourist attraction in the local shop windows. As many as 100,000 murres are shot annually by the Faeroese (Fisher and Lockley, 1954), especially by people from settlements where there are no fowling cliffs. They are cured or preserved for winter food by smoking in barrels over burning peat, or by salting in brine and wind drying in *skeos* or *cletts*, which are wooden sheds or unmortared stone huts.

The soft, white breast feathers of murres are extensively used for stuffing pillows and the large quilts which are the only bed-covers in the Faeroe home. For many years before World War II, quantities of murre and puffin feathers were exported to Denmark for a similar purpose. Plucking is a woman's job and a good worker can deal with 300 birds in a day.

An important piece of equipment to the Faeroese fowler is the *fleygustong* or fowler's net. It is a pole, 12 to 16 feet long, forked at the end, with a net between the two prongs. The fowler rests on a ledge on the cliff, awaits the birds in flight and swings out his net as they fly past. An experienced fowler can catch up to 1,000 birds a day. This method of fowling, most in use nowadays, is called *fleyging*.

Another method of fowling in the Faeroes, called *fygling*, consists in putting the net over the birds while they are sitting on the ledges. A third method is *omanfleyg*, when the fowlers row in to the cliffs in boats and startle the birds. Panic ensues and hundreds of birds fly down from the ledges to dive into the sea and are caught in nets on the way down.

Fowlers engaged in *fygling* or *fleyging* often spend several weeks at a time on the cliffs, living in small cramped dug-outs or even on the open ledges. Boats put out daily from the settlements, weather permitting, to collect the catch thrown down by the fowlers. It is a dangerous and adventurous occupation. Occasionally, a party must spend the night on an exposed ledge, roped together for safety.

Another method for catching murres at sea was introduced to the Faeroes from Iceland some 30 years ago. Large planks, six or seven feet long and three or four feet wide, on which 50 or more loops of plaited horsehair are arranged, and at one end of which a stuffed skin is mounted on stiff wires, are floated on the water. The murres are attracted to this lure, climb up on it and are snared as they attempt to leave. A crew usually has ten such boards and on a good day can capture up to 600 birds by this method.

Murre chicks are sometimes hunted by the Faeroese after they have left the cliffs and are congregated on the sea below. Being unable to fly, they are herded into narrow inlets and there dispatched with a *kast*, a stone attached to a fishing line.

A unique method of catching murres at St. Kilda is described by Mackenzie (1905). The fowler hides himself as close to the edge of a ledge as possible and holds up a white object such as a handkerchief. A flying murre thinks this is another bird and settles down beside it. It is at once pounced upon, killed and placed in a sitting position to induce others to alight beside it. Other accounts describe how the St. Kildans sometimes covered their heads with a large white sheet to simulate a guano-white ledge rather than the flashing underparts of a sitting bird.

It is interesting to compare the tools of the traditional fowlers in the Old World. The *fleyg* used in the Faeroes does not appear to have been used at St. Kilda, although it was in use in the Orkneys about 1808. The nearest the Hebrideans could get to the *fleyg* was a simple pole, with which they struck down murres in mid-air, as was done in Newfoundland. The *fleyg* is used in some localities in Iceland, at the Westermann Islands for example, as is also the raft snare, which was later adopted by the Faeroese.

A method of catching murres used in Iceland is snaring with a "running noose" of fine wire or twine, which is slipped over their necks. A long pole to which it is attached enables the fowler to reach the birds more easily (Gudmundsson, *in litt.*). This tool is like a St. Kilda puffin-gin.

Venables and Venables (1955) describe the Shetland techniques for capturing murres. They are shot, snared with hair nooses and caught by hand on the breeding ledges.

A type of *fleyg*, actually a dip-net, is used for catching murres in parts of West Greenland, as at Thule (Salomonsen, 1951). Quite independently, the Aleuts in the North Pacific developed a *fleyg* hooped like a giant butterfly net for catching the tufted puffin.

The tradition of hunting murres, then, is highly developed only in the Old World. In most places in the New World, without a background of tradition, the use of murres was commercialized and sporadic. It was eventually prohibited, largely because commercialization in the New World was competitive and very damaging to the nesting colonies. In Japan and Russia, the harvesting of murre eggs is still of substantial economic importance. In the latter country at least, efforts are now made to harvest them on a sound, scientific basis.

The Economic and Ecological Importance of Murres

Since the dominance of man in the natural world is only recent, murres have been more important on the whole for fertilizing the surface layers of the sea than as a source of food and clothing.

The total world population of murres is in the order of fifty million birds. The adult almost certainly consumes its weight in food each week. Therefore murres consume at least fifty million pounds of plankton and fish weekly. Human utilization is about two million eggs and one million birds annually. Although those figures are rough estimates, it is safe, I think, to generalize on the importance of murres, not only to man, but also to the rest of their environment (Fig. 33). I shall consider the natural environment first.

Sea-bird excrement is especially rich in nitrates and phosphates, without which the phytoplankton, the basic life in the sea, cannot exist. Murres feed on a large number of bottom fishes during the summer and, by excretion, replenish the surface layers with nutrients where they can be most readily utilized by the phytoplankton. There is no extensive circulation in the arctic marine regions and this surface replenishment may be more important than is generally realized. Surface replenishment of nutrients to the surface layers seems to be so important that murres may be referred to as the fertilizer factories of the northern seas. Murres are not the only source of such nutrients (Fig. 34), but since they are circumpolar in distribution and probably the most abundant sea-birds in the Northern Hemisphere, they are the most important.

The cold climate and waters of the arctic marine zones are more favourable for the seasonal growth of phytoplankton than the warm regions of the world. As a direct result, the world's great fisheries are carried out in regions influenced by arctic waters. Dunbar (1955b) gives four reasons for this:

1 Low temperatures allow high concentration of dissolved gases, both carbon dioxide for photosynthesis and oxygen for energy requirements, since the solubility of gases in water is inversely proportional to the temperature.

2 Photosynthesis can continue for longer periods during the long summer days in the Arctic than in regions close to the equator.

3 The greater viscosity of the cold water has an important effect on the flotation of plant cells, so that the period of their sojourn in the euphotic zone is more extended than in warmer waters.

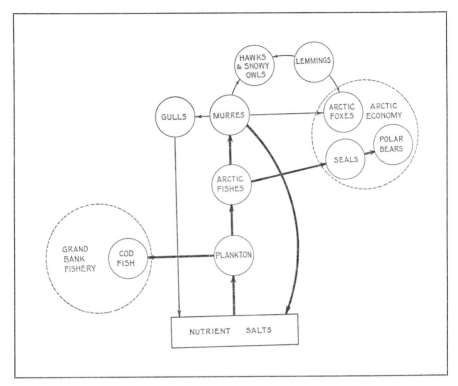

FIGURE 33. *An ecological relationship of murres*

4 The enormous numbers of sea-birds which breed in the North provide in their excrement a constant supply of nutrient salts, or fertilizers, during the whole summer.

The upwelling and mixing of waters that bring to the surface submerged nutrients is not characteristic of the purely arctic waters, where both salinity and temperature remain fairly constant. In those regions, as has been stated, the surface replenishment of nutrients by sea-bird excrement is most important to the economy of the waters. Moreover, the nutrients provided by excrement which are not immediately utilized, perhaps because they sink to lower levels, are eventually carried southward by the continuous flow of arctic waters. There, through upwelling and vertical circulation, they become available for the development of phytoplankton in regions far from their origin. It is amazing to think that the unutilized nutrients from the excrement of murres at the large colonies in Digges Sound and Akpatok Island may eventually reach the Grand Banks, but that is almost certainly the fact.

The guano industry of the coastal regions of Peru is a classic example of the economic importance to man of large sea-bird colonies. Because of vertical circulation, the seas in that region are especially fertile in plankton, small fishes and crustaceans. Probably the nutrients responsible for this phenomenon come largely from the immense penguin and other sea-bird populations in the Antarctic.

222

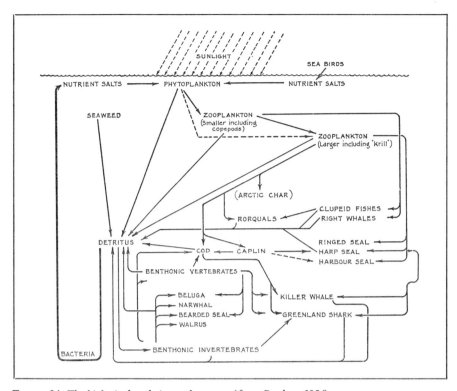

FIGURE 34. *The biological cycle in northern seas (from Dunbar, 1954)*

Immense colonies of cormorants and pelicans, attracted by the abundant food supply, occupy the coastal islands. Because there is practically no rainfall off the Peruvian coast, their excrement is not washed off the nesting islands into the sea. In fact, the richly nitrogenous guano is baked almost immediately. Thus the nutrients are not returned to the waters there and the fertility of the waters must be replenished by flow from the Antarctic. The excrement which accumulates on those islands provides the main source of the world's supply of natural fertilizers. Many millions of tons of this highly valuable fertilizer have been "mined" and transported to the Northern Hemisphere.

According to the best estimates, more than ten million tons of Peruvian guano, worth many millions of dollars, were mined and exported from a single group of islands during the period 1851-1872. The original deposits are exhausted, but more than 100,000 tons are deposited annually by the birds.

Because of the high humidity of the coastal regions in the Northern Hemisphere, murre excrement from the nesting sites is quickly washed into the sea so its value cannot be measured in the same way. At all large murre colonies, a continuous stream of murky water flows into the surrounding sea. The murky colour of this water is largely due to the excrement originally deposited on the ledges. During rainy weather, when the flow is greatest, the surrounding seas may be discoloured for many square miles.

Nitrate guano is not formed in those latitudes because the high humidity causes the nitrogen to dissipate rapidly in the air. The nest sites, facing or sloping towards the sea, do not permit extensive accumulation of phosphate guano. All the excrement rather quickly reaches the sea.

Since nitrogenous guano is not formed in regions of high humidity, the large sea-bird colonies along the coasts of the Northern Hemisphere have never been the source of commercial fertilizers to any considerable extent. Locally, the richly organic and nitrogenous soil is used in a number of places. In 1863, the Colonial Government of Newfoundland granted to Mr. Glindon, a United States citizen, the "privilege" of removing the soil from Funk Island. That soil, especially enriched by the carcasses of great auks, was deemed valuable as a manure when imported to Boston and other places in North America. In all 35 tons of "guano" were obtained, four labourers producing 20 tons in ten days. Five tons were sold at St. John's for $19 a ton, and the remainder consigned to a firm in Boston, whence it was eventually shipped to Baltimore and Washington.

The relationship of murres to the economy of the Arctic is an important one. On Akpatok Island in Ungava Bay and along the west coast of Greenland, where there are no lemmings, arctic foxes depend entirely on murres and other sea-birds. As previously described, there was no evidence on Bylot Island that murres acted as an alternate food for foxes in low lemming years in that locality. The carcasses of adults killed on the cliffs by rock slides and of chicks drowned during the sea-going period are often washed ashore many miles from the scene of those mortalities. They all provide food for foxes. I have often watched arctic foxes burying the carcasses, presumably against a day when food might be scarce. Since arctic fox pelts are at present the principal article of trade for the Eskimos of the Canadian Arctic, the contribution of murres to the Eskimo economy in certain areas may be a valuable one.

Although murres, as demonstrated, play a most significant role in marine ecology and are indirectly important to man in that way, their direct importance as a source of food and material for clothing is more readily recognized.

In a few regions, as in the Aleutian Islands and West Greenland, the skins and feathers are sometimes used in articles of clothing or blankets. Experiments carried out in Russia in 1941 showed that the skins and other parts of murres usually discarded could be used to advantage. The plucked skins were processed and made into children's outer garments, collars, caps and muffs. The fat proved suitable for industrial use and the dried or salted mucous membrane of the gullet for sausage casings. During the long history of murre use, their eggs at one time or another have been used in sugar refineries, for making patent leather, and for making soap.

Actually the murre is not the most important wild-egg producer. Cott (1953 and 1954a) gives an informative summary of human exploitation of wild birds. Sea-birds top the list because most of them are colonial nesters. The world's most important wild-egg producer is the sooty tern (*Sterna fuscata*). Statistics from the Colonial Office show that in some years as many as 1,996,400 sooty tern eggs from the Seychelles and 617,000 from Morant and Pedro Cays have reached the Caribbean markets.

Many writers have spoken of the value of murre eggs for table use. Elliott (1880) found the thick-billed murre's egg the most popular of all eggs of sea-birds breeding in the Pribilof Islands. He maintained that it was excellent, whether soft-boiled or fried, and best of all scrambled. He added: ". . . when perfectly fresh, I can testify to its practical equality with our deservedly prized hen's eggs". Kane (1856) stated that the eggs of murres were well known as a delicacy along the coast of Labrador and described a concoction of "raw eggs and cochlearia" as "the best salad in the world". Also Audubon (1844) wrote that: "They afford excellent food, being highly nutritive and palatable, whether boiled, poached or in omelette".

It is not surprising then that the panel on the palatability of the eggs of birds conducted by Cott (1954b) at the University of Cambridge assigned the thick-billed murre egg a provisional rating of 8.0 and the common murre a mean edibility rating of 7.7. This compares very favourably with that of domestic fowl, which was rated 8.7 by the same panel.

The results of an analysis of murre eggs by Tyrova (1939), made at the request of the All-Union Scientific Research Institute of Aviculture at Moscow, are as follows:

Table 28: *Chemical composition of eggs in percentages*

SPECIES	*Water*	*Fat*	*Protein*	*Ash*
Thick-billed murre	69.7	12.1	12.7	1.03
Common murre	77.0	10.0	12.03	1.15
Hen	73.0	12.57	12.02	1.07
Duck	70.81	12.77	15.04	1.08

Table 29: *Vitamin A and carotene content of egg yolk (micrograms per gram of yolk).*

SPECIES	*Vitamin A*	*Carotene*	*Total Carotenoids*
Thick-billed murre	9.8	14.0	26.5
Common murre	10.0	18.5	30.1
Hen	8 to 10	—	7 to 15
Duck	10 to 18	—	15 to 30

As the tables indicate, the food value of murre eggs is high and is comparable with that of the eggs of domestic poultry. In addition, carotene, presumably not found in domestic poultry eggs, is found in rather large quantities in murre eggs.

The caloric content of murre eggs is also fairly high. Tyrova (1939) gives the following comparative figures:

Product	Calories per kg.
Thick-billed murre egg	1,988
Average beef	1,358
Poultry meat	1,288
Whole cow's milk	683

225

Since murre eggs contain about as much Vitamin A as domestic poultry eggs and far more calories per unit than whole cow's milk, they are of substantial nutritional value to peoples in the Arctic or other regions where neither domestic eggs nor milk are available. Uspenski *et al.* (1948) stated that the nutritional value of murre meat is well below that of poultry meat, but did not give data to support their contention. In winter, at least, murres are high in fat content, which is an important factor in the diet of peoples living in cold climates.

The number of murre eggs consumed annually in the world is approximately two million. The present monetary value of two million hens' eggs (Canadian standard) is approximately $135,000. This is scarcely a fair standard of comparison, because in regions in which murre eggs are most heavily utilized, the cost of domestic hens' eggs would be substantially higher than that used to calculate the above figure; indeed likely would not be available at any cost. A similar situation affects the value of murres used as meat. In regions where they are so used, they may at times be the only meat available and they may be a welcome change from a staple and monotonous diet.

CHAPTER XXI

Management

In most regions of the Northern Hemisphere murres are given some protection in one way or another, by tradition, by closed seasons, or by the establishment of refuges and sanctuaries. Some of the most important colonies in the Arctic are virtual sanctuaries because of their inaccessibility.

An interesting document in the Newfoundland Archives of the Memorial University at St. John's may well be the earliest document in the New World concerned with the protection of sea-birds (but see Appendix E). It is a proclamation by Governor Admiral John Holloway, dated October 1, 1807. In view of Anspach's comments (see p. 214) it must have referred especially to murres. It reads as follows:

"Whereas the birds which formerly abounded on the shores of Newfoundland and the adjacent islands and were of great use to mariners on their approaching the coast in foggy weather have been wantonly destroyed for the sake of their feathers; I do hereby issue this my proclamation forbidding all persons whomsoever from taking or destroying those birds, their nests or eggs in future, in order that the breed may be restored, and hereby direct all Magistrates, Surrogates, and others His Majesty's officers to enforce this proclamation, and anyone being found to offend against it will be prosecuted as the law directs. Given under my hand, etc. . . . "

The oldest form of protection given to murres—husbandry along traditional lines by the private owners of breeding colonies—is still in effect in parts of the Old World. In the Faeroe Islands, fowling cliffs are hereditarily owned; in Iceland, they belong to certain farms or communities. In each case, the results are the same—the eggs are considered an annual crop and harvested accordingly. No shooting or other disturbances are permitted within a mile or two of the breeding cliffs. Harvesting of eggs from the various ledges is usually on a rotational basis from year to year. At St. Kilda, eggs were taken traditionally on May 18 and again 18 days later. At Grimsey, eggs are collected at the end of May and again on Midsummer's day—three weeks later. The management practices which have been in effect in those localities for several centuries must have been wise ones, since the murre populations have remained stable there. In contrast, practices used elsewhere in many cases have brought drastic reduction of the colonies because of over-utilization.

Some of the first murre colonies given complete protection in the Old World were the Karlsoarna in the Baltic Sea. In 1880, a group of private Swedish citizens, disturbed at the reduction of the Baltic murre population, purchased the breeding islands and formed a club for their protection. The remarkable increase in the colonies shows how effective complete protection of the breeding sites can be when a population is threatened with extinction.

The large common murre colony at Teurejimo has been protected since 1938 by being designated as a National Monument by the Japanese Government. Common murres and their eggs are now totally protected in Great Britain under the Protection of Birds Act of 1954. Recently Russia stopped commercial use of the colonies at Seven Islands on the Murman coast and at Gribovaya and Bezymyannaya Bay in Novaya Zemlya until they recover from the effects of over-utilization. In West Greenland, magistrates now impose local regulations to assure an adequate annual breeding stock at certain colonies.

In the New World, where commercial egging contributed to the decline in population of most of the accessible common murre colonies, protection of the main breeding colonies is now complete. All the large murre colonies off the Pacific coast of North America are now parts of wildlife refuges under the aegis of the U.S. Fish and Wildlife Service. The principal colonies in the Gulf of St. Lawrence are now migratory bird sanctuaries administered by the Canadian Wildlife Service.

Three Arch Rocks, the famous common murre colony off the Oregon coast, was established as a wildlife refuge in 1907. In the same year, a wildlife refuge was established at Copalis off the Washington coast. This latter is a five-acre nesting rock for murres among other sea-birds. The Farallon Islands, which were the scene of commercial egging in the past century in defiance of the U.S. Coast Guard, which attempted to put a stop to the traffic, were created a wildlife refuge in 1909.

A large number of wildlife refuges in the North Pacific were set up for the preservation of sea-lions or the conservation of fur seals, but they also benefit murre colonies. The Aleutian Island National Wildlife Refuge covers some 4,250 square miles. Its eastern boundary is at Unimak Island, off the Alaskan Peninsula, and it extends westward along the Aleutian chain to Attu. In that refuge there are about fifty islands, many of which are nesting sites for murres. Bogoslof Island, one of the most famous murre islands in the Aleutians, has been established as a separate refuge. Forrester Island, Hazy Island and Kodiak Island Refuges off the Alaskan coast have murre colonies, as does Nunivak National Wildlife Refuge, off the west coast of Alaska, and the Semedi National Wildlife Refuge—eight islands southwest of Kodiak.

The Pribilof Islands Reservation (Saint George Island, Saint Paul Island and Walrus Island) was established primarily for the conservation of fur seals, but it accords protection to the main colonies of murres breeding in the Pribilofs, some of which may be the largest in the world.

The Migratory Birds Treaty between the United States and Canada has afforded almost complete protection for murres in North America since 1916. Indians and Eskimos are permitted to take murres and their eggs for food or clothing, although they may not sell them or take them from a sanctuary, The only regions within the range of murres in North America not affected by the treaty at the time it was signed were the French islands of St. Pierre and Miquelon (off the south coast of Newfoundland) and

Newfoundland and Labrador, then a separate unit of the British Commonwealth.

Since murres are a traditional source of meat in winter for the coastal residents of Newfoundland, the Migratory Bird Regulations were amended after Newfoundland became a province of Canada. Murres may still be shot for food in Newfoundland, but at present only in the rural areas from September 1 to March 31. Only residents of those rural areas are permitted to shoot murres in open season and it is unlawful to sell them.

Fisher and Lockley (1954) wrote: "A conclusion from a study of the fowling on St. Kilda, the Faeroes and Iceland is that sea-birds were (and are) a source of cheap and good food, which can be indefinitely enjoyed, provided a calculated harvest can be taken from the cliffs which leaves a strong adult population behind. Further, this harvest can be large and yet not materially affect the size of the colony. Experience over some hundreds of years shows that large numbers of eggs can be taken from such species as the murre which readily lay replacements, and that from all others a crop of fat young can be taken most easily just before the young fly or swim from the colony. Furthermore, it seems that it is safe to take up to half as many young as there are in the nests".

It may be necessary some day to consider, more seriously than at present, the scientific exploitation of sea-birds for food. The ability of murres to replace their first laying is exceptionally good if eggs are taken within two or three days. Some 50 to 60 per cent of the eggs are normally lost as a result of nesting hazards. Thus it would be good management to harvest the part of the egg crop, most of which would be lost in any case. Factors which should be considered in working out a scientific program for the harvest of murres and their eggs are discussed in Appendix F.

Habitat improvement is considered one of the fundamental techniques of wildlife management. Rather little work of this type has been done with sea-birds, perhaps because there has seemed little need for it and because sea-birds are not generally considered game species. Results of a few experiments indicate that this approach has great promise.

Improvement of nesting habitat at Green Island, Newfoundland, in 1953, by clearing away debris and stacking small rocks at the edges of the slopes, indicated that habitat improvement for murres is an excellent and simple management technique. In one area of 200 square feet, completely unoccupied in 1953, clearing provided for a nesting group of 136 birds in the following year. The breeding population of two other areas, nearly 700 square feet in total area, was increased by 18 per cent in the following year. It was not possible to follow those experiments through to the sea-going period, but on two similarly improved nesting sites at Cape Hay, an average of 74.5 per cent of the eggs hatched and 97.5 per cent of the chicks got away to sea (see Table 19).

Uspenski (1956) shows that it is possible to establish a nesting colony of murres on the flat top of a cliff or island, where predation is not a factor. The first essential of occupation of horizontal surfaces is that they should be on the summits of isolated cliffs and islands, sufficiently high and having steep rocky sides. The desired results may be obtained by clearing the soil from coastal promontories and surrounding them with wire netting.

229

Concerning an experiment made in 1950, Uspenski (1956) writes:

"During the pre-nesting period in 1950 one might constantly see flocks of murres flying along the coasts. The birds' behaviour was unusual. They would fly far inland, pass by unoccupied parts of the coastal cliffs, and try to settle on very small projections or even the grass-covered flat surfaces of the upper terraces. Coming to the conclusion that the birds that were flying past the bazaars were looking for nesting-places, we cleared the soil and vegetation from the summit of a cliff where up to that time only two glaucous gulls had nested. Within three days—at the time of commencement of laying—about 20 murres were seen sitting on the cleared area and nine eggs had been laid. The total number of birds that settled there is unknown, but on August 19, when the bird bazaars were generally breaking up, there were still nine chicks of various ages at that spot. L. O. Belopolski obtained similar results in Seven Islands."

Nesting sites can be improved by combining several small ledges into one large one, as was done in one experiment at Green Island. Ledges may be combined and strengthened by paving them.

Construction of artificial ledges of concrete would appear to be quite practical. Such ledges, to meet the needs of both species of murres, should be built on those parts of the coast where the sea comes to the foot of the cliff. The height of the ledge above sea-level should not be less than 30 feet. The width and length should be as great as possible. The slope should not exceed five degrees.

Habitat improvement seems to offer almost limitless possibilities. Existing colonies could be improved so that a greater proportion of chicks could survive to reach the sea and thus contribute to the annual increment. In favourable locations murres might be induced to breed where it has hitherto been impossible because of the absence of suitable nesting ledges.

APPENDICES

Common murres banded in Newfoundland Island and Labrador, 1951-57

	Banded		Recoveries	
			Banded as	
	Adults	Chicks	Adults	Chicks
Green Island	477	4,353	2	129
Funk Island	1,000	15,100	5	281
Labrador	238	1,169	—	44
Totals:	1,715	20,622	7(0.415%)	454(2.202%)

APPENDIX B

Thick-billed murres banded in eastern North America, 1951-57

	Banded		Recoveries	
	Adults	Chicks	Adults	Chicks
Labrador	117	204	1	7
Digges Sound	2,002	8,027	6	47
Coats Island	525	—	6	—
Cape Hay	1,363	1,137	7	33
Other	128	—	—	—
Totals:	4,135	9,368	20(0.484%)	87(0.929%)

APPENDIX C

Seasonal changes in cliff populations at Cape Hay, 1957

(Ten sections or faces of the cliffs were chosen for this project. Each was clearly visible from the ice in early summer and from the land for the remainder of the season. As many as ten daily counts were made of the individual birds on those faces at varying times of the day. Two or three counts late in the evening gave the most consistent results. The following statistics are the maximum counts of a particular face of the cliff on a particular day.)

Date	1	2	3	4	5	6	7	8	9	10	Total
June 13	216	321	387	404	456	396	387	403	400	583	3953
June 14	214	322	382	404	452	397	388	402	398	582	3941
June 15	216	320	388	404	456	399	388	404	400	584	3959
June 16	—	—	—	—	—	—	—	—	—	—	
June 17	—	—	—	—	—	—	—	—	—	—	
June 18	198	313	368	388	425	383	381	388	386	562	3792
June 19	188	297	350	370	401	365	368	374	372	540	3625
June 20	188	295	350	372	404	365	367	375	370	541	3627
June 21	178	282	324	360	388	366	354	366	370	526	3514
June 22	179	281	324	361	386	367	355	366	370	528	3517
June 23	180	282	324	360	388	366	356	366	370	528	3520
June 24	180	282	326	362	388	368	356	364	371	528	3525
June 25	180	282	324	360	388	366	356	362	370	524	3512
June 26	183	284	326	361	388	368	361	361	374	532	3538
June 27	190	286	330	362	389	367	362	364	378	536	3564
June 28	188	286	329	363	389	368	360	363	378	534	3558
June 29	—	—	—	—	—	—	—	—	—	—	
June 30	190	285	332	362	389	368	361	364	376	537	3564
July 1	192	286	333	363	393	371	362	364	378	557	3599
July 2	213	301	—	—	—	—	—	—	—	—	
July 3	210	308	340	391	404	394	390	384	401	600	3822
July 4	212	308	340	—	—	—	—	—	—	—	
July 5	206	307	336	—	—	—	—	—	—	—	
July 6	210	308	335	390	403	398	392	385	401	592	3814
July 7	207	308	336	391	401	397	393	383	402	595	3813
July 8	199	308	335	390	402	398	392	385	401	590	3800
July 9	201	307	337	392	403	401	392	386	400	593	3812
July 10	200	308	335	390	402	395	391	383	401	591	3796
July 11	194	308	336	387	403	393	390	384	399	589	3783
July 12	196	307	—	—	—	—	—	388	401	590	
July 13	195	310	—	—	—	—	395	389	402	597	
July 14	195	307	338	386	404	398	394	388	401	593	3804

Date	1	2	3	4	5	6	7	8	9	10	Total
July 15	194	306	338	384	405	395	394	387	—	—	
July 16	193	306	339	386	403	395	395	384	—	—	
July 17	196	307	340	388	406	393	394	389	402	591	3806
July 18	194	305	341	388	404	394	391	386	400	594	3797
July 19	196	307	340	386	405	393	390	384	401	594	3796
July 20	195	306	341	387	405	392	390	384	400	595	3795
July 21	194	306	340	386	402	391	390	385	389	594	3777
July 22	194	307	343	385	403	394	392	384	388	601	3791
July 23	195	307	343	385	404	394	392	385	389	603	3797
July 24	—	—	—	—	—	—	—	—	—	—	
July 25	190	307	340	386	401	390	391	380	383	588	3756
July 26	191	307	342	385	399	392	390	380	387	601	3774
July 27	191	308	347	383	400	393	392	384	391	613	3802
July 28	192	308	345	384	400	395	392	388	390	615	3809
July 29	197	312	356	387	408	399	397	401	397	629	3883
July 30	199	314	360	389	408	401	398	408	396	632	3905
July 31	208	327	383	399	415	407	420	423	418	664	4064
August 1	—	—	—	—	—	—	—	431	432	681	
August 2	217	331	390	404	419	419	428	430	436	689	4163
August 3	215	332	387	404	418	416	423	432	437	683	4147
August 4	209	331	387	403	413	412	421	433	432	677	4118
August 5	215	339	401	402	411	418	424	438	436	680	4164
August 6	—	—	—	—	—	—	—	—	—	—	
August 7	—	—	—	—	—	—	—	—	—	—	
August 8	211	331	398	392	404	417	421	436	428	673	4111
August 9	209	321	396	387	401	415	418	429	416	669	4061
August 10	—	—	—	—	—	—	—	—	410	658	
August 11	—	—	—	—	—	—	—	—	403	651	
August 12	197	311	379	376	384	391	401	402	391	638	3870
August 13	—	—	—	—	—	—	—	—	—	—	
August 14	183	293	352	362	376	380	382	389	381	601	3699
August 15	183	289	343	359	382	372	380	380	385	584	3657
August 16	181	287	328	357	381	375	—	—	—	—	
August 17	180	284	321	353	379	368	371	369	382	547	3554
August 18	180	284	321	358	378	365	368	361	378	534	3527
August 19	161	207	300	293	322	308	291	287	258	357	2784
August 20	122	171	192	208	257	243	267	208	193	204	2065

APPENDIX D

List of West Greenland murres recovered in Newfoundland

Band No.	Date Banded	Date Recovered
47099	August 9, 1946	November 12, 1946
470814	August 9, 1946	February 7, 1947
472520	July 16, 1948	April 16, 1949
472548	July 16, 1948	November 26, 1949
478636	August 4, 1950	April 10, 1951
478721	August 5, 1950	March 20, 1951
474024	August 6, 1950	May, 1956
474030	August 6, 1950	February 20, 1951
474154	August 6, 1950	May 28, 1951
474017	August 6, 1950	January 28, 1952
474033	August 6, 1950	December 5, 1950 (Quebec)
474914	August 14, 1950	November 10, 1951
475815	July 27, 1951	November 6, 1951
475365	July 27, 1951	December 3, 1951
475186	July 27, 1951	January 17, 1952
475155	July 27, 1951	January 25, 1952
475133	July 27, 1951	March 13, 1952
475213	July 27, 1951	January 10, 1952
450110	July 13, 1952	February 6, 1953
474686	August 7, 1952	February, 1953
450911	August 10, 1952	December 1, 1952
451033	August 10, 1952	March 9, 1953
474530	August 3, 1954	March 14, 1956
473051	August 4, 1954	February 3, 1955
475067	August 7, 1954	November, 1954
475097	August 8, 1954	October, 1954
457431	August 3, 1955	January 21, 1956
457802	August 3, 1955	February 11, 1956
458543	August 3, 1955	March 20, 1956
457417	August 4, 1955	January, 1956
457307	August 3, 1955	March, 1956
457810	August 9, 1955	December 30, 1955
573636	July 28, 1955	February 20, 1956
456654	August 7, 1955	April 3, 1956
450715	August 9, 1956	November 15, 1956
477430	August 8, 1956	February 7, 1957
477153	August 7, 1956	February, 1957

Note: It will be noted from the above that thick-billed murres from West Greenland arrive in Newfoundland waters in late October or early November and remain at least throughout March. The occasional bird is recovered in April and more rarely in May. At least three of the birds recovered had been banded for more than two years and one was in its fifth winter.

APPENDIX E

Early attempts to protect sea-birds in Newfoundland

The early fishing ships depended on the presence of certain sea-birds to indicate that they had reached the fishing banks off Newfoundland. The great auk was one of those birds and possibly murres or "Baccalieu birds", since murres do not normally occur at any time outside the off-shore zone.

There are frequent references in the early Newfoundland literature to the value of Baccalieu birds in summer as an indicator in times of fog that land was near. It was perhaps for this reason that Baccalieu Island became a famous landmark for early voyages to Newfoundland and most, if not all ships, tried to make land at that point. It was not surprising then, that a conflict arose between the first colonists, who recognized the navigational aid of the birds, and the crews of fishing ships, who looked upon the island as peculiarly their own possession and used the birds for bait. In ARTICLES OF GRIEVANCES MENTIONED IN THE PETITION OF THE WESTERN PORTES TOUCHING THOSE OF PLANTERS OF NEWFOUNDLAND, DECR. 1618, we read:

"That they have denied and letted the Peticioners from taking birdes upon the Island of Baccalieu, the flesh of which birdes the Peticioners have heretofore used for baite until the ordinaire baite come upon the Coasts".

To which the Crown replied:

"If any their Colonie have denied the taking of birdes for fishermen's baites being a thing altogether unknown to them here—It shall be ordered to the contrary."

As the island became more colonized, the importance of the protection of sea-birds was again stressed in THE PETITION OF THE MERCHANTS, BOATKEEPERS AND PRINCIPAL INHABITANTS OF ST. JOHN'S, PETTY HARBOUR, TOR BAY, IN THE ISLAND OF NEWFOUNDLAND, 1775 TO THE HONOURABLE THE COMMONS OF GREAT BRITAIN IN PARLIAMENT ASSEMBLED:

"Contiguous to the Northern Part of this Island are a great many islands where Birds breed in vast abundance which were of great service to the inhabitants residing near them, for food in winter, and also for bait in catching of fish during the summer, of which valuable resource they are now almost entirely deprived, as great part of the birds are destroyed within a few years by the crews of men who make it their business to kill them in the breeding season, for their feathers (of which they make a Traffic) and burning the carcasses, we have applied to get this with many other grievances redressed but have yet retained a partial relief, therefore pray that an entire stop may be put to destroying the birds otherwise than for food or bait as before excepted."

The early colonists, although they apparently made laws from time to time protecting the sea-birds of Newfoundland, had no means of enforcing them. The first real protection, then, was the Proclamation of Governor Holloway in 1804 (Chapter 21). The first actual legislation for protection was "An Act for the Protection of the Breeding of Wildfowl in this Colony" on April 23, 1845. Under this act all wildfowl and the eggs of all wildfowl were protected during the breeding season, that is between May 10 and the September 1 in each year.

APPENDIX F

Principles of utilization

If rational economic utilization of murres is to be undertaken, it is necessary to establish a norm for collecting eggs and taking immature and adult birds. The problem is to determine the amount of harvest that would not diminish the adult breeding population.

In considering limits for utilization it must be borne in mind that different limits must be set, depending upon whether eggs, young birds or adult birds are taken. Obviously, most of the crop to be harvested should consist of eggs and immature birds. There is no uniformity of opinion with respect to desirable limits of harvest.

The annual increment at Cape Hay in 1957 was calculated at 41 chicks going to sea for every 100 pairs. This is an increment of approximately 20 per cent. Further losses to the young birds can be anticipated before they achieve independence. It appears very unlikely that more than 25 per cent of the potential increment gets safely to sea from any murre colony, even on flat stacks where the danger of the eggs and chicks falling into the sea is slight. Thus 75 per cent of the eggs and chicks of each murre colony perish from various causes. This large natural loss could be avoided by prior harvesting and use for human food without any drain on the reproductive potential of the colony. In fact a substantial number of fully grown but immature birds could also be safely utilized, since stable populations could be maintained if only about five per cent of the potential annual increment reached maturity.

Salomonsen (1955a) considered that stable populations could be maintained in Greenland by adhering to the following regulations:

1 Catch of birds in dip-nets to be allowed but restricted to 10 per cent of the breeding birds.

2 Egg collecting to be similarly limited to 10 per cent of the eggs.

3 Prohibition of shooting or any disturbance whatsoever within a distance of one kilometre from the colonies.

4 All catching and egg-collecting to cease after June 30.

Gorbunov (1925) suggested that egg collecting could be safely as high as 90 per cent of the birds in a colony. Portenko (1931) took a more cautious approach and estimated that the eggs should not exceed 25 per cent of the breeding population. Krasovski (1937) estimated the productivity of the Novaya Zemlya colonies at not more than 20 per cent and limited the maximum number of eggs to be taken in a colony to 10 per cent of the number of birds. Kaftanovski (1951) placed the average loss of eggs and chicks at 30 per cent and assumed that each female is capable of three layings. He concluded that eggs up to 40 or 50 per cent of the number of nesting birds could be collected annually. He considered it possible to take the whole of the first laying and even a small part of the second. Kartashev (1950) considered that in Seven Islands the eggs collected should not exceed 20 per cent of the number of nesting birds.

Work in the Soviet colonies has shown that under protection the annual increase of a murre population is about 10 per cent. Therefore, it is likely that from three to five per cent is the normal increase for murre colonies being utilized. That amount of growth is ensured by the increasing reproduction of the birds during exploitation.

It seems possible to maintain that rate of increase when eggs up to 40 per cent of the number of nesting birds are collected annually. Uspenski (1956) presented the following calculations to prove this:

1 *With protection.* One hundred birds normally produce and incubate 50 eggs and hatch 50 chicks. Egg and chick losses among murres amount to 50 per cent, so that only 25 chicks survive to enter the water. Of those 25 chicks (if it is assumed that there is no loss of adult birds), 10 young birds (40 per cent of the chicks entering the water) return to the colony two years later, increasing the total population by 10 per cent.

2 *With economic utilization.* One hundred birds produce 50 eggs, 40 of which (practically the whole of the first laying) are collected. After the eggs are taken, 60 per cent of the females (30) re-lay and produce 30 eggs, of which 50 per cent (15 eggs and chicks) are lost during the nesting period, 15 chicks surviving to enter the water.

Assuming that 40 per cent of the young birds return to the colony two years later, the annual increase of the murre population would be six per cent. Actually, a fairly large number of chicks are required to replace losses in the adult population. The rate of increase would be somewhat lower, say from three to five per cent.

At Cape Hay in 1957, 400 thick-billed murre females produced 632 eggs. That was a replacement of 58 per cent. Since the eggs replaced were normal losses in various stages of incubation, the replacement would have been considerably higher had the eggs been removed by exploitation within a day or two of laying. Uspenski (1956) determined that first replacement could be as high as 77.3 per cent of freshly collected eggs. With this evidence, I think it fairly safe to collect up to 50 per cent of the first laying without unduly disturbing the productivity of the colony.

At this time, I cannot agree that the collection of the entire first laying is advisable, even if possible. Losses of eggs and chicks from a second laying may be substantially higher than from the first laying. This is suggested by observations on losses of chicks from the first and second layings in Bezymyannaya Bay (Uspenski, 1956). Of 42 chicks from the first laying, 64.2 per cent survived to enter the water but of 34 chicks from the second laying, only 38.2 per cent survived. The probability of mortality from exposure or even starvation increases as the summer advances. I cannot agree that it would be wise to harvest even a small part of the second laying. Chicks raised from second replacements must remain at least six weeks later on the nesting cliffs than those from the first laying. It is most unlikely that late chicks have a high survival rate. In fact, if they reach the fledgling stage, they may very well be stunted and inferior.

In my opinion, egg collection at a murre colony should commence as soon as the birds begin to lay and the collecting period should not exceed two weeks. By that time, most of the birds have laid their first egg. If a large part of the colony is inaccessible, a system of rotation might be established. Collection of the complete first laying on certain ledges should alternate with years of rest. Details of management of each colony should, however, be judged on the particular conditions which exist there. Every project should be under the supervision of a biologist whose duty would be to assure an adequate survival of eggs.

Because of the rapid cessation of ovary activity in the females, eggs in exploited colonies should be collected at least every two days of the suggested two-week period. This would assure that all eggs taken were fresh and could be used for human food. Because of the thickness of the shell, candling murre eggs to determine their freshness by submerging them in fresh water and discarding those that barely sink with the large end uppermost, is not entirely effective.

Collected eggs spoil quickly under the conditions of high humidity and fluctuating air temperatures typical of most regions along the coasts of the Northern Hemisphere. Serious attention should be given to the primary care and preservation of collected eggs. None of the primitive methods of keeping them in salt, ashes, or sand or on ice is effective for long.

Murre eggs remain edible as long as four months if placed in a saturated solution of lime. This method is widely used for preserving domestic eggs. Its chief defect is that the eggs acquire a faint but definite limey taste. A thin layer of melted paraffin also gives very good results. It prevents the loss of weight and preserves the eggs for two months or longer.

The method now most widely used in Russia for preserving murre eggs is pasteurization, combined with a covering of melted paraffin. This method, also commonly used in the Soviet poultry industry, is simple, cheap and effective (97 per cent in room temperatures at four months). The eggs are pasteurized for five seconds in a boiling solution of ash lye. After being well dried, the pasteurized eggs are covered with a thin film of melted paraffin.

When murres are exploited at their breeding sites, only the eggs should be taken. Young murres are rarely utilized, even at the traditional fowling cliffs of the Old World. In addition to the fact that such harvesting would be undesirable biologically, the young birds on the cliffs are small (one-quarter the weight of an adult) and not very fat. This is in contrast to nestling gannets and fulmars, the young of which are excessively fat and before leaving the nesting colonies may actually weigh more than the adults.

Throughout the world some one million adult murres are utilized annually, providing some two million pounds of meat. In terms of the world population, this is not excessive, since it is only about two per cent of the estimated world population and includes a preponderance of birds of the first year.

Shooting murres in Newfoundland, the only region in North America where this is now permitted, accounts for from 100,000 to 200,000 birds annually. It is probably closer to the former figure at present. Since a minimum of five million murres winter off the coast of Newfoundland, approximately two per cent of the winter population is taken. Banding murres has revealed some very interesting facts about this population. The largest proportion of the take in Newfoundland is composed of first-year thick-billed murres from the colonies in West Greenland and the eastern Canadian Arctic. The take of adults is very low (one-tenth of one per cent), since adults tend to stay farther north and farther off shore and are generally less accessible.

So long as eggs are not utilized in eastern North America, it would be feasible to harvest from 10 to 20 per cent of the wintering populations off Newfoundland, or five to ten times the present utilization in that region. Such an increase in the harvest should be limited to the months of October and November and to the northeastern coast of Newfoundland, where the impact would be largely on immature thick-billed murres.

Some local common murres in their first year are shot off Newfoundland. This is because local birds are available throughout the year. Local immature common murres winter largely off the south and southeast coasts. Since the local colonies are increasing, there appears to be no excess utilization. Local adults, since they remain farther off shore, are less accessible and are rarely shot (one in 1,000).

Should it ever be possible to allow a larger harvest of murres in Newfoundland, there should be no shooting within a 20-mile radius of the breeding sites at any time of the year, because the adults are largely sedentary except for a brief period after the nesting season is concluded.

REFERENCES

AHLMANN, H. W.
1953. Glacier variations and climatic fluctuations. New York.

ALDRICH, ELMER C.
1938. Oil contamination of California murres. Bird-Lore 40:110.

ALDRICH, JOHN W., and DAVID C. NUTT
1939. Birds of eastern Newfoundland. Sci. Pub. Cleveland Mus. nat. Hist. 4:13–42.

ALLEN, ARTHUR A.
1948. Sea-bird cities off Audubon's Labrador. Nat. geog. Mag. 93:755–774.

ALLEN, G. M.
1909. List of the Aves of New England. Occ. Pap. Boston Soc. nat. Hist. Vol. 7, No. 11.

ANSPACH, LEWIS A.
1819. A history of the Island of Newfoundland. London.

ATKINSON, ROBERT
1949. Island going. London.

AUDUBON, JOHN JAMES
1840-1844. The birds of America. New York.

AUSTIN, OLIVER LUTHER, JR.
1932. The birds of Newfoundland Labrador. Mem. Nuttall orn. Cl., No. VII. Cambridge, U.S.A.

AUSTIN, OLIVER L., JR., and
NAGAHISA KURODA
1953. The birds of Japan—their status and distribution. Bull. Mus. comp. Zool., Harv. 109:280–637.

BAGENAL, T. B.
1950. Birds of the North Atlantic and Newfoundland Banks in July and August, 1950. Brit. Birds 44:187–195.

BAILEY, ALFRED M.
1943. The birds of Cape Prince of Wales, Alaska. Proc. Colo. Mus. nat. Hist. 18:1–113.

BAILEY, ALFRED M.
1948. Birds of arctic Alaska. Colo. Mus. nat. Hist.

BAIRD, S. F., T. M. BREWER and
R. RIDGWAY
1884. A history of North American birds. Boston.

BARABASH—NIKIFOROV, I.
1938. Mammals of the Commander Islands and the surrounding seas. J. Mamm. 19:423–429.

BAXTER, E. V. and L. J. RINTOUL
1953. The birds of Scotland. Edinburgh.

BAYLEY, IVAN A.
1925. The birds of Bird Islands, Nova Scotia. Canad. Field Nat. 39:183–187.

BELOPOSKAYA, M. M.
1947. Parasitic fauna of the Seven Islands Sanctuary (East Murman). Lecture, Leningrad State Univ. (In Russian).

BENT, A. C.
1919. Life histories of North American diving birds. U.S. nat. Mus. Bull. 107.

BERNIS, F.
1949. Las aves de las Islas Sisargas en junio. Bol. Soc. Hist. nat. 46:647–648

BERTHET, G.
1947. La nidification de Rissa tridactyla et Uria aalge (variété ringia) en France. Alauda, 15:203–208.

BERTRAM, G. C. L. and DAVID LACK
1933. Notes on the birds of Bear Island. Ibis, Ser. 13, 3:283–301.

BERTRAM, G. C. L., D. LACK, and
S. B. ROBERTS
1934. Notes on East Greenland birds, with a discussion of the periodic non-breeding among arctic birds. Ibis Ser. 13, 4:816–831.

BIGELOW, HENRY B., and WILLIAM C. SCHROEDER
1953. Fishes of the Gulf of Maine. Woods Hole oceanogr. Inst., Contr. No. 592.

BIRD, C. G. and E. G. BIRD
1940. Some remarks on non-breeding in the Arctic, especially in Northeast Greenland. Ibis Ser. 14, 4:671–678.

BISHOP, LOUIS B.
1889. Notes on the birds of Magdalen Islands. Auk 6:144–150.

BOARDMAN, GEORGE A.
1862. Catalogue of the birds found in the vicinity of Calais, Maine, and about the islands at the mouth of the Bay of Fundy. Proc. Boston Soc. nat. Hist. 9:122–132.

BONNYCASTLE, RICHARD H.
1842. Newfoundland in 1842. London.

BRAESTRUP, F. W.
1941. A study on the arctic fox in Greenland. Medd. Grønland, Nr. 4. København.

BREWSTER, WILLIAM
1883. Notes on the birds observed during a cruise in the Gulf of St. Lawrence. Proc. Boston Soc. nat. Hist. 22:364.

BRUN, ESKE
1957. Greenland to-day. Arctic 10:119–121.

BRYANT, HENRY
1861. Remarks on some of the birds that breed in the Gulf of St. Lawrence. Proc. Boston Soc. nat. Hist. 8:65–75.

BRYANT, WALTER E.
1888. Birds and eggs from the Farallone Islands. Proc. Calif. Acad. Sci. 1:25–50.

CADE, TOM
1952. Notes on the birds of Sledge Island, Bering Sea, Alaska. Condor 54:51–54.

CARSON, RACHEL L.
1950. The sea around us. Oxford.

CLARKE, C. H. D.
1944. Notes on the status and distribution of certain mammals and birds in the Mackenzie River and Western Arctic area in 1942 and 1953. Canad. Field Nat. 58:97–103.

CLARKE, W. EAGLE
1890. The birds of Jan Mayen Island. Zoologist 14:1–16, 41–51.

CLARKE, W. E.
1898. The birds of Franz Josef Land. Proc. R. phys. Soc. 14:87–112.

CORDEAUX, J.
1884. The sea-birds at Flamborough. Naturalist 9:93–95.

COTT, HUGH B.
1953. The exploitation of wild birds for their eggs. Ibis 95:409–449, 643–675.

COTT, HUGH B.
1954a. The exploitation of wild birds for their eggs. Ibis 96:129–149.

COTT, HUGH B.
1954b. The palatability of the eggs of birds; mainly based upon observations of an egg panel. Proc. zool. Soc. Lond. 124:335–463.

COUES, E.
1861. Notes on the ornithology of Labrador. Proc. Acad. nat. Sci. Philad. 13.:215–257.

CULLEN, J. M.
1954. The diurnal rhythm of birds in the arctic summer. Ibis 96:31–46.

DARLING, F. F.
1938. Bird flocks and the breeding cycle. Cambridge, England.

DAVIES, D. H.
1956. Bird predators, 1954–55. Investig. Rep. No. 23, Div. Fish., Dep. Comm. and Indust., Union of South Africa.

DAVIES, O. J. H., and R. D. KEYNES
1948. The Cape St. Mary gannet colony. Ibis 90:538–546.

DAVIS, D. H. S.
1936. A reconnaissance of the fauna of Akpatok Island, Ungava Bay. J. Anim. Ecol. 5:319–331.

DEMENTEV, G. P. et al.
1951. Birds of the Soviet Union, Vol. 2. Moscow. (In Russian).

DEMME, MRS. N. P.
1934. Life on a bird rock (Rubini Rock on Hooker Island, Franz Josef Land). Trans. arct. Inst., Leningr. (In Russian).

DIONNE, C. E.
1920. Liste des oiseaux de l'isle d'Anticosti. Nat. Canad. 47:25–29.

DOBSON, R.
1952. The birds of the Channel Islands. London.

DUFFEY, ERIC and DAVID E. SERGEANT
1950. Field notes on the birds of Bear Island. Ibis. 92:554–563.

DUNBAR, M. J.
1954. A note on climatic change in the sea. Arctic 71:27–30.

DUNBAR, M. J.
1955a. Water masses. *In* Geography of the Northlands. Washington.

DUNBAR, M. J.
1955b. Marine life. *In* Geography of the Northlands. Washington.

DUNBAR, M. J. and H. H. HILDEBRAND
1952. Contribution to the study of the fishes of Ungava Bay. J. Fish. Res. Bd. Canada 9:83–128.

ELLIOTT, HENRY WOOD
1880. Report on the Seal Islands of Alaska. Washington.

ELLIS, D. V.
1956. Observations on the migration, distribution and breeding of Canadian birds in the Canadian Arctic during 1954 and 1955. Dansk orn. Foren. Tidsskr. 50:207-229.

EMERSON, W. OTTO
1904. The Farallone Islands revisited, 1887-1903. Condor 6:61.

ENGLISH, ARTHUR
1918. Gannet colonies. Ottawa Nat. 32:98.

EVANS, WILLIAM
1891. On the periods occupied by birds in the incubation of their eggs. Ibis 33:52–93.

FENCKER, E.
1889. The birds of Greenland. Medd. Grønland, Nr. 7. København. (In Danish).

FERDINAND, L.
1947. Studier af fuglelivet paa Faerøerne. Dansk. orn. Foren. Tidsskr. 41:1–37.

FISHER, JAMES
1956. Are guillemots decreasing? Country Fair, July. London.

FISHER, JAMES and R. M. LOCKLEY
1954. Sea-birds. London.

FISHER, JAMES and H. G. VEVERS
1943-44. The breeding distribution, history and population of the North Atlantic gannet (*Sula bassana*). J. Anim. Ecol. 12:173–213; 13:49–62.

FLEMING, J. H.
1907. The unusual migration of Brunnich's murre (*Uria lomvia*) in eastern North America. Proc. 4th int. orn. Congr.

FOSTER, R. J., R. L. BAXTER, and P. A. J. BALL
1951. A visit to Grimsey (Iceland), July-August, 1944. Ibis 93:53–59.

FRAZAR, MARTIN ABBOTT
1887. An ornithologist's summer in Labrador. Orn. and Oolog. 12:1–3.

FREUCHEN, PETER and FINN SALOMONSEN
1958. The arctic year. New York.

FROHAWK, F. W.
1928. Speed of the guillemot. Field, 152:995. London.

GABRIELSON, IRA N.
1940. America's greatest bird concentrations. Bird-Lore 42:497–506.

GABRIELSON, IRA N.
1952. Notes on the birds of the North Shore of the Gulf of St. Lawrence. Canad. Field Nat. 66:44–59.

GABRIELSON, IRA N., and FREDERICK C. LINCOLN
1959. Birds of Alaska. Wildl. Mgmt. Inst., Washington, D.C.

GÄTKE, H.
1895. Heligoland as an ornithological observatory, the result of fifty years of experience. Edinburgh.

GIBSON, J. A.
1951. The breeding distribution, population and history of the birds of Ailsa Craig. Scot. Nat. 63:73–100, 159–177.

GIBSON, L.
1922. Bird notes from North Greenland. Auk 39:350–363.

GILLIARD, E. THOMAS
1937. The gannets of Funk Island. Auk 54:379–381.

GIZENKO, A. I.
1955. Birds of the Sakhalin area. Acad. Sci. (Sakhalin Dep.), Moscow. (In Russian).

GODFREY, W. EARL
1958. Birds of Cape Breton Island, Nova Scotia. Canad. Field Nat. 72:7–27.

GORBUNOV, G. P.
1925. The bird bazaars of Novaya Zemlya. Trans. Inst. Northern Studies, Moscow. (In Russian).

GORBUNOV, G. P.
1929. Mammal and bird fauna of Novaya Zemlya. Trans. Inst. Northern Studies, Moscow. (In Russian).

GRAYCE, ROBERT
1947. Birds of the MacMillan Labrador Expedition. Auk 64:275–280.

GRIEVE, SYMINGTON
1885. The great auk or garefowl, its history, archeology and remains. London.

GROSS, ALFRED O.
1937. Birds of the Bowdoin-MacMillan Arctic Expedition. Auk 54:12–42.

GUDMUNDSSON, FINNUR
1951. The effects of the recent climatic changes on the bird life of Iceland. Proc. 10th. int. orn. Cong.

GUIGUET, C. J.
1950. Notes on common murres nesting in British Columbia. Murrelet 31:12–13.

GURNEY, J. H.
1913. The gannet. London.

HAKLUYT, RICHARD
1660. Collection of voyages. Vol. 3. London.

HANNA, G. DALLAS
1917. The summer birds of the St. Matthew Island Reservation. Auk 34:403–410.

HANTZSCH, BERNARD
1908. Beitrag sur Kenntniss der Vogelwelt des Nordostlichsten Labradors. J. Orn., Lpz. 56:177–202, 307–392.

HARDY, MANLY
1897. Regarding the Brunnich's murre. Osprey 2:26.

HARE, F. KENNETH
1952. The climate of the island of Newfoundland: a geographical analysis. Geogr. Bull. No. 2, Dep. Mines and Tech. Surv., Ottawa.

HARE, F. KENNETH
1955. Weather and climate. *In* Geography of the Northlands. Washington.

HARTLEY, C. J. and J. FISHER
1936. The marine foods of birds in an inland fjord in West Spitsbergen. J. Anim. Ecol. 5:370–389.

HATTON, JOSEPH and REV. M. HARVEY
1883. Newfoundland, the oldest British colony, its present condition and its prospects in the future. London.

HAYES, I. I.
1867. The open polar sea. London.

HEERMAN, A. L.
1859. Reports of explorations. (*In* Cott, 1954a).

HEWITT, OLIVER H.
1950. Fifth census of non-passerine birds in the bird sanctuaries of the North Shore of the Gulf of St. Lawrence. Canad. Field Nat. 64:73–76.

HÖHN, E. O.
1955. Birds and mammals observed on a cruise in Amundsen Gulf, N.W.T., July 29th-August 16th, 1953. Canad. Field Nat. 69:41–44.

HOLGERSON, HOLGER
1951. Hvor Kommer Alkene Fra? Saertrykk av Stavanger Museums Arbok.

HORR, A. R.
1947. The log of the schooner *Bowdoin.* (With appendix on Labrador birds by A. M. Bailey.) New York.

HØRRING, R.
1937. Report of the Fifth Thule Expedition, 1921-24. Vol. 2, No. 6. Copenhagen.

JACQUES, FRANCIS LEE
1930. Water birds observed on the Arctic Ocean and the Bering Sea in 1928. Auk 47:353–366.

JAGERSKIOLD, L. A., and G. KOLTHOFF
1926. Norden Faglar. Stockholm.

JEWETT, STANLEY G. *et al.*
1953. Birds of Washington State. Univ. of Washington.

JOHNSON, R. A.
1938. Predation of gulls in murre colonies. Wilson Bull. 50:161-170.

JOHNSON, R. A.
1940. Present range, migration and abundance of the Atlantic murre in North America. Bird-banding 11:1–17.

JOHNSON, R. A.
1941. Nesting behaviour of the Atlantic murre. Auk 58:153–163.

JOHNSON, R. A.
1944. Weight records for some Atlantic Alcidae. Wilson Bull. 56:161–168.

JOURDAIN, REV. F. C. R.
1922. The birds of Spitsbergen and Bear Island. Ibis 64:159–179.

KAEDING, HENRY B.
1905. Birds from the west coast of Lower California and adjacent islands. Condor 7:105.

KAFTANOVSKI, YU. M.
1938. Colonial nesting of murres and factors in egg and chick loss. Zool. Zh. 17:695–705. (In Russian).

KAFTANOVSKI, YU. M.
1951. Alcids of the East Atlantic. Moscow. (In Russian).

KANE, ELISHA K.
1856. Arctic explorations: the second Grinnell Expedition in search of Sir John Franklin in 1853, '54, '55. Philadelphia.

KARPLUS, MARTIN
1947. Massachusetts Alcids. Bull. Mass. Audubon Soc. 31:21–32.

KARTASHEV, N. N.
1950. Biology of the development of alcids in the East Atlantic. Lecture, Moscow State Univ. NIIZ lib. (In Russian).

KAY, G. T.
1947. The young guillemot's flight to the sea. Brit. Birds, 40:156–157.

KEIGHLEY, J. and R. M. LOCKLEY
1947. Fledging periods of the razorbill, guillemot and kittiwake. Brit. Birds 40:165–171.

KIRKMAN, F. B.
1912. The British bird book. London.

KRASOVSKI, S. K.
1937. Studies on the biology of Brunnich's murre. Trans. arct. Inst., Leningrad. (In Russian).

KUMLIEN, L.
1879. Birds. *In* Contributions to the Natural History of Arctic America. U.S. Nat. Mus. Bull. 15:69–105.

LEGENDRE, R.
1926. Un poisson qui pêche des oiseaux. Nature, Paris, No. 20725:413–414.

LEMIEUX, LOUIS
1956. Seventh census of non-passerine birds in the bird sanctuaries of the North Shore of the Gulf of St. Lawrence. Canad. Field Nat. 70:183–185.

LE ROI, O.
1911. Spezieller Teil. *In:* A. Koenig, Avifauna Spitsbergenis. Bonn.

LEWIS, HARRISON F.
1924. List of birds recorded from the Island of Anticosti, Quebec. Canad. Field Nat. 38:43–46; 72–75.

LEWIS, HARRISON F.
1930. Notes on banding operations on the North Shore of the Gulf of St. Lawrence in 1929. Bird-banding 1:95–103.

LEWIS, HARRISON F.
1931. Five years' progress in the bird sanctuaries of the North Shore of the Gulf of St. Lawrence. Canad. Field Nat. 45:73–78.

LEWIS, HARRISON F.
1937. A decade of progress in the bird sanctuaries of the North Shore of the Gulf of St. Lawrence. Canad. Field Nat. 51:51–55.

LEWIS, HARRISON F.
1942. Fourth census of non-passerine birds in the bird sanctuaries of the North Shore of the Gulf of St. Lawrence. Canad. Field Nat. 56:5–8.

LEWIS, STANLEY
1936. Birds of the Island of Steep Holm. Brit. Birds 30:219–223.

LOCKLEY, R. M.
1942. Shearwaters. London.

LONGSTAFF, T. G.
1924. Notes from Spitsbergen, 1923. Ibis 6:480–495.

LOPPENTHIN, B.
1932. Die Vogel Nordostgronlands swichen 73°11′ und 75°30′ N. Medd. Grønland, Nr. 91. (In German).

LOW, ALBERT P.
1906. Report on the Dominion Government Expedition to Hudson Bay and the Arctic Islands, D.G.S. 'Neptune', 1903-4. Canada, Dep. Mar. Fish., Ottawa.

LUCAS, FREDERICK A.
1888. The expedition to the Funk Island, with observations upon the history and anatomy of the great auk. U.S. nat. Mus. Rep., 1887-88: 493-529.

LYSGAARD, L.
1950. On the present climatic variation. Cent. Proc. roy. met. Soc.

MACKENZIE, N.
1905. Notes on birds of St. Kilda. Ann. Scot. nat. Hist. 14:75–80, 141–153.

M'CLINTOCK, ADMIRAL SIR F. LEOPOLD
1859. The voyage of the "Fox" in arctic seas, in search of Franklin and his companions. London.

MACOUN, JOHN and JAMES M. MACOUN
1909. Catalogue of Canadian birds. Canada, Dep. Mines, Ottawa.

MANNICHE, A. L. V.
1910. The terrestrial birds and mammals of northeast Greenland. Danmark-Ekspeditionen til Grønlands Nordøstkyst 1906-1908. Bd. 5 Nr. 2. (Medd. Grønland, 1912. Bd. 45.)

MANNING, T. H., E. O. HÖHN, and A. H. MACPHERSON
1956. The birds of Banks Island. Nat. Mus. Canada Bull. No. 143.

MARKHAM, C. R.
1881. The voyages of William Baffin, 1612-1622. Hakluyt Soc., London.

MARKOV, G. S.
1937. Changes with age in the parasitic fauna of the Novaya Zemlya murre (*Uria lomvia lomvia*). Trans. Leningrad Nat. Soc., Vol. 56, No. 3. (In Russian).

MARTIN, M.
1698. A late voyage to St. Kilda, the remotest of all the Hebrides, or western isles of Scotland. London.

MELA, A. J.
1904. *Uria arra* Pall., tavattu Suomen valtiollisella alalla. Medd. Soc. Fauna Fl. fenn. Vol 29.

MILLER, ALDEN H. and FRANK E. PEABODY
1941. An additional pleistocene occurrence of the murre, *Uria aalge*. Condor 43:78.

MILLER, LOYE and HILDEGARDE HOWARD
1948. The flightless Pliocene bird Mancalla. Publ. Carneg. Inst. No. 584.

MILNE, JOHN
1875. Relics of the great auk on Funk Island. Field, March 27, April 3, and April 10.

MODESTOV, V. M.
1941. Ecology of colonial-nesting birds. Lecture, Moscow State Univ. NIIZ Lib. (In Russian).

MÜLLER, R.
1906. Vildtet og Jagten i Sydgrønland. København.

MURPHY, R.
1936. Oceanic birds of South America. Amer. Mus. nat. Hist., New York.

NELSON, EDWARD WILLIAM
1883. Birds of the Bering Sea and the Arctic Ocean. *In* Cruise of the Revenue-Steamer Corwin in Alaska and N.W. Arctic Ocean in 1881. Washington.

NELSON, EDWARD WILLIAM
1887. Birds of Alaska and a partial bibliography of Alaskan ornithology. *In* Report upon Natural History Collections made in Alaska Between the Years 1877 and 1881. Washington.

NEWTON, ALFRED
1865. Notes on the birds of Spitsbergen. Ibis 7:199–219, 6–525.

NØRREVANG, ARNE
1955. Changes in the bird-life of the Faeroes in relation to the climatic changes in the North Atlantic area. Dansk. Orn. Foren. Tidsskr. 49:206–229.

NØRREVANG, ARNE
1958. On the breeding biology of the guillemot (*Uria aalge* (Pont.)). Dansk. Orn. Foren. Tidsskr. 52:48–74.

NORTON, ARTHUR H.
1923. Notes on the birds of the Knox
County region (pts. 1 and 2), Maine
Nat. 3:1–4, 31–35.

OSGOOD, W. H., E. A. PREBLE, and
G. H. PARKER
1915. The fur seals and other life of the
Pribilof Islands, Alaska, in 1914.
Senate Documents, Vol. 6, No. 980,
Washington.

PACKARD, A. S.
1891. The Labrador coast. A journal of
two summer cruises in that region. (List
of birds by L. M. Turner, revised by
J. A. Allen). New York.

DE PAILLERETS, B.
1927. Catalogue des oiseaux du
Départment de la Charente-Inférieure.
Rev. franç. Orn.

PALMER, RALPH S.
1949. Maine birds. Cambridge, U.S.A.

PARIS, P.
1921. Faune de France. Vol. 2. Paris.

PEDERSON, ALWIN
1931. Fortgesetzte Beitrage zur
Kenntnis der Saugetier und Vogelfauna
Ostkuste Grønlands. Medd. Grønland,
Nr. 77. (In German).

PENNYCUICK, C. J.
1956. Observations on a colony of
Brunnich's guillemots, *Uria lomvia*, in
Spitsbergen. Ibis 98:80–89.

PERRY, R.
1940. Lundy, isle of puffins. London.

PERRY, R.
1944. Five months with guillemots.
Geogr. Mag., Lond. 17:84–95.

PERRY, R.
1948. Shetland sanc ary. London.

PETERS, HAROLD S.
1942. A new gannet colony in
Newfoundland. Auk 59:100.

PETERS, HAROLD S. and THOMAS D.
BURLEIGH
1951. The birds of Newfoundland.
St. John's.

PETERSON, ROGER TORY, and JAMES
FISHER
1955. Wild America. Boston.

PITT, T. K.
1958. Distribution, spawning and
racial studies of the capelin, *Mallotus
villosus* (Müller) in the offshore
Newfoundland area. J. Fish. Res. Bd.
Canada 15:275–293.

PORTAZ, REGINALD
1928. Speed of the guillemot. Field
152:819. London.

PORTENKO, L.
1931. Productive potentialities of the
bird fauna of Novaya Zemlya. Trav.
Lab. Biogeochim., Acad. Sci. U.R.S.S.
Appendix II. (In Russian).

PORTENKO, L.
1944. New subspecies of birds from
Wrangel Island. C. R. (Doklady)
Acad. Sci. U.R.S.S. 43:225–228.
(In Russian).

RAY, MILTON S.
1904. A fortnight on the Farallones.
Auk 21:425–442.

REAGAN, A. B.
1910. Destruction of young water birds
in a storm. Auk 37:92.

ROLNIK, V. V.
1948. Development of thermoregulation
in various birds of the north. Zool. Zh.,
Vol. 27, No. 6.

RUSANOFF, V.A.
1910. Description of the coasts and
interior parts of Novaya Zemlya from
Admiralteystva Peninsula to
Krestovaya Bay and from the latter to
Neznayemyy Bay. *In* Materials on the
Exploration of Novaya Zemlya, Part 1.
I. V. Sosnovski, ed. Moscow. (In
Russian).

SADOVSKI, B. I.
1910. Russian Colonization of Novaya
Zemlya. *In* Materials on the
Exploration of Novaya Zemlya, Part 1.
I. V. Sosnovski, ed. Moscow. (In
Russian).

SALOMONSEN, FINN
1932. Descriptions of three new
guillemots (*Uria aalge*). Ibis
73:128–132.

SALOMONSEN, FINN
1935. Zoology of the Faroes, Vol. 3.
København.

SALOMONSEN, FINN
1943. Fugetaelinger 1936–1942 paa Hirsholmene og Christiansø. Dansk. orn. Foren. Tidsskr. 37:151–181.

SALOMONSEN, FINN
1944. The Atlantic alcidae; the seasonal and geographical variation of the auks inhabiting the Atlantic ocean and the adjacent water. Sjatte följder, Ser. B., Vol. 3, No. 5. Goteborg.

SALOMONSEN, FINN
1948. The distribution of birds and the recent climatic change in the North Atlantic area. Dansk. orn. Foren. Tidsskr. 42:85–99.

SALOMONSEN, FINN
1951. The birds of Greenland. Vol. 3. København.

SALOMONSEN, FINN
1955. Bird preservation in Greenland. Dansk. orn. Foren. Tidsskr. 49:1–11. (In Danish, with English summary).

SALOMONSEN, FINN
1956. The Greenland bird-banding system. Arctic 9:258–264.

SAXBY, H. L.
1874. The birds of Shetland. Edinburgh.

SCHAANING, H. THO. L.
1923. Zoological results of the Norwegian Scientific Expedition to Novaya Zemlya in 1921. Kristiania.

SCHERMAN, KATHERINE
1956. Spring on an arctic island. Boston.

SCHMIDT-NIELSON, KNUT, and RAGNAR FANGE
1958. The function of the salt gland in the brown pelican. Auk 75:282–289.

SCHMITT, JOSEPH
1904. Monographie de l'ile d'Anticosti. Oiseaux: 289–309. Paris.

SCHULTZ, H.
1947. Die Welt der Seevogel ein Fuhrer durch die Vogelbrutstatten der deutschen Kusten. Hamburg.

SELIGMAN, O. R. and J. M. WILCOX
1940. Some observations on the birds of Jan Mayen. Ibis 82:464–479.

SELOUS, E.
1905. The bird-watcher in the Shetlands. London.

SERGEANT, D. E.
1951. Ecological relationships of the guillemots *Uria aalge* and *Uria lomvia*. Proc. 10th. int. orn. Cong.

SERGEANT, D. E.
1952. Little auks in Britain, 1948 to 1951. Brit. Birds 45:122–133.

SMITH, H. W.
1953. From fish to philosopher. Boston.

SNYDER, L. L.
1957. Arctic birds of Canada. Toronto.

SOPER, J. D.
1946. Ornithological results of the Baffin Island expeditions of 1928-29 and 1930-31, together with more recent records. Auk 63:1–24, 223–239, 418–427.

SOUTHERN, H. N.
1939. The status and problems of the bridled guillemot. Proc. zool. Soc. Lond. 109:31–41.

SOUTHERN, H. N.
1951. Change in status of the bridled guillemot after ten years. Proc. zool. Soc. Lond. 121:657–671.

SQUIRES, W. AUSTIN
1952. The birds of New Brunswick. Monogr. Ser., No. 4, New Brunsw. Mus., Saint John.

STECHOW, J.
1938. Ueber die jahreszeitliche Verbreitung der europaischen Lummen (*Uria aalge* (Pont.)). Vogelzug 9:125–138.

STEENSTRUP, J.
1855. Et Bidrag til Gejrfuglens, *Alca impennis* Lin. Medd. fra Naturhist. Forening i Kjobenhavn. (French translation: Bull. Soc. orn. Suisse 2, No. 1, 1868. German translation: Bull. Scient. de l'Acad. de St. Petersbourg, No. 6, 1863).

STORER, ROBERT W.
1952. A comparison of variation, behaviour and evolution in the sea-bird genera *Uria* and *Cepphus*. Univ. Calif. Publ. Zool. 52:121–222.

SUTTON, GEORGE MIKSCH
1932. The birds of Southampton Island. Mem. Carneg. Mus., Vol. 12, Part 2, Sec. 2.

SVERDRUP, H. U., N. M. JOHNSON, and R. H. FLEMING
1942. The oceans, their physics, chemistry and general biology. New York.

SWARTH, HARRY SCHELWALD
1934. Birds of Nunivak Island, Alaska. Pacif. Cst. Avif., No. 22.

TAIT, W. C.
1924. The birds of Portugal. London.

TANING, A. V.
1930. Sortfugle og fisk ved Island. Nat. Verd., Kbh., Vol. 14.

TECHAU, G.
1936. Die Nasendruse der Vogel. J. Orn., Lpz. 84:511–617.

TEMPLEMAN, WILFRED and A. M. FLEMING
1953. Long term changes in hydrographic conditions and corresponding changes in the abundance of marine animals. Annu. Proc. int. Comm. N.W. Atlantic Fish. 3(5):3–10.

TEMPLEMAN, WILFRED
1945. Observations on some Newfoundland sea-birds. Canad. Field Nat. 59:136–147.

TENER, JOHN
1951. Sixth census of non-passerine birds in the bird sanctuaries of the North Shore of the Gulf of St. Lawrence. Canad. Field Nat. 65:65–68.

TOCQUE, PHILIP
1846. Wandering thoughts, or solitary hours. London.

TOWNSEND, CHARLES W.
1920. Notes on the summer birds of the Gaspé Peninsula. Canad. Field Nat. 34:78–80.

TREVOR-BATTYE, AUBYN
1896. On the common guillemot in Kolguev. Ibis 38:155.

TREVOR-BATTYE, AUBYN
1897. The birds of Spitsbergen. Ibis 39:574–600.

TUCK, LESLIE M., and H. J. SQUIRES
1955. Food and feeding habits of Brunnich's murre (*Uria lomvia lomvia*) on Akpatok Island. J. Fish. Res. Bd. Canada 12:781–792.

TUCKER, EPHRAIM W.
1839. Five months in Labrador and Newfoundland. Concord, N.H.

TURNER, LUCIEN M.
1885. List of the birds of Labrador, including Ungava, East Maine, Moose, and Gulf Districts of the Hudson Bay Company, together with the Island of Anticosti. Proc. U.S. nat. Mus. 8:233–254.

TYROVA, G. A.
1939. Murre eggs and reindeer meat. Collection scientific works of the Archangel branch of the San.–Bact. Inst. for 1935-1937, Vol. 1, Archangel. (In Russian).

USPENSKI, A. A., M. A. PODLEGAYEFF, and V. S. TONGUR
1948. Technology of poultry products. Moscow. (In Russian).

USPENSKI, S. M.
1956. The bird bazaars of Novaya Zemlya U.S.S.R. Acad. Sci., Moscow. (English translation: Canad. Wildl. Serv., Translations of Russian Game Reports, No. 4.).

USPENSKI, V. S.
1941. Birds of Seven Islands. Trans. Seven Islands Sanctuary, Vol. 1. Moscow. (In Russian).

VENABLES, L. S. V., and U. M. VENABLES
1955. Birds and mammals of Shetland. London.

VERRILL, A. E.
1865. Catalogue of the birds observed at Anticosti and vicinity. Proc. Boston Soc. nat. Hist. 9:137–143.

VOUS, K. H.
1948. Notes on the races of *Uria aalge* (Pont.) occurring along the Dutch North sea coast. Limosa 21:10–14.

WAHLIN, B.
1944. The murre population of the Baltic region. Svensk faun. Rev. 4/44. (In Swedish).

WASHBURN, A. L.
1951. Geography and arctic lands. *In* Taylor's Geography in the Twentieth Century. New York.

WATSON, ADAM
1957. Birds in Cumberland Peninsula, Baffin Island. Canad. Field Nat. 71:87–109.

WATT, G.
1951. The Farne Islands. London.

WIGELSWORTH, J.
1903. St. Kilda and its birds. Liverpool.

WILLET, H. C.
1950. Temperature trends of the past century. Cent. Proc. roy. met. Soc.

WILLIAMSON, K.
1945. The economic importance of sea-fowl in the Faeroe Islands. Ibis 87:249–269.

WINGE, H.
1898. Grønlands Fugle. Medd. Grønland, Nr. 21. (In Danish; also contains unpublished notes by J. Vahl and E. Fencher).

WITHERBY, H. F.
1924. A practical handbook of birds, Vol. 2. London.

WITHERBY, H. F. *et al.*
1941. The handbook of British birds. Vol. 5. London.

WYNNE-EDWARDS, V. C.
1935. On the habits and distribution of birds on the North Atlantic. Proc. Boston Soc. nat. Hist. 40:233–346.

WYNNE-EDWARDS, V. C.
1952. Zoology of the Baird Expedition, 1950: The birds observed in central and southeast Baffin Island. Auk 69:353–391.

YAMASHINA, Y.
1931. Die Vogel der Kurilen. J. Orn., Lpz. 79:491–541.

INDEX

PART B: VERTEBRATE ANIMALS OTHER THAN MURRES

PART C: SELECTED LOCALITIES

PART D: AUTHORITIES